FLUORESCENCE
AND
PHOSPHORESCENCE
ANALYSIS

FLUORESCENCE AND PHOSPHORESCENCE ANALYSIS

Principles and Applications

Edited by DAVID M. HERCULES

Department of Chemistry and Laboratory for Nuclear Science
Massachusetts Institute of Technology
Cambridge, Massachusetts

Interscience Publishers

a division of John Wiley and Sons

New York • London • Sydney

PREFACE

Although fluorescence has been used for a long time as a technique for certain trace analyses, only recently have its uses been expanded to a wide variety of materials. Phosphorescence as a technique for trace analysis is a veritable infant. However, it is apparent that use of these techniques by the analytical chemist is increasing and will continue to do so for some time.

While some recent publications have dealt with details of fluorescence analysis and with certain specific procedures, there remains a gap in the literature of analytical chemistry regarding basic information about fluorescence, phosphorescence, and other excited-state processes. In an attempt to fill this gap, a one-day symposium on the uses of Fluorescence and Phosphorescence in Chemistry was organized by the Analytical Division of the American Chemical Society at the 148th meeting of the American Chemical Society, held in Chicago in 1964. This symposium consisted of eight invited papers, and the present book represents an expansion of these eight papers.

It is intended that this book be educational in nature, and at the same time present some selected recent developments in the field. The book is intended for the novice, or the practicing chemist who needs to acquire a limited knowledge of fluorescence techniques, rather than for the spectroscopist or expert in the field. The outline of topics reflects this intention. The first four chapters deal with theory, instrumentation, and fluorescence in organic and metal–chelate systems. The second four chapters deal with some recent developments, such as application to biomedical problems, fluorescence polarization, phosphorescence, and chemiluminescence.

It is hoped that the papers presented here will also serve to stimulate among analytical chemist an interest in the use of excited-state processes for chemical analysis in a much wider scope than has been accomplished to date.

I want to thank Miss K. M. Kelly for typing the manuscript for my chapter, as well as for relieving much of the tedium of the editing process. I want to thank Prof. W. E. Ohnesorge for many valuable and helpful discussions during the editing of the manuscripts. Finally, I want to thank all of the authors for their cooperation in meeting rather rigid deadline requirements.

David M. Hercules

Cambridge, Massachusetts
October, 1965

AUTHORS

D. W. ELLIS, Department of Chemistry, University of New Hampshire, Durham, New Hampshire

D. M. HERCULES, Department of Chemistry and Laboratory for Nuclear Science, Massachusetts Institute of Technology, Cambridge, Massachusetts

W. E. OHNESORGE, Department of Chemistry, University of Rhode Island, Kingston, Rhode Island, and Department of Chemistry and Laboratory for Nuclear Science, Massachusetts Institute of Technology, Cambridge, Massachusetts

J. P. PARIS, Radiation Physics Laboratory, Engineering Department, E. I. du Pont de Nemours and Company, Wilmington, Delaware

L. B. ROGERS, Department of Chemistry, Purdue University, Lafayette, Indiana

B. L. VAN DUUREN, Institute of Environmental Medicine, New York University Medical Center, New York, New York

G. WEBER, Division of Biochemistry, University of Illinois, Urbana, Illinois

E. L. WEHRY, Department of Chemistry, Indiana University, Bloomington, Indiana

J. D. WINEFORDNER, Department of Chemistry, University of Florida, Gainesville, Florida

CONTENTS

Chapter 1. **Theory of Luminescence Processes.** *By David M. Hercules*

I. *Nature of Electronic States* 2
    A. Ethylene: π,π^* Excited States 4
    B. Formaldehyde: n,π^* Excited States 6

II. *Population of Excited States* 9
    A. The Nature of the Absorption Process 9
    B. The Intensity of Absorption Bands 11
    C. Properties of Excited States 13

III. *Luminescence Processes* 16
    A. Vibrational Relaxation 18
    B. Fluorescence 19
    C. Internal Conversion 19
    D. Phosphorescence and Intersystem Crossing 21

IV. *Effect of Transition Type on Luminescence* 23

V. *Effect of Molecular Structure and Environment on Luminescence* . . 24

VI. *Processes Competing with Luminescence* 29
    A. Energy Transfer: Collisional Quenching 32
    B. Noncollisional Energy Transfer 33
    C. Chemical Reactions 36
    General References 39
    References 39

Chapter 2. **Luminescence Instrumentation and Experimental Details.** *By David W. Ellis*

I. *General Principles of Luminescence Instrumentation* 41

II. *Instrumental Problems* 45
    A. Source 45
    B. Monochromator 45
    C. Detectors 46
    D. Standardization of Fluorescence Intensity 47
    E. Sample Cell, Cell Geometry, and Scattered Light 47
    F. Inner Filter Effect 49

III. *Chemical Problems*   49

      A. Fluorescent Reference Compounds   49
      B. Media   50
      C. Impurities and Interferences   51
      D. Quenching   51
      E. Photolysis   51
      F. Temperature Effects   52
      G. Adsorption   52

IV.   *Data Analysis*   53

      A. Definition of Sensitivity   53
      B. Reporting of Spectral Data   54
      C. Correction of Excitation and Emission Spectra   54
      D. Calibration Curves   58
      E. Quantum Efficiency   58
      F. Comparison between Instruments   59
      G. Comparison with Absorption   60
      H. Identification of Compounds Using Absorption and
          Fluorescence   62

V.   *Types of Instrumentation*   62

      A. Filter Fluorometers   62
      B. Accessories for Spectrophotometers   67
      C. Spectrofluorometers   68
      D. Compensating Spectrofluorometers   71
      E. Phosphorescence Instrumentation   73
      F. Specialized Instruments   74
      General References   75
      References   76

Chapter 3. **Fluorescence and Phosphorescence of Organic Molecules.** *By*
            E. L. Wehry and L. B. Rogers

I.   *Introduction*   81

II.   *Photoluminescence and the Structure of Organic Molecules*   81

      A. Aliphatic Compounds   82
      B. Aromatic Compounds   84
          1. Aromatic Hydrocarbons   85
          2. Substituted Aromatic Hydrocarbons   88
              a. Alkyl Groups   88
              b. Halogens   88
              c. Nitro Groups   89
              d. Hydroxyl and Amino Groups   91
          3. Aromatic Carbonyl Groups   91
          4. Nitrogen Heterocyles   92
          5. Other Heterocyclic Compounds   93
          6. Organic Polymers   94

    7. Dyes 95
  C. Effects of Molecular Geometry upon Luminescence of
      Organic Compounds 98

III. *Fluorescence Quenching and Energy Transfer in Organic*
     Compounds 100
  A. Transfer of Singlet and Triplet Excitation Energy 101
  B. Energy Transfer in Organic Crystals 103
  C. Intramolecular Energy Transfer 104
  D. Quenching of Fluorescence in Liquid Solution 105
  E. Organic Liquid Scintillators 109
  F. Organic Plastic Scintillators 111
  G. Organic Crystal Scintillators 112
  H. Summary 113

IV. *Special Effects in the Luminescence of Organic Molecules* 113
  A. "Excimer" Fluorescence 113
  B. Delayed Fluorescence 118
  C. Effects of pH on Fluorescence: Excited-State Dissociation . 125
    1. Analytical Implications 134
  D. Solvent Effects: Hydrogen Bonding 135
    1. Polarization Shifts 137
    2. Hydrogen Bonding 138
    3. Temperature Effects 139
    4. Solvent Quenching 141
    5. Conclusion: Analytical Implications 141
  E. Stimulated Emission from Organic Compounds 142

V. *Conclusion* 143
    References 143

Chapter 4. Fluorescence of Metal Chelate Compounds. *By William E.*
     Ohnesorge

I. *Introduction* 151

II. *Theory* 151
  A. Internal Conversion 152
  B. Intersystem Crossing 152
  C. Collisional Deactivation 152
  D. Energy Transfer 153
  E. Excited-State Dissociation 153

III. *Characteristics of Typical $\pi^* \rightarrow \pi$ Fluorescent Metal Chelate*
     Compounds 155

IV. *Chelates Emitting by Pathways Other Than $\pi^* \rightarrow \pi$* 158

V. *Applications* 162
    References 165

Chapter 5. **Analytical Uses of Phosphorescence.** *By J. D. Winefordner*

I.   *Introduction*   169

II.   *Comparison with Other Methods*   170
        A.   Mechanisms   170
        B.   Sensitivity   170
        C.   Selectivity   171
        D.   Accuracy, Precision, and Speed   171
        E.   Temperature   173
        F.   Concentration   173
        G.   Impurities 174
        H.   Sample Tubes   174

III.   *Applications of Phosphorimetry*   175
        A.   Trace Concentration of Organic Molecules of Interest to
             Biochemistry   176
        B.   Organic Compounds on Paper and on Thin-Layer
             Chromatograms   178
        C.   Analysis of Organic Compounds of Interest in
             Petrochemistry   180

IV.   *Limits of Detection*   181
        References   183

Chapter 6. **Chemiluminescence and Other Luminescence Processes.** *By*
        J. P. Paris

I.   *Introduction*   185

II.   *Reaction Mechanisms*   185
        A.   Radical–Radical Reactions   187
        B.   Carbene Reactions   188
        C.   Peroxide Dissociation   189
        D.   Electron Transfer Reactions   190
        References   193

Chapter 7. **Fluorescence in Biomedical Research.** *By B. L. Van Duuren*

I.   *Introduction*   195

II.   *The Binding of Dyes to Nucleic Acids*   195

III.   *The Fluorescence of Tetramethyluric Acid Complexes of Aromatic*
        Hydrocarbons, Heterocyclics, and Related Compounds   205
        References   215

Chapter 8. **Polarization of the Fluorescence of Solutions.** *By Gregorio Weber*

I. *The Fluorescence Transition* 217

II. *Origin of the Polarization of the Fluorescence* 217

III. *Molecular Geometry and Polarized Light Absorption* 218

IV. *Polarization in Solution and Molecular Orientation* 220

V. *The Fluorescence Polarization Spectrum* 224

VI. *Depolarization Owing to Extrinsic Causes* 227

VII. *Fluorescence Polarization and Energy Transfer* 233

VIII. *Polarization of the Fluorescence in an Electric Field* 237

IX. *Other Uses of Fluorescence Polarization* 238
  A. Determination of Lifetimes of the Excited State 238
  B. Energy Migration in Biological Systems 238
  C. Binding Equilibria 239
  References 239

Author Index 241

Subject Index 253

chapter 1

Theory of Luminescence Processes

David M. Hercules

*Department of Chemistry and Laboratory for Nuclear Science,
Massachusetts Institute of Technology, Cambridge, Massachusetts*

Luminescence is most conveniently defined as the radiation emitted by a molecule, or an atom, after it has absorbed energy to go to an excited state. Insofar as the analytical chemist is concerned, luminescence consists of *fluorescence* and *phosphorescence*; the distinction between the two generally being phenomenological although there is a more subtle theoretical distinction. Both fluorescence and phosphorescence have been used by the analytical chemist for trace analysis, and the electronic theory underlying these two processes will be the subject of the present chapter.

As a start it is appropriate to review the current status of luminescence analysis from four different viewpoints: instrumentation, kinds of analyses generally performed, sensitivity, and selectivity. Fluorescence instrumentation is currently available commercially and ranges in quality from simple filter fluorometers to highly complex self-correcting spectrophotofluorometers. Generally, there is instrumentation available to fill the needs of most analytical chemists for fluorescence analysis. On the other hand, there is not a wide variety of commercially available instrumentation for phosphorescence. Only one manufacturer offers a spectrophosphorimeter and/or a filter phosphorimeter.

The kinds of analyses which have been performed to date using fluorescence have been varied, including such things as trace metal determination, analysis for traces of organic materials, and particularly for determining trace constituents of biological systems. Phosphorescence has had only a relatively few applications, mainly to organic compounds, particularly in the area of biochemistry.

1

The sensitivity of fluorescence analyses has largely justified the use of fluorescence for many determinations. Lower limits of detectability for many methods lie in the sub-parts per million (ppm) to parts per billion (ppb) range. Generally, phosphorescence methods have shown sensitivities in the ppm range, although there is no reason why phosphorescence inherently should be less sensitive than fluorescence. The selectivity of fluorescence analysis has been good; variation in excitation and/or analytical wavelengths has allowed simultaneous determinations of components in many mixtures. Potentially, phosphorescence offers a higher degree of selectivity than fluorescence, for not only does the analyst have the exciting and analyzing wavelengths as variables, but also the lifetime of phosphorescence.

In order to understand better and to apply luminescence to analysis more intelligently, it is essential for the analytical chemist to become familiar with the nature of excited states and excited state processes. First off, such an approach may not seem to be too appropriate to analytical chemistry, because in general excited states are rather short-lived species having vanishingly small steady-state concentrations. However, excited state chemistry offers some new, sensitive, and highly selective methods to the analytical chemist which are particularly attractive because many of the experimental techniques in this field have already been developed to a high degree of sophistication by spectroscopists and photochemists. Therefore, a second purpose of this chapter will be to introduce the analytical chemist to excited states of molecules and some of their reactions. The chapter will be divided into four sections: the nature of electronic states, population of excited states, luminescence processes, and processes competing with luminescence.

I. Nature of Electronic States

It is necessary when discussing the nature of electronic states to distinguish between the terms *electronic state* and *electron orbital*. Although this distinction is very elementary, the two terms are quite often confused by chemists when discussing excited states and molecular spectra. An *orbital* is defined as that volume element of space in which there is high probability (99.9%) of finding an electron. It is calculated from a one-electron wave function and is assumed to be independent of all other electrons in the molecule. *Electronic states*, on the other hand, are concerned with the properties of all of the electrons in all of the orbitals. In other words, the wave function for an electronic state (state wave function) is a combination of the wave functions of each of the electrons in each of the orbitals of the molecule. When an electron in a molecule is moved from one orbital to another, the state of the molecule is changed and it is important to consider the states of the molecule involved rather than considering only the orbitals involved in such an electron promotion. The reason it is so important to make this distinction is that the interactions between electrons are quite significant and require that a major correction be applied to orbital energies calculated from simple one-electron wave functions.

Another important distinction is that between excited electronic states and the transition states so familiar to organic chemists. Generally transition states correspond to vibrationally excited ground states (i.e., ground state molecules in a strained configuration), whereas excited electronic states may contain no excess vibrational energy, but are still of much higher energy than the ground state. In fact, a molecule in an excited state is best regarded as a completely new entity, only remotely related to the same molecule in the ground state. An excited state will have a completely different electron distribution from the ground state, a different geometry, and more than likely will undergo chemical reactions quite different from those of ground state. Consider 9,10-anthraquinone, for example. In the ground state, anthraquinone dissolved in alcohol is quite stable and shows no tendency to react. However, anthraquinone in an excited state rapidly abstracts a hydrogen atom from the alcohol and is reduced to 9,10-dihydroxyanthracene, at the same time oxidizing the alcohol to its corresponding aldehyde.

It is important to consider the kinds of electronic states one may encounter in organic molecules. The state of any molecule which is most familiar to chemists is the *ground state*, the normal state of the molecule, or the state of lowest energy. Another way of defining the ground state is to say that it is the state in which a molecule exists in a bottle on the shelf. There is only one ground state for any given molecule. However, there are many different possible excited states for even very simple molecules, the exact nature of which depend upon the particular types of orbitals involved, as will be shown below.

Electronic states of organic molecules can be grouped into two broad categories: singlet states and triplet states. A *singlet state* is one in which all of the electrons in the molecule have their spins paired. (For example, the ground state of most organic molecules will be a singlet state.) *Triplet* states are those in which one set of electron spins have become unpaired—that is, all electrons in the molecule except two have paired spins. (The nomenclature *singlet* and *triplet* arise from the multiplicity considerations of atomic spectroscopy.) It should be noted that free radicals which contain one unpaired electron do not have a singlet ground state, but rather the ground state is a doublet (because of one unpaired spin), and the corresponding higher spin state would be a quartet state (because of three unpaired spins). However, the present discussion will be limited to singlet and triplet states because these are the states of importance in most molecules.

Although the exact nature of excited states shows a great deal of variability depending upon the specific parameters in a given molecule, a qualitative picture of the nature of electronic states can be gotten by considering very simple molecules. The concepts developed in such a treatment are directly applicable to more complicated molecules and therefore it is worthwhile to look at some simple molecules in considerable detail.

A. ETHYLENE: π,π^* EXCITED STATES

Because fluorescence and phosphorescence generally occur in molecules having π-electron systems, ethylene has been chosen as a simple example of such a system. Each of the carbon atoms in ethylene is in an sp^2 configuration forming three sp orbitals in a plane, $120°$ to each other, and having a p orbital perpendicular to the plane containing the three sp orbitals. When bonding in ethylene, each of the carbon atoms uses two of its three sp orbitals to form σ bonds with hydrogen, and the remaining sp orbital to form σ and σ^* molecular orbitals, as indicated in the energy level diagram of Figure 1-1. (A σ orbital is one that is totally symmetrical around the bond axis and an antibonding orbital, indicated by an asterisk, is the one which has an additional nodal plane perpendicular to the bond axis.) The two p orbitals on the carbon atoms combine to form π and π^* orbitals as shown in Figure 1-1. (A π orbital is one that has one nodal plane

containing the bond axis.)   Because each of the two carbon atoms
involved contributes two electrons to the σ and π orbital systems,
the lowest energy state (ground state) of ethylene is that in which
two electrons are in the σ orbital and two electrons are in the π orbital
with the σ^* and π^* orbitals being vacant.   This corresponds to a
ground state configuration, $\sigma^2\pi^2$, which is given the state symmetry
notation ^1A_g.   (Terms such as ^1A_g arise from group-theoretical notations, based on the overall symmetry of the state wave function.   A
treatment of these terms is beyond the scope of the present discussion,
but they may be regarded as convenient labels for the states involved.)

Because the energy of the σ orbital is very low and the energy of
the σ^* orbital is very high, the only excited states of ethylene which
are of any significance in chemistry are those which involve π electrons.   This gives rise to the possibility of two excited singlet states
in ethylene, corresponding to the configurations $\sigma^2\pi\pi^*$, and $\sigma^2\pi^{*2}$,

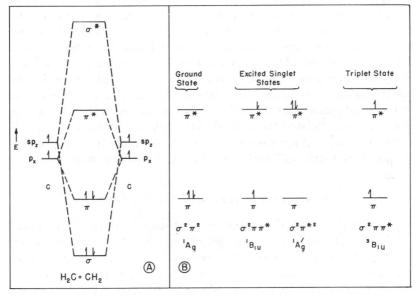

Figure 1-1.   The electronic states of ethylene: A, a diagram showing the
molecular orbitals of ethylene and their relationship to the atomic orbitals of the
carbon atoms.   The Z axis is the axis of the C—C bond.   B, a summary of the
electron configurations of the states of ethylene resulting from promotions of π
electrons.   The orbital occupancy and state symbols are given below each
configuration.

having the symmetry state notations $^1B_{1u}$ and $^1A_g'$, respectively. The $^1B_{1u}$ state corresponds to removing an electron from the π orbital and putting it into π^*, while the $^1A_g'$ state requires promoting both electrons from π to π^*.   A third excited state is also possible, corresponding to the promotion of a π electron to π^*, but with a subsequent change of spin.   This state is given the notation $^3B_{1u}$ and is a triplet state.

The three states presented above are the only possible excited states which can arise from π electron promotion in ethylene.   Because all of these states involve only π electrons, they are all said to be π,π^* excited states (which result from $\pi \rightarrow \pi^*$ transitions).   It is interesting to compare the electron distribution of the π,π^* excited states with the electron distribution of the ground state.   The states $^1B_{1u}$ and $^3B_{1u}$ will have a smaller electron density between the carbon atoms, and a greater density at the carbon atoms than will the ground state because of the nodal plane in the π^* orbital between the carbon atoms.   Likewise the excited state $^1A_g'$ will have an even greater electron density on the carbon atoms and an even smaller electron density between them.   Also, it should be noted that, whereas in the ground state both CH_2 groups in ethylene are coplanar (i.e., all four hydrogen atoms lie in the same plane), in the $^1B_{1u}$ state the π electron stabilization of the planar structure of ethylene is lost, and the most stable configuration of the molecule is that in which the CH_2 groups have become twisted 90° out of plane relative to each other (13). This is a rather interesting example of a molecule having geometry in an excited state different from that of the ground state.

B. Formaldehyde: n,π^* Excited States

To enlarge upon the types of electronic transitions in organic molecules, consider next formaldehyde, which has a π electron system similar to that of ethylene.   As shown in Figure 1-2, the carbon atom of formaldehyde is an sp^2 hybrid, and the oxygen atom can be considered to bond using unhybridized p orbitals.   The sp_z hybrid orbital of carbon and p_z orbital of oxygen combine to form σ and σ^* orbitals.   The overlap of the p_x orbital of carbon and the p_x orbital of oxygen give rise to the π orbital system, consisting of π and π^*.

The difference between formaldehyde and ethylene arises from the p_y orbital on the oxygen atom which lies in the HCH plane (on the

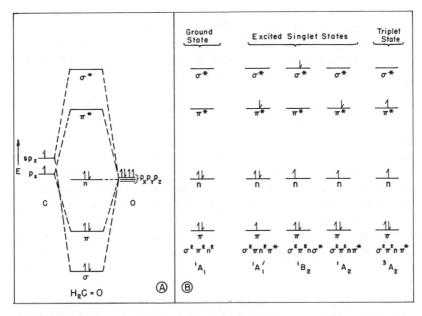

Figure 1-2.   The electronic states of formaldehyde: A, a diagram showing the molecular orbitals of formaldehyde and their relationship to the atomic orbitals of the carbon and oxygen atoms.   (The Z axis is the axis of the C—O bond. The p orbitals of oxygen are of equal energy.)   B, a summary of the electron configurations of some of the states of formaldehyde resulting from one-electron promotions.   The orbital occupancy and state symbols are given below each configuration.

y axis) perpendicular to the C—O bond (z axis).   This orbital cannot combine with any of the carbon orbitals and therefore goes through the bonding sequence relatively unperturbed from its energy in the oxygen atom.   Because of this it is considered to be a nonbonding orbital, and is given the symbol n in Figure 1-2.   Therefore the ground state electron configuration of formaldehyde is written $\sigma^2\pi^2 n^2$ and has the state symbol $^1A_1$.   (There is no subscript g on the state symbol of formaldehyde because the symmetry center of ethylene is not present in formaldehyde.)

Figure 1-2 also shows four of the possible excited electronic states of formaldehyde, produced by the promotion of either an n or a π electron since, as in the case of ethylene, the σ electrons are very low in energy.   The $^1A_1{'}$ excited state of formaldehyde is a π,π^* excited state similar to the $^1B_{1u}$ state of ethylene. It corresponds to the electron configuration $\sigma^2\pi n^2\pi^*$. The electron density distribution of the $^1A_1'$ state is also similar to its corresponding state in ethylene, i.e., the π electron density is greater on the carbon and oxygen atoms than in the ground state, and the electron density between the atoms is reduced.

The $^1B_2$ excited state arises from promotion of an n electron into the σ^* orbital, and therefore is called an n,σ^* excited state. It has the electron configuration $\sigma^2\pi^2 n\sigma^*$. It is interesting to compare the electron density distribution in the $^1B_2$ state of formaldehyde with the $^1A_1'$ state. In the singlet $^1B_2$ state, an electron has been promoted from the nonbonding orbital of the oxygen atom into the σ^* molecular orbital, delocalizing it over the carbon and oxygen atoms. In effect, this promotion decreases the electron density of the oxygen atom and increases the electron density of the carbon atom. Therefore, $^1B_2$ state has a partial negative charge on the carbon atom, while it has a partial positive charge on the oxygen atom relative to the ground state.

The $^1A_2$ excited state is produced by promoting an n electron into a π^* orbital, and is called an n,π^* excited state. It has the electron configuration $\sigma^2\pi^2 n\pi^*$. The n,π^* excited state is similar to the n,σ^* excited state because it involves promotion of an n electron into an antibonding molecular orbital. The partial positive charge (relative to the ground state) found on the oxygen atom in an n,π^* excited state is very significant in the interpretation of many excited state processes, such as photochemical reactions. The $^3A_2$ state of formaldehyde is likewise an n,π^* excited state and is similar to the $^1A_2$ state except that the spin of the electron promoted into the π^* orbital has been reversed, making it a triplet state. The reversal of electron spin in an excited state is not a trivial difference. As will be seen later, triplet states and singlet states differ significantly in their properties as well as in their energies. Borrowing a rule from atomic spectroscopy, triplet states always lie lower in energy than their corresponding singlet states (Hund's Rule).

The energies of the excited states of formaldehyde, relative to the ground state, can be obtained by inspection of Figure 1-2. Those states corresponding to the greatest difference in energy between the orbitals involved in the electron promotion will always be highest in energy. Hence the energy sequence of the excited states of formaldehyde, from the highest to the lowest, will be $\pi,\pi^* > n,\sigma^* > n,\pi^*$; and invoking Hund's Rule, the singlet n,π^* state will be greater in energy than the triplet n,π^* state. In summary then, one sees that a typical organic molecule (based on the simple picture of formaldehyde and ethylene) will have only one ground state but may have a number of excited states, which may be π,π^*, n,π^*, or n,σ^*, and that for every excited state arising from a single electron promotion there will be a singlet state and a triplet state.

II. Population of Excited States

Molecular excitation requires promotion of an electron into an orbital of higher energy than it occupies in the ground state. The most direct way of bringing about such a promotion is for the molecule to absorb a photon of the appropriate energy, thereby changing the state of the molecule from the ground state to an excited state.

A. THE NATURE OF THE ABSORPTION PROCESS

Figure 1-3 shows the energy level diagram for the electronic states of formaldehyde (4, 10, 11). One should note that each of the electronic states (ground or excited) has a number of vibrational levels superimposed on it, and these are numbered 0, 1, 2, 3, 4, 5, 6, etc. The vibrational levels arise because a molecule in a given electronic state may absorb small increments of energy corresponding to changes in vibrational modes, although retaining the same electronic configuration. Another significant fact to be noted is the degree of overlap between the vibrational levels of higher states such as $^1A_1{}'$ and $^1B_2$. By convention, the singlet states in Figure 1-3 are stacked in a vertical column, while the triplet states are stacked in another vertical column displaced to the right of the singlet column. Only the energy level of the $^3A_2$ state is known exactly, and hence the other two triplets are shown by dashed lines. Also, it is important to note that there is overlap between the lowest vibrational level of $^1A_2$ and the intermediate vibrational levels of its corresponding triplet state, $^3A_2$.

The energy of a photon ($E = hc/\lambda$) required to produce a particular excited state is the difference in energy between that state and the ground state as shown in Figure 1-3. It should be observed that a range of wavelengths can bring about a transition between any two

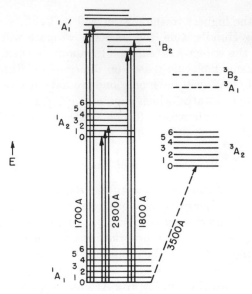

Figure 1-3. Electronic transitions of formaldehyde. The wavelength given by each set of vertical arrows is the band maximum in the ultraviolet absorption spectrum of formaldehyde corresponding to that transition.

electronic states, which accounts for the fact that electronic absorption spectra generally occur as broad bands, rather than as single lines. In some cases it is possible to observe vibrational fine structure superimposed on an electronic absorption band, particularly in gas phase spectra. The lowest energy photon which can bring about a given transition is that corresponding to the energy difference between zeroth vibrational levels of the two states involved. For example, in the $^1A_1 \rightarrow {}^1A_2$ transition (the 2800 A. transition), the lowest energy transition is given by $(^1A_1)_0 \rightarrow (^1A_2)_0$. Generally, the energy separation between two electronic states is taken as the difference between the zeroth vibrational levels, rather than the band maximum which often corresponds to excitation to a higher vibrational level of the excited state.

The $^1A_1 \rightarrow {}^3A_2$ absorption band is shown by a dotted line and occurs at approximately 3500 A. This transition is weak because singlet–triplet transitions are forbidden by formal spectroscopic selection rules. (A good rule of thumb is that singlet–triplet processes have a probability of about 10^{-6} that of a corresponding singlet–singlet or triplet–triplet process.) In fact, if direct excitation of triplet states from the ground state by absorption of radiation was the only mechanism by which these states could be populated, they would be of little significance in spectroscopy, chemical analysis, or photochemistry. However, as will be discussed later, population of triplet states from excited singlet states occurs in many molecules, and in some molecules it is a very efficient process.

Table 1-1 presents a summary of the electronic transitions of formaldehyde giving their wavelengths as well as the corresponding photon energies in electron volts (eV) and kcal/mole. It is important to note that the energy required for an electronic transition in formaldehyde varies from 82–168 kcal/mole (3.54–7.28 eV). Such an amount of energy is more than that required for many chemical reactions in ground state molecules, and hence it is little wonder that excited states of molecules are quite often highly reactive.

TABLE 1-1

Energies of the Excited States of Formaldehyde

State	Wavelength,[a] A.	Energy[b]	
		eV	kcal/mole
$^3A_2$	3500	3.54	82
$^1A_2$	2800	4.43	102
$^1B_2$	1800	6.88	158
$^1A_1'$	1700	7.28	168

[a] Approximate wavelength of absorption maximum.
[b] The energy of the ground is set at zero, arbitrarily.

B. The Intensity of Absorption Bands

The intensity of an electronic absorption band is a measure of the probability of an electronic transition between two states. For example, in formaldehyde the $^1A_1 \rightarrow {}^1A_2$ band is weak, indicating that this electronic transition has a low probability while the $^1A_1 \rightarrow {}^1A_1'$ band is intense, indicative of high probability. The absolute intensity (oscillator strength) of an absorption band may be determined from the integrated absorption spectrum by the relationship (8):

$$f = 0.102 \ (mc^2/N\pi e^2)\int \epsilon_\nu \, d\nu = 4.315 \times 10^{-9}\int \epsilon_\nu \, d\nu \qquad (1\text{-}1)$$

where m = mass of the electron, c = the velocity of light, N = Avogadro's number, e = the charge on the electron, ϵ_ν = the molar extinction coefficient at a particular frequency, ν. A totally allowed electronic transition has an absolute intensity of $f = 1$.

Although the absolute intensity of an absorption band is significant to spectroscopists, chemists are used to thinking in terms of ϵ_{max} (the molar extinction coefficient of the absorption band maximum). There is a fairly good correlation between f and ϵ_{max}, if one assumes that an electronic absorption band is a reasonably narrow symmetrical Gaussian curve (14). Then for $f = 1$, the corresponding value of ϵ_{max} is 10^5; for $f = 0.1$, $\epsilon_{max} = 10^4$, for $f = 0.01$, $\epsilon_{max} = 10^3$, etc.

The question now arises as to what factors cause f to be less than 1 for an electronic transition in any given molecule. Although a detailed discussion of this problem is beyond the scope of the present treatment, there are some factors which can be discussed that will allow one to draw distinctions between the major transition types which have been considered. Basically, there are three major factors which influence the intensity of an electronic transition: (1) the multiplicities of the ground state and the excited state; (2) the degree of overlap between the orbitals involved in electron promotion (i.e., the orbital from which the excited electron came and the one to which it was promoted); (3) the symmetries of the wave functions of the ground state and the excited state. One can consider that each of the above factors introduces some degree of forbiddenness (thereby reducing the probability of the transition) into an electronic transition and that the absolute intensity of the transition is the product of the probabilities of each of the individual factors. This is expressed as follows:

$$f = P_m P_o P_s \ldots \tag{1-2}$$

where P_m is the probability factor introduced by multiplicity, P_o the factor introduced by orbital overlap, and P_s the factor introduced by symmetry. (For a totally allowed transition, $P_m = P_o = P_s = 1$.)

For most organic molecules the value of P_m will be equal to 1 for transitions between states of the same multiplicity (i.e., singlet–singlet transitions), and will have a value of approximately 10^{-5} to 10^{-6} for transitions involving changes in multiplicity (such as singlet–triplet transitions). Therefore, if one deals with a singlet–triplet transition, which is by all other factors allowed, an f value of 10^{-6} is to be expected. This would correspond to ϵ_{max} of 10^{-1}, i.e., an extremely weak electronic transition. This accounts for the weakness of singlet–triplet transitions, and the fact that they are seldom observed (and often overlooked) in absorption spectra.

The orbital overlap factor, P_o, will generally have a value between 1 and 10^{-4}, depending upon the exact placement of the orbitals in the molecule. For example, the $\pi \rightarrow \pi^*$ transition in ethylene has P_o nearly equal to 1, since there is a high degree of overlap between the π and π^* orbitals in this molecule. On the other hand, the $n \rightarrow \pi^*$ transition in formaldehyde has P_o approximately equal to 10^{-4} and therefore it is weaker than the $\pi \rightarrow \pi^*$ transition. This arises from the fact that the n orbital is oriented 90° to the axis of the π electron system, thereby allowing only small overlap between the n and the π^* orbitals.

The symmetry forbiddenness factor, P_s, generally will vary between 1 and 10^{-3}. This factor is more important in highly symmetrical molecules, such as highly substituted aromatic compounds, or polyenes. For example, the well known 2500 A. band of benzene (the long wavelength absorption band) is weak and part of the weakness is due to symmetry forbiddenness of the transition.

From the foregoing discussion one would expect that the order of intensity among the types of electronic transitions would be singlet–singlet $\pi \rightarrow \pi^* >$ singlet–singlet $n \rightarrow \pi^* > > >$ singlet triplet $\pi \rightarrow \pi^* >$ singlet–triplet $n \rightarrow \pi^*$. Although the correlation is generally valid for singlet–singlet transitions, $n \rightarrow \pi^*$ singlet–triplet transitions often are more intense than $\pi \rightarrow \pi^*$ singlet–triplet transitions. This results from mixing which occurs between excited states, imparting considerable singlet character to most n,π^* triplet states. (See Section IV.)

C. Properties of Excited States

At this point it is appropriate to discuss briefly some of the chemical properties of excited states, particularly in contrast to the same chemical properties of the ground state. Quite often, chemists have difficulty in visualizing excited states of molecules as unique chemical entities, and it is hoped that this brief discussion will introduce a bit of chemical realism into the subject.

To talk about the geometry of the formaldehyde molecule, one must consider two planes: the plane containing the carbon atom and

the two hydrogen atoms, and the plane containing the oxygen atom
and the two hydrogen atoms. In the ground state of formaldehyde
these two planes coincide, and the molecule as a whole is planar. In
the lowest excited singlet state ($^1A_2$), however, the angle between the
H—C—H plane and the H—O—H plane is 20° and the C—O bond
length has increased to 1.32 A., as compared to 1.22 A. in the ground
state, with a corresponding reduction in the carbonyl stretching
frequency to 1177 cm^{-1}. In the lowest triplet state ($^3A_2$), the C—O
bond length is 1.31 A., but the angle between the H—C—H and the
H—O—H planes has increased to 35° (13). These changes are shown
in Figure 1-4. These data for formaldehyde indicate not only that
differences in geometries exist between the ground state and excited
states, but also that differences exist between excited singlet states
and their corresponding triplet states.

Another very interesting example of the changes in geometry which
can occur on excitation is given by acetylene, as shown in Figure 1-4.
In the ground state, acetylene is linear having a C—H bond length of

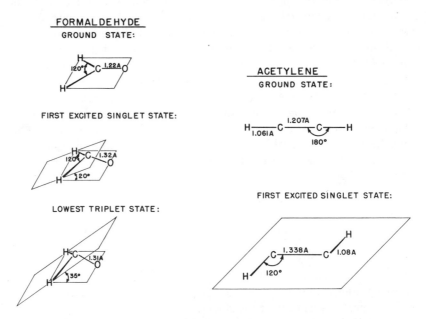

Figure 1-4.   Geometries of some electronic states of formaldehyde
and acetylene.

1.06 A. and a C—C bond length of 1.207 A. In the first excited singlet state, the C—H bond length has changed to 1.08 A., and the carbon–carbon bond length has increased to 1.338 A. However, the most significant feature is that the H—C—C bond angle has become 120° in the excited state, compared to 180° in the ground state. Effectively what has happened in acetylene is that after excitation the carbon atom has undergone a rehybridization from sp to sp^2 and has adopted an ethylene configuration with the hydrogens in the *trans* positions. Although it has never been observed, it is conceivable that one could encounter a *cis* isomer of acetylene in the excited state. In other words, one could have *cis–trans* isomerization among excited state configurations.

Another important change is the difference in π electron distribution between excited states and the ground state, and the effect this difference has on chemical properties. Figure 1-5 shows the electron distributions for the ground state and the first excited singlet state of phenol, based on molecular orbital calculations for anisole (15). In the ground state, there is a partial electron deficiency on the oxygen atom and an increased electron density at the *ortho* and *para* positions (relative to benzene). This is responsible for the slight acidity of phenol in the ground state, as well as accounting for the predominant *ortho–para* direction observed for electrophilic substitution reactions of phenol. However, if one compares the ground state electron distribution with that of the first excited singlet state, one sees some remarkable differences. For example, the oxygen atom has a much lower electron density in the excited state than in the ground state, corresponding to a partial promotion of the electron from the oxygen atom into the ring. Also the major electron density lies in the *ortho* and *meta* positions with a decrease in electron density at the *para* position, a situation quite different from that of the ground state. From these considerations, one might expect phenol to be a stronger acid in the excited state than in its ground state because of the decrease of electron density on the oxygen atom. This is borne out in experiment as shown by the data at the bottom of Figure 1-5. The pK_a for phenol changes from 10.02 in the ground state to 5.7 in the excited state, a difference in pK_a of 4.3. Even more startling changes are observed for other phenols. For example, α- and β-naphthol show pK_a changes of approximately 7 pK units on excitation, changing from weak acids in the ground state to moderately

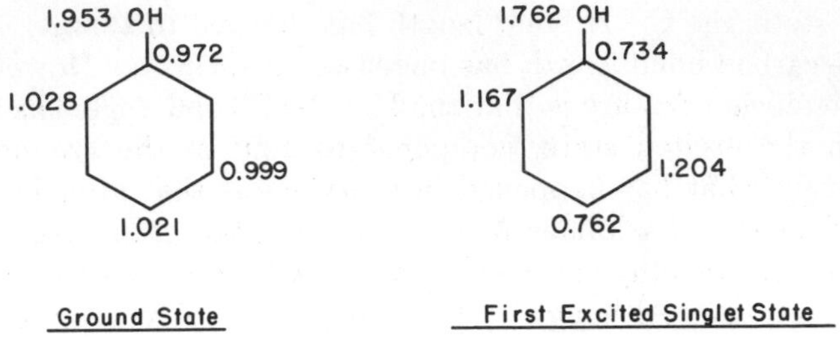

1.953 OH
0.972
1.028
0.999
1.021

Ground State

1.762 OH
0.734
1.167
1.204
0.762

First Excited Singlet State

Compound	pK$_A$	pK$_A$*	Δ pK$_A$	
Phenol	10.02	5.7	4.3	(16)
α−Naphthol	9.23	2.0	7.2	(17)
β−Naphthol	9.46	2.5	7.0	(17)
p−Chlorephenol	9.38	3.6	5.8	(16)

(NB   pK$_A$* is the pK$_A$ in the excited state)

Figure 1-5.   Electron distributions for the ground state and the first excited singlet state of phenol.   Tabulation of pK$_a$'s for ground states and first excited singlet states of some phenols.

strong acids in the excited state.   The fact that substituent groups can significantly affect the acidity of an excited state is seen by comparison of the pK$_a$ changes for p-chlorophenol with that for phenol.

III. Luminescence Processes

Luminescence processes can be interpreted only in terms of the excited state from which luminescence emission occurs and its relationship to the ground state of the molecule.   Although the simple picture of photon absorption by a molecule and subsequent re-emission of a photon to give luminescence seems to be quite straightforward, there are nonradiative processes which precede and/or compete with photon emission.   Therefore, it is important to consider all processes which occur after photon absorption by a molecule and their relationship to luminescence.

As a model for the discussion of luminescence processes, consider the electronic states of benzene shown in Figure 1-6 (7,10).   Benzene in many respects is an ideal model for discussing luminescence because only π electrons are involved in excitation. The ground state of benzene is $^1A_{1g}$, and the excited singlet states are $^1B_{2u}$, $^1B_{1u}$, and $^1E_{1u}$, in increasing order of energy, giving rise to absorption bands peaking at approximately 2550, 2000, and 1800 A., respectively. The triplet states of benzene in increasing order of energy are $^3B_{1u}$, $^3E_{1u}$, $^3B_{2u}$, although the higher triplet states are drawn with dotted lines indicating that the nature of these states is not known exactly. The $^1A_{1g} \rightarrow {}^3B_{2u}$ transition is weak although it has been observed under perturbation. Also it is possible to observe the triplet–triplet

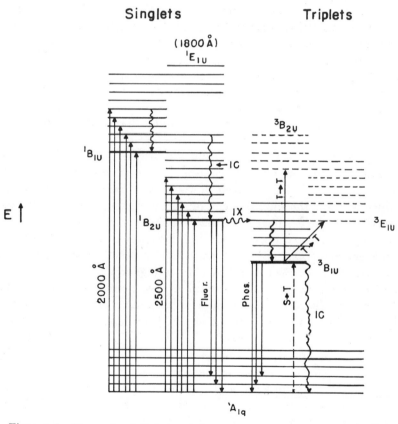

Figure 1-6. Energy level diagram of the electronic states of benzene: Fluor = fluorescence; IC = internal conversion; IX = intersystem crossing; Phos. = phosphorescence.

transitions in benzene, $^3B_{1u} \rightarrow {}^3E_{1u}$ and $^3B_{1u} \rightarrow {}^3B_{2u}$, by flash photolysis. In discussions about luminescence processes, mean lifetimes (i.e., reciprocal rate constants) of all processes will be stressed because the relative rates of these processes are very important in determining the luminescence behavior of a molecule.

A. Vibrational Relaxation

One may assume that all molecules are in the lowest vibrational level of the ground state in solution at room temperature. Therefore, absorption occurs from the zeroth vibrational level of the $^1A_{1g}$ state of benzene to various vibrational levels of an excited state as discussed previously. The actual time required for photon absorption, i.e., the time required for a molecule to go from one electronic state to another, is 10^{-15} s (according to the Franck-Condon principle) which is short relative to the time required for all other electronic processes and for nuclear motion. This means that immediately after excitation a molecule has the same geometry and is in the same environment as it was in the ground state. In this situation it can do one of two things: emit a photon from the same vibrational level to which it was excited initially, or undergo changes in vibrational levels prior to emission of radiation. Which of these two processes is dominant depends upon the environment of the molecule. For an isolated molecule in the gas phase, the only way to lose vibrational energy is to emit an infrared photon, which is less probable than undergoing an electronic transition to return to the ground state. Therefore, one tends to see photon emission from higher vibrational levels of excited states in gas phase spectra at low pressures. In solution, however, thermal relaxation of a vibrationally excited molecule is quite rapid through transfer of excess vibrational energy from the solute molecule to the solvent. In fact, this process is so efficient that not just one or two quanta of vibrational energy are lost by thermal relaxation, but all of the excess vibrational energy of the excited state, this process occurring in 10^{-13} to 10^{-11} s. This is an extremely important point. It means that before an excited molecule in solution can emit a photon, it will undergo vibrational relaxation, and therefore photon emission will always occur *from the lowest vibrational level of an excited state.*

B. Fluorescence

Once a molecule arrives at the lowest vibrational level of an excited singlet state, it can do a number of things, one of which is to return to the ground state by photon emission. This process is called *fluorescence.* The lifetime of an excited singlet state is approximately 10^{-9} to 10^{-7} s and therefore the decay time of fluorescence is of the same order of magnitude. If fluorescence is unperturbed by competing processes, the lifetime of fluorescence is the intrinsic lifetime of the excited singlet state. The *quantum efficiency* of fluorescence is defined as the fraction of excited molecules that will fluoresce. For highly fluorescent molecules the quantum efficiency of fluorescence approaches unity (such as rubrene, Rhodamine B, and fluorescein), while for other molecules fluorescence is so weak that one is unable to observe it and the quantum efficiency of fluorescence approaches zero. It should be noted that even though a quantum of radiation is emitted in fluorescence, this quantum will be of lower energy on the average than the quantum absorbed by the molecule, due to vibrational relaxation (both after absorption and after emission). The change in photon energy causes a shift of the fluorescence spectrum to longer wavelengths, relative to the absorption spectrum, and is referred to as a Stokes Shift.

To summarize, then, the process of fluorescence consists of photon absorption by a molecule to go to an excited singlet state, relaxation from higher vibrational levels of that state to its lowest vibrational level, photon emission to a vibrationally excited level of the ground state, and again relaxation of the molecule to the lowest vibrational level of the ground state.

C. Internal Conversion

In addition to fluorescence, one also encounters *radiationless* processes whereby molecules in an excited singlet state may return to the ground state without the emission of a photon, converting all of the excitation energy into heat. The process, called *internal conversion*, is not well understood and its efficiency is very difficult to measure. Generally, internal conversion between an excited singlet state and the ground state should be an inefficient process and it probably accounts for only a small fraction of the total excitation energy in most molecules. This is particularly true in aromatic hydrocarbons, where it is thought that internal conversion between the lowest excited singlet state and the ground state is nonexistent (18).

So far, the discussion has been concerned with the $^1A_{1g} \rightarrow {}^1B_{2u}$ transition in benzene, and the question might be raised as to the nature of excited state processes if the molecule is excited to a higher singlet state such as $^1B_{1u}$. If the molecule is excited to a higher vibrational level of the $^1B_{1u}$ state, it undergoes vibrational relaxation as discussed before. The question then arises as to the fate of the molecule when it reaches the zeroth vibrational level of the $^1B_{1u}$ state. Generally, the energy separation between excited singlet states in an aromatic molecule is smaller than the energy separation between the lowest excited singlet state and the ground state. This means that the zeroth vibrational level of $^1B_{1u}$ will overlap with higher vibrational levels of the $^1B_{2u}$ state that do not involve extremely large differences in nuclear configuration from the lowest vibrational level of the $^1B_{2u}$ state. This situation gives rise to a high degree of coupling between the vibrational levels of the $^1B_{1u}$ and $^1B_{2u}$ states, which provides an extremely efficient path for crossing from the $^1B_{1u}$ state to the $^1B_{2u}$ state. In fact, this process is so efficient that the molecule undergoes internal conversion from the $^1B_{1u}$ state to the lowest vibrational level of the $^1B_{2u}$ state in about the same time that it requires to convert from an excited vibrational level of the $^1B_{2u}$ state to its zeroth vibrational level (i.e., 10^{-13} to 10^{-11} s). Because of this situation one may formulate the following general rule: a molecule may be considered to undergo internal conversion to the *lowest vibrational level of its lowest excited singlet state* in a time that is short, relative to photon emission, *regardless of the singlet state to which it was excited initially.*

The rule just quoted is an empirical rule and occasionally an exception will be observed. For example, in azulene fluorescence, emission is observed from the lowest vibrational level of the *second* excited singlet state but not from the first excited singlet state (19,20). This situation arises because the energy separation between the first and second excited states of azulene is large and therefore vibrational coupling between these two states is small. This decreases the probability of internal conversion between them, while increasing the probability of emission from the higher state to the ground state. On the other hand, the energy separation between the ground state and the first excited singlet state is small, and therefore an efficient internal conversion process removes the excitation energy from the first excited singlet state.

D. PHOSPHORESCENCE AND INTERSYSTEM CROSSING

Although population of triplet states by direct absorption from the ground state is insignificant, a very efficient process exists for population of triplet states from the lowest excited singlet state in many molecules. This process is referred to as *intersystem crossing*, and is a spin-dependent internal conversion process. Because singlet–triplet processes are generally less probable than singlet–singlet processes, one may be startled that a singlet–triplet process such as intersystem crossing can occur within the lifetime of an excited singlet state (10^{-8} s). The mechanism for intersystem crossing involves vibrational coupling between the excited singlet state and a triplet state. Remembering that singlet–triplet processes are less probable than singlet–singlet processes by a factor of 10^{-5} to 10^{-6}, and that radiationless vibrational processes (such as internal conversion) occur in approximately 10^{-13} s, the time required for a spin-forbidden vibrational process would be approximately 10^{-8} to 10^{-7} s, which is the same order of magnitude as the lifetime of an excited singlet state. Therefore, intersystem crossing can compete with fluorescence emission from the zeroth vibrational level of an excited singlet state but cannot compete with vibrational deactivation from higher vibrational levels of a singlet state.

The mechanism for intersystem crossing presented above has some interesting ramifications. First, if the energy difference between the lowest singlet state and the triplet state just below it is small, intersystem crossing should be more favorable than if the energy difference between these states is large. In general, this has been observed to be true. For example, in aromatic hydrocarbons where the singlet–triplet split is large, intersystem crossing is less efficient than in certain dye molecules where the singlet–triplet split is small (4). Second, increasing the lifetime of an excited singlet state should increase the fraction of excited molecules which undergo intersystem crossing, compared with those that fluoresce, and therefore should decrease the quantum efficiency of fluorescence. Again, this has generally been found to be true. Once intersystem crossing has occurred, the molecule undergoes the usual internal conversion process (10^{-13} to 10^{-11} s) and falls to the zeroth vibrational level of the triplet state.   Because the difference in energy between the zeroth vibrational level of the triplet state and the zeroth vibrational level of the lowest excited singlet is large compared to thermal energy, repopulation of a singlet state from a triplet state is highly improbable.

There are two factors which tend to enhance a *radiationless* transition between the lowest triplet state and the ground state. First, the energy difference between the triplet state and the ground state is smaller than the difference between the lowest singlet state and the ground state, which tends to enhance vibrational coupling between these two states, and therefore to enhance internal conversion.   Second, and more importantly, the lifetime of a triplet state is much longer than that of an excited singlet state (ca. 10^{-4} to 10 s) and therefore loss of excitation energy by collisional transfer is greatly enhanced.   In fact, this second process is so important that in solution at room temperature it is often the predominant pathway for the loss of triplet state excitation energy.

If a molecule is placed in a rigid medium so that collisional processes are minimized, a radiative transition between the lowest triplet state and the ground state is observed, and this emission is called *phosphorescence*.   Because phosphorescence originates from the lowest triplet state, it will have a decay time approximately equal to the lifetime of the triplet state (ca. 10^{-4} to 10 s).   Therefore phosphorescence often is characterized by an afterglow which is not observed for fluorescence.   Although this phenomenological difference between fluorescence and phosphorescence exists, it should be stressed that a more fundamental distinction also exists, i.e., that fluorescence arises from a *singlet–singlet transition*, while phosphorescence arises from a *triplet–singlet transition*.

Because of the reasons discussed above, phosphorescence is almost never observed in solution at room temperature (biacetyl is an exception) (21), although it has been detected for some molecules by using a very sensitive detector (22).   Generally, phosphorescence is observed from rigid glasses at the temperature of liquid nitrogen (77°K).   One of the most popular of such glasses is EPA, consisting of a mixture of ethyl ether, isopentane, and ethyl alcohol in a ratio of 5:5:2.   Because phosphorescence lifetimes are in the region where they are measurable by mechanical means, phosphorescence offers the added dimension of lifetime measurements to the analytical chemist using luminescence techniques.

IV. Effect of Transition Type on Luminescence

Internal conversion to the lowest excited singlet state of a molecule prior to emission of a photon is very important in determining the luminescence characteristics of a molecule. This means that the behavior of a molecule after excitation will not depend upon the state to which it was excited initially, but rather on the nature of the lowest excited singlet state. If the lowest excited singlet state is a π,π^* state, the molecule will show behavior characteristic of a π,π^* state, whereas if the lowest excited singlet state is an n,π^* state, it will show characteristics of an n,π^* state. Because π,π^* and n,π^* states represent the two major types of excited states found in organic molecules, it is important to compare those characteristics which affect their luminescence.

Table 1-2 compares approximate values for maximum extinction coefficient, lifetime of the state, singlet–triplet split, and relative rate of intersystem crossing for n,π^* and π,π^* states. Because $n \rightarrow \pi^*$ transitions generally are less intense than $\pi \rightarrow \pi^*$ transitions, n,π^* excited states have longer lifetimes, a factor which tends to enhance intersystem crossing from n,π^* states. The smaller singlet–triplet split for n,π^* states also tends to enhance intersystem crossing. These two factors account for the fact that intersystem crossing occurs with a much greater probability from an n,π^* excited state than from a π,π^* state. This situation is illustrated in Figure 1-7. Absorption of a photon to produce an excited state is indicated by A, with internal conversion to the lowest excited singlet state by IC. For molecule "a", where the lowest excited singlet state is π,π^*, competition between the usual processes for the loss of excitation energy occurs. This means that the molecule may fluoresce or may undergo intersystem crossing to the triplet state and then return to the ground state by phosphorescence. If the lowest excited singlet state is n,π^* as in the case of molecule "b", intersystem crossing is enhanced at the expense of fluorescence, removing fluorescence as a major pathway for the loss of excitation energy, but retaining all other processes.

TABLE 1-2

Comparison of n,π^* and π,π^* Singlet States

	n,π^* states	π,π^* states
ϵ_{max}	$10-10^3$	10^3-10^5
Lifetime	10^{-7} to 10^{-5}	10^{-9} to 10^{-7}
Singlet–triplet split	Small	Generally large
Rate of intersystem crossing	Greater than for fluorescence	Of the same order as fluorescence

A rather interesting experimental verification of this idea is found for quinoline and acridine (23). It has been established that for these molecules in polar solvents the lowest excited singlet state is π,π^*, whereas in nonpolar solvents the lowest excited state is n,π^*. Therefore, in hydrocarbon solvents, intersystem crossing occurs rapidly and only very weak fluorescence is observed. As the solvent polarity is increased, the nonbonding electrons on the nitrogen atom are solvated more strongly and their energy is lowered, raising the energy of the n,π^* excited state so that at some point interchange of the levels occurs, and the π,π^* excited singlet state becomes lower in energy than the $n \rightarrow \pi^*$ state. Therefore, in more polar solvents where solvation of the electrons is great, quinoline shows fluorescence that is qualitatively, at least, proportional to the polarity of solvent. For example, the relative fluorescence quantum yields of quinoline in benzene, ethanol, and water are $1:30:1000$ (27).

V. Effect of Molecular Structure and Environment on Luminescence

The effect of molecular structure on luminescence is best discussed in terms of the rate constants for excited state processes, as outlined in Figure 1-8. S_0, S^*, and T represent the ground state, the first excited singlet state, and the lowest triplet states, respectively. The rate constants k_c, k_f, k_x, k_p, k_c' are for radiationless energy loss from the first excited singlet state, fluorescence, intersystem crossing, phosphorescence, and radiationless energy loss from the lowest triplet to the ground state, respectively.

The quantum yield of fluorescence is given by

$$\phi_f = k_f/(k_f + k_c + k_x) \tag{1-3}$$

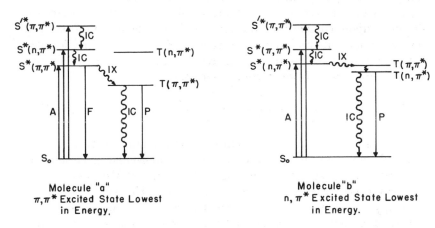

Molecule "a"
π,π^* Excited State Lowest
in Energy.

Molecule "b"
n, π^* Excited State Lowest
in Energy.

Figure 1-7.   Comparison of electronic processes for molecules having lowest n,π^* and π,π^* states: A, absorption; IC, internal conversion; IX, intersystem crossing; P, phosphorescence; F, fluorescence; S*, excited singlet state; T, triplet state; S_0, ground state.

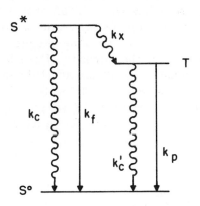

Figure 1-8.   Summary of rate constants for excited state processes: S_0, ground state; S*, lowest excited singlet state; T, lowest triplet state; k_c, internal conversion for lowest excited singlet state; k_c', internal conversion between lowest triplet state and ground state; k_p, phosphorescence; k_x, intersystem crossing.

If k_f is much greater than both k_c and k_x, the quantum efficiency of fluorescence will approach unity, while if k_x or k_c is much greater than k_f, ϕ_f will approach zero. The quantum efficiency of phosphorescence depends upon competition between internal conversion from the lowest triplet state and phosphorescence emission, as well as depending upon the rate of intersystem crossing relative to fluorescence and internal conversion from excited singlet state:

$$\phi_p = \frac{k_p}{k_p + k_c'} \times \frac{k_x}{k_f + k_c + k_x} \qquad (1\text{-}4)$$

In general, k_f and k_p are dependent upon molecular structure and are affected only slightly by the nature of the molecular environment. The value of k_x depends on molecular structure but also is influenced by certain perturbations of the environment. However, k_c and k_c', although determined to some extent by the nature of the electronic states of a molecule, are strongly dependent upon the molecular environment. The most reasonable way to discuss the effect of molecular structure on ϕ_f and ϕ_p is to consider how changes in structure affect the rate constants of Figure 1-8. It is important to remember that fluorescence and phosphorescence are only two of several processes that can occur after molecular excitation. Therefore structural or environmental changes that affect rate constants other than k_f of k_p can have profound effects on ϕ_f or ϕ_p.

First, consider those factors which will affect k_f. This rate constant is a measure of the probability of an electronic transition between the lowest excited singlet state and the ground state. This means that those factors which affect the intensity of the longest wavelength absorption band in a molecule will also affect the rate of spontaneous emission from the lowest excited singlet state. Therefore, the maximum molar extinction coefficient, ϵ_{max}, of the long-wavelength absorption band can serve as a qualitative measure of k_f. As ϵ_{max} decreases, one will expect to see a corresponding decrease in k_f (and a corresponding increase in the lifetime of the excited singlet state). Therefore, when symmetry and/or orbital overlap restrictions are introduced into the long-wavelength transition, one would expect to see a decrease in fluorescence efficiency. For example, ϵ_{max} for the long-wavelength absorption band of anthracene is approximately 10^4, while the ϵ_{max} for the long wavelength band of triphenylene is approximately 10^3. The fluorescence efficiency of anthracene is 0.46 (28), while the fluorescence from triphenylene can barely be measured.

The rate of intersystem crossing, k_x, is largely determined by two molecular parameters: the extent of singlet–triplet mixing, and the energy separation between the lowest singlet state and the triplet state immediately below it. According to spectroscopic selection rules, all transitions involving a change in multiplicity are formally forbidden. However, in organic molecules, considerable state mixing occurs so that triplet states are not pure triplets, but have some degree of singlet character to them (29). It is this singlet character which is largely responsible for the observed intensity of triplet–singlet transitions. Therefore, the greater amount of singlet character in a triplet state, the greater will be the probability of intersystem crossing. Another parameter affecting k_x is the triplet–singlet split. The smaller the difference in energy between the singlet and the triplet, the greater will be the probability of intersystem crossing. This situation arises because intersystem crossing is brought about by a vibrational coupling between a vibrational level of the triplet state and the lowest vibrational level of the lowest excited singlet state. For a molecule to go from the singlet state to a very high vibrational level of a triplet state is unlikely because of the large changes in nuclear configuration required. However, if the singlet–triplet split is small, intersystem crossing will require only a modest change in nuclear configuration and the probability of its occurring will be increased. It is difficult to determine the percentage of singlet character in a triplet state, but the energy separation between the singlet and triplet is easily measurable, a good first approximation being the differences in energies between the fluorescence and phosphorescence spectra.

The extent to which singlet–triplet mixing occurs in a molecule is dependent upon the electromagnetic field in which an electron finds itself—the greater the potential field, the greater the singlet–triplet mixing (spin–orbit coupling). Therefore, if a π electron is allowed to interact with the field near the nucleus of a heavy atom, the mixing between triplet and singlet states will increase as will the rate of intersystem crossing, k_x (30). This is a brief explanation of the so-called heavy atom effect in molecular spectroscopy, in which substitution of a heavy atom into a π electron system decreases fluorescence and increases phosphorescence. For example, in the halobenzene series the fluorescence efficiency of fluorobenzene is approximately 0.16, chlorobenzene is 0.05, and bromobenzene is approximately 0.01, with iodobenzene being nonfluorescent (31).

Therefore, one may formulate the general rule that perturbation of a π electron system by an atom of high atomic number will tend to enhance the rate of intersystem crossing.

Another rather interesting effect is that of a paramagnetic species on the intersystem crossing rate (32). In general, species with unpaired electron spins will enhance intersystem crossing. This effect operates independently of the atomic number effect discussed above. For example, in mesoporphyrin (IX) dimethyl ester (33), one sees strong fluorescence and weak phosphorescence; but its zinc chelate ($Z = 30$) shows medium intensity of fluorescence and weak phosphorescence due to intersystem crossing enhanced by the increase in atomic number. If, however, one observes the luminescence of the copper chelate ($Z = 29$) of this molecule, no fluorescence is observed but very strong phosphorescence occurs. This additional decrease in fluorescence and increase in phosphorescence of the copper chelate cannot be attributed to an atomic number effect, since its atomic number is one less than that of zinc, and therefore must be attributed to the enhancement in intersystem crossing by the paramagnetic character of the copper ion.

The intramolecular factors affecting the rate of radiationless deactivation of an excited state are not well understood although some work has been done recently to investigate the nature of this very important process. One of the most important environmental factors in this regard is temperature. During the lifetime of an excited singlet state, a molecule will undergo many collisions with other molecules in solution. Some of these collisions will be such that the excitation energy can be transferred to another molecule, perhaps to a solvent molecule, and lost as heat. As one increases the temperature of the solution, the number of collisions is increased, increasing the probability of radiationless loss of excitation energy by collisional transfer, resulting in a net increase in k_c. This accounts for the fact that the fluorescence efficiency of most molecules decreases with increasing temperature. The effect of temperature is even more important in regard to k_c' because of the longer lifetime of triplet states. The radiationless deactivation process for most molecules in triplet states is so efficient that phosphorescence can be observed only when the solution is frozen into a rigid glass, as discussed in Section III-D. It should be stressed, however, that the environmental aspects of radiationless deactivation do not tell the whole story. For example, pyridine shows neither fluorescence nor phosphorescence in solution at room temperature, or in rigid glasses at liquid nitrogen temperature (34).

In general, it has been assumed that those factors which enhance intersystem crossing should also enhance k_p relative to k_c', since both intersystem crossing and phosphorescence involve a change in spin. In fact, since intersystem crossing must precede phosphorescence emission, it has been difficult to evaluate independently changes in k_x and k_p.   One piece of evidence which supports the contention that similar changes in k_x and k_p should be observed for the same perturbation is the fact that paramagnetic species are known to quench emission from triplet states effectively (for example, oxygen) as well as to enhance intersystem crossing.   Recently a method has been developed for estimating independently the quantum efficiency of phosphorescence and the quantum efficiency of intersystem crossing (35).

The question which naturally arises when considering the effect of molecular structure on luminescence is how substituent groups will affect luminescence relative to the unsubstituted π electron system (for example, functional groups on an aromatic nucleus vs. the unsubstituted aromatic hydrocarbon).   Although there are no rigorous rules which govern the effect of substituents, a few generalities can be given.   First, electron-donating groups generally tend to enhance fluorescence efficiency because they tend to increase the transition probability between the lowest excited singlet state and the ground state.   Those groups, which have a small interaction with the π electron system, tend to produce a small change in quantum efficiency, such as SO_3H, NH_4^+, and alkyl groups.   A second generalization can be made that those functional groups which tend to introduce a long wavelength $n \to \pi^*$ transition into the absorption spectrum of a molecule tend to reduce the fluorescence efficiency of that molecule to zero.   The third generalization which may be made is that introduction of a high atomic number atom into a π electron system generally enhances phosphorescence and decreases fluorescence.   The effect of molecular structure on fluorescence will be discussed in greater detail in Chapter 3.

VI. Processes Competing with Luminescence

Any excited state process that occurs instead of luminescence competes with luminescence.   For example, intersystem crossing and internal conversion to the ground state are processes which compete with fluorescence, the latter also competing with phosphorescence. The reason these processes have been dealt with earlier is that the understanding of luminescence requires discussion of these two competing processes at the same time. However, there are other processes which compete with luminescence and these will be the topic of this section.

The process of molecular excitation and subsequent loss of excitation energy can be treated by considering four states: the ground state, the state to which excitation occurred initially, the lowest excited singlet state, and the triplet state. A process competing with luminescence can occur from any of the three excited states mentioned, subject to certain kinetic restrictions. For a process to compete effectively with the normal radiative processes, it must have a rate constant greater than the spontaneous decay of the excited state from which it must occur. Expressed mathematically,

$$k_{cp} > 1/\tau_s$$

where k_{cp} is the rate constant for the competing process and τ_s is the lifetime of the state involved. Figure 1-9 shows the relationship between the four states mentioned and both radiative and nonradiative processes.

Basically, there are two types of processes that compete with luminescence (other than internal conversion and intersystem crossing): radiationless transfer of excitation energy to an appropriate acceptor, and chemical reactions, both reversible and irreversible. Each of the three important excited states will be discussed in relation to these two types of processes and their kinetic requirements.

The initial excited state can be either a higher excited singlet state or a vibrationally excited level of the lowest excited singlet state. Remembering that internal conversion occurs to the lowest vibrational level of the lowest excited singlet state in approximately 10^{-13} to 10^{-11} s, any competing process that is to occur from this state must have a first-order rate constant of at least 10^{11} l/mole-s. This restriction is sufficiently limiting that, to date, energy transfer from higher excited singlet states has been observed only in solid matrices, and it is questionable whether any chemical reactions from higher excited singlet states have been observed. Certainly if a chemical reaction

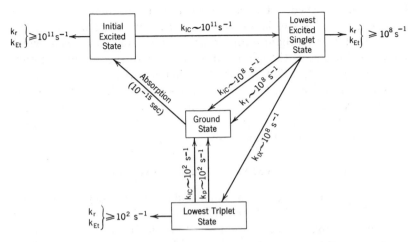

Figure 1-9.   The relationship between radiative and nonradiative processes from excited states: k_r = rate constant for chemical reaction; k_{Et} = rate constant for energy transfer; k_{IC} = rate constant for internal conversion; k_{IX} = rate constant for intersystem crossing; k_p = rate constant for phosphorescence.

is to occur, it *cannot* be a diffusion-controlled reaction (diffusion-controlled reactions have rate constants in the vicinity of 10^9 l/mole-s), but the molecule will have to react with its nearest neighbor within the solvent cage.   This virtually restricts one to very rapid reactions such as electron exchange, since the time for reaction is on the order of that required for one molecular vibration.

In the lowest excited singlet state (lowest vibrational level), a molecule has a lifetime of approximately 10^{-8} s, and hence both energy transfer and chemical reactions can occur from such a state. Also, diffusion controlled processes are possible.   Energy transfer can occur by both "collisional" mechanisms and noncollisional mechanisms, and both singlet–singlet and singlet–triplet energy transfer are known.   Both reversible and irreversible chemical reactions have been observed for a molecule in an excited singlet state.   The restriction on the rate constant for a chemical reaction is that k_r, $k_{Et} \gg k_f$, k_{IX}, k_{IC}, as shown in Figure 1-9.   This still restricts one to rather rapid processes having rate constants around 10^8 l/mole-s.

The lifetime of the lowest triplet state is long, on the order of 10^{-2} s, and therefore both energy transfer and chemical reactions occur from triplet states.   Both triplet–triplet and triplet–singlet energy transfer have been observed. The major restriction on chemical reactions involving triplet states is not that $k_r \geqslant k_p$, but rather that $k_r \geqslant k_{ic}$, since in solution at room temperature it is internal conversion which limits the lifetime of the triplet state rather than the intrinsic lifetime of the state itself. This means that chemical reactions having rate constants of the order of 10^3 l/mole-s are possible from triplet states and not from singlet states. It is this type of argument which has led many authors to postulate the triplet as the reactive state for a wide variety of photochemical reactions.

A. Energy Transfer: Collisional Quenching

Collisional quenching is a bimolecular process depending upon "contact" between the excited molecule and the quencher. It is a diffusion-controlled process requiring that the lifetime of the excited state involved be greater than 10^{-9} s. The mechanism for collisional quenching may be written in the following way:

$$F + h\nu \rightarrow F^* \tag{1-5}$$

$$F^* \rightarrow F + h\nu' \tag{1-6}$$

$$F^* + Q \rightarrow F + Q \tag{1-7}$$

The fluorescent molecule F absorbs a photon to give F^*, the equilibrium level of the lowest excited singlet state. F^* can either emit a photon, $h\nu'$, and return to the ground state, or it can interact with a quencher molecule Q, thereby losing excitation energy and returning to the ground state without emission of fluorescence. This very simple mechanism is described by the Stern-Volmer law (36):

$$(f_0/f) - 1 = kC_Q \tag{1-8}$$

where f_0 is the fluorescence intensity in the absence of the quencher, f is the fluorescence intensity at concentration, C_Q, of the quencher, and k is a proportionality constant.

Although this simple mechanism adequately describes collisional quenching mathematically, the physical process requires dissipation of approximately 50–100 kcal/mole of excitation energy, a quantity too great to be lost by a simple collisional transfer. Basically there are two mechanisms by which "collisional" loss of excitation energy can occur: enhancement of intersystem crossing by the quencher, or electron transfer.

The effect of the quencher on intersystem crossing is well known; for example, oxygen, alkyl halides, and paramagnetic metal chelates (37) all are effective quenchers. The enhancement of intersystem crossing during collision is a very efficient process; it appears that external perturbations by quenchers are more effective at enhancing intersystem crossing than comparable internal perturbations (38). For example, complex formation with an alkyl iodide is more effective in bringing about intersystem crossing in aromatic molecules than is substitution of an iodine atom directly into the aromatic system.

The concept of quenching by an electron transfer mechanism is relatively new and extremely interesting (39). It may be summarized by the following sequence of reactions:

$$F^* + Q \rightarrow F^- \cdot Q^+ \xrightarrow{\text{solvent}} F^-_{\text{solv}} + Q^+_{\text{solv}} \qquad (1\text{-}9)$$
$$^3F + Q \qquad \qquad F + Q$$

The excited fluorescent molecule, F^*, reacts with the quencher, Q, abstracting an electron from it to form the ion pair $F^- \cdot Q^+$. This ion pair can dissociate to give either a triplet state, ^3F, and quencher, or simply a ground state and quencher, either process dissipating the excitation energy thermally. In the presence of a polar solvent, however, both F^- and Q^+ can be solvated, and can then carry out characteristic radical ion reactions in solution. The electron abstraction mechanism has been studied for the quenching of perylene fluorescence by amines (39). Flash photolysis was used to observe the presence of the perylene triplet, and the perylene negative radical ion.

B. NONCOLLISIONAL ENERGY TRANSFER

Energy transfer that occurs over distances larger than the contact distances of molecular collision is called a noncollisional energy transfer (40-42). These processes are true, nonradiative transfer processes and should not be confused with the trivial process of emission of radiation by one molecule and reabsorption of emitted radiation by another. Also, noncollisional energy transfer is not spin forbidden per se, singlet–triplet and triplet–singlet transfer occurring as well as singlet–singlet and triplet–triplet transfer. The process of noncollisional energy transfer is summarized below:

$$D + h\nu \rightarrow D^* \qquad (1\text{-}10)$$
$$D^* + A \rightarrow D + A^* \qquad (1\text{-}11)$$
$$A^* \rightarrow A + h\nu \qquad (1\text{-}12)$$

The donor molecule, D, absorbs radiation and goes to an excited state, D^*. D^* and A, the acceptor, interact and the excitation energy is transferred from D to A.   Molecule A in its excited state, A^*, emits its own characteristic fluorescence, the net effect being that the energy of excitation has been transferred from D to A.   This mechanism has been studied for a number of molecules, although studies on energy transfer between 1-chloroanthracene and perylene (43) were the first to establish clearly that noncollisional transfer was not brought about by the trivial process.   Noncollisional energy transfer can occur over distances of 50–100 A., and the probability of transfer falls off as the reciprocal sixth power of the distance between the donor and the acceptor.

Noncollisional energy transfer most likely arises from a vibrational coupling interaction between the excited states of the donor and the acceptor, as shown in Figure 1-10.   If the donor and acceptor have a common vibrational frequency, resonant energy transfer between them is possible, because of the quantum mechanical identity of the system:

$$D^* \ldots . A \leftrightarrow D \ldots . A^*$$

If both D and A have a common single energy level, the energy will be transferred back and forth between them until one emits.   If, however, the lowest vibrational level of the excited state of the acceptor lies lower than the equilibrium state of the donor, once the energy has been transferred to A, rapid internal conversion occurs to its lowest vibrational level.   Under these circumstances, A does not have sufficient thermal energy to overcome the barrier for transferring energy back to D, and therefore A has acted as an energy sink. The acceptor will remain in its lowest excited state until it can emit radiation (or undergo internal conversion), as shown in Figure 1-10. An interesting characteristic of this transfer process is that its efficiency depends upon the overlap of the absorption spectrum of A with the fluorescence spectrum of D (exactly the same as would be true for the trivial case), as well as on the lifetime of the excited state of the donor and the intensity of the transition between the ground state and the active excited state of the acceptor.

A very striking (and practically useful) example of noncollisional transfer is the triplet–triplet energy transfer between benzophenone as donor and naphthalene as acceptor (44,45).   Phosphorescence of

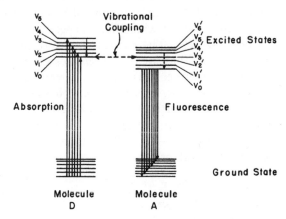

Figure 1-10.   The mechanism of noncollisional nonradiative energy transfer.

naphthalene is not excited by 3650 A. because radiation of this wavelength is not absorbed by naphthalene and, furthermore, the phosphorescence of naphthalene is excited only with poor efficiency by its long-wavelength singlet–singlet absorption band.   Benzophenone has its singlet state lower in energy than the lowest excited singlet state of naphthalene, but its lowest triplet state higher in energy than the lowest triplet state of naphthalene.   Furthermore, the phosphorescence of benzophenone is excited readily by 3650 A., probably with unit quantum efficiency.   If both benzophenone and naphthalene are present in a rigid glass at 77°K and irradiated with 3650 A. radiation, benzophenone absorbs the exciting radiation, intersystem crosses to its triplet, transfers its excitation energy to naphthalene, and naphthalene phosphorescence is observed.   As it turns out, this method of excitation is far more effective for exciting the phosphorescence of naphthalene than is the direct excitation by absorption of naphthalene.   This particular type of energy transfer process has been used in a number of instances to photosensitize chemical reactions (46).

Another energy transfer process is delayed fluorescence, an emission which has the spectral characteristics of fluorescence but a lifetime just shorter than the lifetime of phosphorescence.   Delayed fluorescence has been observed in the gas phase, in solution, and in rigid glasses at liquid nitrogen temperature (47–49).   It should be stressed that the delayed fluorescence spectrum is identical with the fluorescence spectrum of the molecule, and should not be confused with the so-called "excimer" fluorescence which has a spectrum different from normal fluorescence (50–52).   The excitation spectrum for delayed fluorescence is the same as that for regular fluorescence.

Delayed fluorescence has been studied for a variety of aromatic hydrocarbons and its intensity is proportional to the square of the intensity of the exciting radiation and to the square of the phosphorescence intensity, indicating that it is a biphotonic process involving two triplet states (53–55).   These data suggest the following mechanism for delayed fluorescence:

$$S_0 + h\nu \rightarrow S^* \tag{1-13}$$

$$S^* \rightarrow T \tag{1-14}$$

$$T + T \rightarrow S^* + S^0 \tag{1-15}$$

$$S^* \rightarrow S^0 + h\nu' \tag{1-16}$$

The molecule in its ground state, S_0, absorbs a photon and goes to the lowest excited singlet, S^*, which undergoes intersystem crossing to the triplet state.   At a sufficiently high concentration of the hydrocarbon, two triplet states can interact according to eq. (1-15) to produce an excited singlet state and a ground singlet state; the excited singlet state then emits its normal fluorescence as shown in eq. (1-16).   This mechanism accounts for the observed relationships between phosphorescence intensity and intensity of exciting radiation, and accounts for the fact that the delayed fluorescence has a lifetime just shorter than that of phosphorescence.

C. Chemical Reactions

Another process which may compete with luminescence is a chemical reaction by a molecule in an excited state, such reactions being reversible or irreversible.   Quite often, excited state reactions are different from reactions of the same molecule in the ground state. A detailed review of chemical reactions of excited states is beyond the scope of the present treatment and therefore only one specific example of each type will be considered.

Irreversible chemical reactions may occur either from a triplet state or from the lowest excited singlet state of a molecule.   A good example is the photochemistry of quinones. Usually it has been thought that triplet states are the active states in the photoreduction of quinones, although this is not always true. For example, duroquinone reacts from the lowest excited singlet state (56) while anthraquinone reacts from the triplet state (57).

Consider the photoreduction of anthraquinone in alcohol. It should be noted that anthraquinone is stable in alcohol in the ground state, but that the triplet state reacts rapidly with alcohol (51,58).

$$AQ + h\nu \rightarrow {}^1AQ^* \rightarrow {}^3AQ \qquad (1\text{-}17)$$

$${}^3AQ + RCH_2OH \rightarrow AQH\cdot + R\dot{C}HOH \qquad (1\text{-}18)$$

$$R\dot{C}HOH + AQ \rightarrow AQH\cdot + RCHO \qquad (1\text{-}19)$$

$$2AQH\cdot \rightarrow AQ + AQH_2 \qquad (1\text{-}20)$$

Anthraquinone, AQ, absorbs radiation to go first to the excited singlet state and then to the triplet state. The triplet state reacts with alcohol to form the semiquinone radical, AQH· (Structure 1-I), and the corresponding alcohol radical, R\dot{C}HOH. The alcohol radical reacts with a ground state anthraquinone molecule to produce a second AQH· and an aldehyde molecule. Two of the anthraquinone radicals then combine in a disproportionation reaction to give anthraquinone and 9,10-dihydroxyanthracene (Structure 1-II) as shown in eq. (1-20). The overall reaction, per photon, is the production of one molecule of AQH_2 and one molecule of the aldehyde.

(1-I)   (1-II)

The photoreduction of anthraquinone is a rapid, highly efficient reaction having a quantum efficiency approaching unity. It is particularly interesting to note that although photoreduction of anthraquinone hypothetically competes with phosphorescence, the reaction produces a highly fluorescent species, AQH_2. Therefore, when this reaction is carried out in solution at room temperature, fluorescence is induced into a solution of anthraquinone rather than being quenched. Photolysis in the anthraquinone system does not stop at 9,10-dihydroxyanthracene, but under 2537 A. radiation, AQH_2 is reduced further—first to 9-anthranol and then to 9,9'-bianthryl (59). These reactions also cause changes in the fluorescence of a solution since both 9-anthranol and 9,9'-bianthryl fluoresce blue.

A good example of an excited state reaction which is reversible is the ionization of molecules in their excited singlet states (60). As was discussed in Section II-C, compounds such as β-naphthol show different acidities in their lowest excited singlet state, and in their ground state. Because of this, one often observes "anomalous" fluorescence behavior as a function of pH. For example, at pH 5 one can observe fluorescence emission corresponding to the ionic form of β-naphthol, even though the ground state pK_a of β-naphthol is 9.46. Also it should be noted that the pK_a of a triplet state will be different from the pK_a's of the lowest excited singlet state and the ground state, although generally being closer to the latter (61).

The mechanism for the ionization of a phenol in its excited state is shown below (62).

$$ROH + h\nu \rightarrow ROH^* \qquad (1\text{-}21)$$

$$ROH^* \rightarrow ROH + h\nu' \qquad (1\text{-}22)$$

$$ROH^* \rightarrow RO^{-*} + H^+ \qquad (1\text{-}23)$$

$$RO^{-*} \rightarrow RO^- + h\nu'' \qquad (1\text{-}24)$$

The molecular form of the phenol, ROH, absorbs radiation to go to its lowest excited singlet state, ROH^*, which can then either emit its molecular fluorescence [eq. (1-27)], or can ionize to produce an excited-state ion, as shown in eq. (1-23). If the latter reaction occurs in a time short compared to the lifetime of the excited singlet state, the excited ion RO^{-*} can then emit its own characteristic fluorescence, as shown in eq. (1–24). The net outcome of this process is that one can see fluorescence characteristic of an ionic species in solutions where no ions exist in the ground state. By comparing changes in fluorescent spectra as a function of pH with changes in absorption spectra as a function of pH, one can utilize fluorescence measurements to determine excited-state ionization constants. A number of molecules have been studied by this technique, indicating that functional groups, such as phenol and arylammonium compounds, become stronger acids in the excited state, while carboxylate groups become stronger bases.

This work is supported in part through funds provided by the United States Atomic Energy Commission under Contract AT (30-1)-905.

General References

1. R. S. Becker and M. Kasha, in F. H. Johnson, Ed., *The Luminescence of Biological Systems*, American Association for the Advancement of Science, Washington, D. C., 1955.
2. Th. Förster, *Fluoreszenz Organischer Verbindungen*, Vandenhoeck and Ruprecht, Göttingen, 1951.
3. H. H. Jaffé and M. Orchin, *Theory and Applications of Ultraviolet Spectroscopy*, Wiley, New York, 1962.
4. M. Kasha, *Radiation Res. Suppl.*, *2*, 243 (1960).
5. M. Kasha, in M. Burton, J. S. Kirby-Smith, and J. Magee, Eds., *Comparative Effects of Radiation*, Wiley, New York, 1960.
6. M. Kasha, in W. D. McElroy and B. Glass, Eds., *Light and Life*, Johns Hopkins University Press, Baltimore, Md., 1961.
7. L. Lang, *Absorption Spectra in the Ultraviolet and Visible Region*, Vol. I, Academic Press, New York, 1961.
8. J. N. Murrell, *The Theory of the Electronic Spectra of Organic Molecules*, Wiley, New York, 1961.
9. P. Pringsheim, *Fluorescence and Phosphorescence*, Interscience, New York, 1949.
10. G. W. Robinson, in W. D. McElroy and B. Glass, Eds., *Light and Life*, Johns Hopkins University Press, Baltimore, Md., 1961.
11. J. W. Sidman, *Chem. Rev.*, *58*, 689 (1958).
12. W. West, Ed., *Chemical Applications of Spectroscopy* (Technique of Organic Chemistry, Vol. 9) Interscience, New York, 1956, Chaps. 1, 5, 6, 7.
13. D. A. Ramsay, in F. C. Nachod and W. D. Phillips, Eds., *Determination of Organic Structure by Physical Methods*, Vol. 2, Academic Press, New York, 1962.

References

14. J. R. Platt, *J. Opt. Soc. Am.*, *43*, 252 (1953).
15. H. E. Zimmerman and V. R. Sandel, *J. Am. Chem. Soc.*, *85*, 915 (1963).
16. W. Bartok, P. J. Lucchesi, and N. S. Snider, *J. Am. Chem. Soc.*, *84*, 1842 (1962).
17. A. Weller, *Z. Physik. Chem. (Frankfurt)*, *17*, 224 (1958).
18. E. Lim, quoted in ref. 35.
19. G. Viswanath and M. Kasha, *J. Chem. Phys.*, *24*, 574 (1956).
20. M. Beer and H. C. Longuet-Higgins, *J. Chem. Phys.*, *23*, 1390 (1962).

21. H. L. J. Bäckström and K. Sandros, *Acta Chem. Scand.*, *12*, 823 (1958).
22. C. A. Parker and C. G. Hatchard, *J. Phys. Chem.*, *66*, 2506 (1962).
23. N. Mataga, Y. Kaifu, and M. Koizumi, *Bull. Chem. Soc. Japan*, *29*, 373 (1956).
24. M. Chowdhury and L. Goodman, *J. Chem. Phys.*, *36*, 548 (1962).
25. E. Lippert and W. Voss, *Z. Physik. Chem. (Frankfurt)*, *31*, 321 (1962).
26. M. A. El-Bayoumi and D. R. Kearns, *J. Chem. Phys.*, *36*, 2516 (1962).
27. B. L. Van Duuren, *Chem. Rev.*, *63*, 325 (1963).
28. E. J. Bowen and A. H. Williams, *Trans. Faraday Soc.*, *35*, 765 (1939).
29. D. S. McClure, *J. Chem. Phys.*, *20*, 682 (1952).
30. D. S. McClure, *J. Chem. Phys.*, *17*, 905 (1948).
31. E. H. Gilmore, G. E. Gibson, and D. S. McClure, *J. Chem. Phys.*, *20*, 829 (1952).
32. P. Yuster and S. I. Weissman, *J. Chem. Phys.*, *17*, 1182 (1949).
33. J. B. Allison and R. S. Becker, *J. Chem. Phys.*, *32*, 1410 (1960).
34. G. J. Brealey, *J. Chem. Phys.*, *24*, 571 (1956).
35. R. E. Kellogg and R. G. Bennett, *J. Chem. Phys.*, *41*, 3042 (1964).
36. O. Stern and M. Volmer, *Physik. Z.*, *20*, 183 (1919).
37. J. Nag-Chadhuri, L. Stoessell, and S. P. McGlynn, *J. Chem. Phys.*, *38*, 2027 (1963).
38. S. P. McGlynn and R. Sunseri, *J. Chem. Phys.*, *37*, 1818 (1962).
39. H. Leonhardt and A. Weller, *Z. Physik. Chem. (Frankfurt)*, *29*, 277 (1961).
40. F. Perrin, *Ann. Phys. (Paris)*, *17*, 283 (1932).
41. Th. Förster, *Ann. Physik.*, *2*, 55 (1947).
42. Th. Förster, *Discussions Faraday Soc.*, *27*, 7 (1959).
43. E. J. Bowen and B. Brocklehurst, *Trans. Faraday Soc.*, *51*, 774 (1955).
44. A. N. Terenin and V. L. Ermolaev, *Dokl. Akad. Nauk. SSSR*, *85*, 547 (1952).
45. A. N. Terenin and V. L. Ermolaev, *Trans. Faraday Soc.*, *52*, 1042 (1956).
46. H. L. J. Bäckström and K. Sandros, *Acta Chem. Scand.*, *14*, 48 (1960).
47. R. Williams, *J. Chem. Phys.*, *28*, 577 (1958).
48. C. A. Parker and C. G. Hatchard, *Trans. Faraday Soc.*, *57*, 1894 (1961).
49. T. Azumi and S. P. McGlynn, *J. Chem. Phys.*, *38*, 2773 (1963).
50. Th. Förster and K. Kasper, *Z. Physik. Chem. (Frankfurt)*, *1*, 275 (1954).
51. Th. Förster and K. Kasper, *Z. Elektrochem.*, *59*, 976 (1955).
52. B. Stevens and E. Hutton, *Nature*, *186*, 1045 (1960).
53. C. A. Parker and C. G. Hatchard, *Proc. Chem. Soc.*, *1962*, 147.
54. H. Steinlicht, G. C. Nieman, and G. W. Robinson, *J. Chem. Phys.*, *38*, 1326 (1963).
55. T. Azumi and S. P. McGlynn, *J. Chem. Phys.*, *39*, 1186 (1963).
56. N. K. Bridge and G. Porter, *Proc. Roy. Soc. (London)*, *244A*, 259, 276 (1958).
57. F. Wilkinson, *J. Phys. Chem.*, *66*, 2569 (1962).
58. J. L. Bolland and H. R. Cooper, *Proc. Roy. Soc. (London)*, *225A*, 405 (1954).
59. J. D. Gorsuch, J. P. Paris, and D. M. Hercules, paper presented at the 144th National Meeting, American Chemical Society, Los Angeles, California, 1963.
60. A. Weller, in G. Porter, Ed., *Progress in Reaction Kinetics*, Vol. I, Pergamon Press, New York, 1961.
61. G. Jackson and G. Porter, *Proc. Roy. Soc. (London)*, *260A*, 13 (1961).
62. Th. Förster, *Z. Elektrochem.*, *54*, 42 (1950).

chapter 2

Luminescence Instrumentation and Experimental Details

DAVID W. ELLIS
Department of Chemistry,
University of New Hampshire, Durham, New Hampshire

I. General Principles of Luminescence Instrumentation

The three principal components of any fluorometer are the source of excitation, the sample cell, and the detector. In the earliest instruments, these components were simply the sun, a glass tube, and the eye. Since then, the instrumentation has become far more complicated.

Figure 2-1 shows the basic components which are present in any modern fluorometer or spectrofluorometer. (For the purpose of this chapter, those instruments which select the wavelengths of excitation or emission by use of filters will be called fluorometers, and instruments that incorporate two monochromators will be called spectrofluorometers.)

The source is usually either a mercury or a xenon arc. Lamps are produced by a variety of manufacturers; some of the more commonly used sources are manufactured by Osram, Hanovia lamp division of Englehard Hanovia, Inc., and the PEK Labs, Inc. The mercury arc has the advantage of giving very high intensities at its emission lines. The intensity level of the xenon arc is comparatively lower, but it is nearly uniform over the range of frequencies most commonly used. However, many xenon lamps produce a small number of lines in the 4000 A. and 6600–8000 A. regions which can be a source of error if one is working at high resolution. The aging and ultraviolet distribution characteristics of xenon arcs have recently been studied (1). These and other types of available lamps have been reviewed by Doede and Walker (2).

41

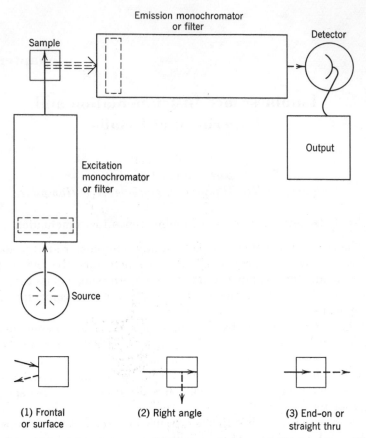

Fig. 2-1. Essential components of a fluorometer or spectrofluorometer. Three common arrangements are shown.

The light passes through the device used to select the excitation radiation, often being focused in order to obtain increased intensity. This device may be either a filter or a monochromator. The major advantage of the filter fluorometer is that it permits a greater quantity of light to strike the sample, an arrangement which is particularly desirable for trace analysis. The lack of selectivity which accompanies the use of filters is their major disadvantage. The possibility that the material from which the filter is made may itself fluoresce, of course, must be checked. Filters are available from Eastman Kodak

Corp., Corning Glass Co., and Bausch and Lomb, Inc.   Interference
filters can also be used to provide greater selectivity.

For some purposes, an excitation monochromator is a necessity.
The choice between a prism or a grating for the excitation monochromator is difficult.   A prism monochromator has the advantage
of greater dispersion in the ultraviolet region, which is usually used
for excitation.   However, quartz prisms, which are needed in this
region, are expensive.   The light loss with grating monochromators
is often less than with prism instruments.   On the other hand, with
gratings the problem of overlapping spectra due to the passage of
different orders can be serious; often simple glass filters can eliminate
most of this problem.   Commercial instruments can be found with
either prism or grating monochromators.

If it is to illuminate the solution, the light must pass through the
sample cell.   The choice of material for the sample cell can be quite
complicated.   It must be made of a material which will not absorb
appreciably the wavelengths of interest.   In most cases a good grade
of glass is suitable; however, for work in the region below 350 mμ,
quartz is often desirable, and below 320 mμ, quartz is essential.
Nevertheless, one should be familiar with the optical characteristics
of each sample cell to be used since the quality of quartz available
can vary considerably.   Parker and Rees (3) state that the fluorescence from optical fused quartz can be as much as 100,000 times
greater than that of some quartzes.   Similarly, the inherent fluorescence of certain glasses is quite high.

Three basic arrangements, shown at the bottom of Fig. 2-1, have
been utilized for placing the cell with respect to the excitation and
detection components.   (1) For solid samples or ones that are very
opaque, the frontal method is the best choice.   (2) For dilute solutions or gases, the right angle arrangement is most advantageous.   It
is important to remember, however, that in this position, the fluorescence monochromator must "see" only the fluorescing solution or
gas and not the side walls of the sample cell.   Otherwise, fluorescence
from the walls of the cell and reflected light from these walls may
seriously reduce the sensitivity of the instrument.   (Reflected light
can further complicate matters by producing additional fluorescence
in the sample; a light trap minimizes this.)   Parker and Rees (3,4)
have shown that the right angle and frontal arrangements are not
without their drawbacks under certain conditions.   (3) The straight

through arrangement is seldom used except in phosphorescence studies.

The fluorescence leaving the sample cell usually passes directly into a fluorescence filter, which is used to eliminate any scattered light of the excitation frequency, or into a fluorescence monochromator; in some cases, both a filter and a monochromator are used. The fluorescence monochromator is usually of the grating type, since it normally will provide better dispersion and less light loss than a prism system. When using monochromators as both the excitation and fluorescence components, the problem of slit widths becomes particularly important. Even when using high intensity sources, the amount of excitation light hitting a sample is small, and the fluorescent light leaving the sample is even smaller. This fluorescence is then passed through another monochromator before being detected. Fortunately, it is seldom necessary to have small slit widths on both monochromators simultaneously. When measuring fluorescence spectra, the slits of the excitation monochromator can be large, and when recording an excitation spectrum, the slits on the fluorescence monochromator can be large.

With both fluorometers and spectrofluorometers, the need for highly sensitive detection systems is acute. In most instruments, high gain photomultiplier tubes with their requisite high voltage power supplies are necessary. Some fluorometers and spectrofluorometers measure fluorescence under DC conditions while others use a chopped light beam and incorporate tuned AC amplifiers. Even though DC systems are usually less complicated, they are inconvenient for differentiating fluorescence from phosphorescence and for the measurement of phosphorescent lifetimes.

The output of the detection system can be displayed in a variety of ways. Most often, simple fluorometers use a meter. With spectrofluorometers, an oscilloscope or recorder is normally used. For particularly low level signals, where the signal-to-noise ratio is the limiting factor, integration with large time constant circuits can be advantageous.

Often it is desirable to obtain fluorescence spectra and excitation spectra. These spectra can be measured only with spectrofluorometers or with spectrographs. When using spectrofluorometers, a fluorescence spectrum is measured by keeping the wavelength of excitation constant and plotting the intensity of emitted fluorescence as a function of its wavelength. An excitation spectrum, on the other hand, is a plot of the intensity of fluorescence at a fixed wavelength as a function of the wavelength of the exciting light. It is measured by keeping the fluorescence monochromator at a preset wavelength and scanning the excitation monochromator. In those cases where the intensity of the exciting light is kept constant over the range of wavelengths for excitation, or differences are corrected for, an excitation spectrum will generally coincide with the absorption spectrum of the compound.

Three important terms which will be used frequently in this chapter are calibration, standardization, and correction. The term "calibration" will be used in those cases where comparisons are made with an absolute standard, for example, in the wavelength calibration of a monochromator. "Standardization" will be used in cases where a relative comparison is made to a standard substance or solution. "Correction" will refer to the process of making adjustments for the wavelength-sensitive components found in spectrofluorometers.

II. Instrumental Problems

A. Source

With the high intensity DC mercury and xenon arc sources which are usually employed in fluorescence analysis, there are some inherent problems. Many of the sources require forced air or water cooling. The most serious problem, however, is the decrease in the emitted intensity with use. It is necessary to correct for this decrease in some manner, such as a reference photodetector, a fluorescent screen (5), or the fluorescence of a fluorescent reference compound. (The correction of spectra which requires compensation for any source changes will be discussed later.)

B. Monochromator

The first step in using a spectrofluorometer is to calibrate the wavelength dial of each monochromator. Low pressure mercury sources are frequently used for this because they emit intense radiation at the mercury lines; several types are readily available (6).

The monochromator is calibrated by scanning the spectrum from the long wavelength end to the short wavelength end of the spectrum, noting the wavelengths at which the mercury lines appear. These can then be compared with the known mercury wavelengths, and the proper adjustments made (7). The calibration is usually carried out first with the fluorescence monochromator. The excitation monochromator is then calibrated against the fluorescence monochromator, using a light scatterer in the cell (8,9). Compounds of known absorption and emission also have been used for purposes of calibration (10).

The resolution of a spectrofluorometer depends on the band-pass of the monochromators, which in turn is determined by the slit width. It is important to remember that with the large slit widths which are used to obtain maximum sensitivity, the stray light and scattered light will be at a maximum. The resolution of the instrument will be at its minimum.

Differences between types of monochromators often confuse individuals working on a variety of instruments. The presence of overlapping second-order spectra is a potential source of error when working with grating monochromators. Differences in transmission of the dispersing element, whether prism or grating, as a function of frequency can be quite serious. For example, King and Hercules (11) have reported a "Wood anomaly" present in a commercial grating. This grating produced a sharp change in intensity in a particular region, causing anomalous shoulders or small peaks to appear.

C. Detectors

Many different types of detectors have been used for fluorescence analysis. Currently, almost all instruments use photomultiplier tubes with their limited wavelength range and wavelength sensitive response. With filter fluorometers, this is often not a handicap, since one can choose a detector with a good response in the region being used. For spectrofluorometers, the wavelength-sensitive response represents a potential source of error and is one factor necessitating the correction of emission spectra. (The correction of spectra will be discussed in a later section.)

For low levels of fluorescence, it is advisable to use a photomultiplier tube having its maximal response in the wavelength region of interest. In addition, with some tubes the signal-to-noise ratio can be improved 50- to 100-fold by cooling.

D. Standardization of Fluorescence Intensity

Because of changes in the lamp intensity with age and changes in the response characteristics of the monochromator–detector system, it is usually necessary to standardize an instrument. The simplest approach to this problem is to measure the fluorescence intensity of a fluorescent reference compound as a standard prior to each measurement. (Note that there are available instruments for which standardization is not necessary; these are discussed in a later section.)

Another approach to instrumental standardization has been suggested by Parker (12), namely, the use of the Raman spectrum of the solvent. If one is using a spectrofluorometer and is working under conditions of high sensitivity and constant band width, the Raman spectrum of the solvent will behave as an internal standard with which fluorescence spectra can be compared. It is then possible to interrelate all fluorescence spectra to one set of conditions using the Raman spectrum.

E. Sample Cell, Cell Geometry, and Scattered Light

Errors due to the sample cell and cell holder were first discussed by Fassel (13). In most instances, the design of the cell holder determines the amount of scattered and stray light; this in turn often limits the sensitivity of the instrument. Fortunately, with both fluorometers and spectrofluorometers, filters can be used to minimize scattered light (14). With right angle illumination, it is extremely important that the exciting radiation is not reflected back into the solution, and that the emission monochromator "sees" only the fluorescing solution, not the walls of the cell.

The glass or quartz used for the sample cell sometimes is a source of error, since many types of glass and quartz emit fluorescence under ultraviolet excitation. Price et al. (15) found that synthetic quartz has a much lower fluorescence than fused quartz. Parker has estimated the difference between his best sample of synthetic silica and a sample of optical quality fused quartz as greater than 100,000 (3). Naturally, the cells should not become scratched or etched. In analytical work using a filter fluorometer, the presence of any colloidal material or other scattering material produces erroneous results. For this reason, secondary filters are used. When using spectrofluorometers, scattered light can distort fluorescence spectra, and it also diminishes the level of fluorescence by scattering the fluorescence emission. Fortunately, the fluorescence spectrum of the blank should detect any background signal due to scattering. As mentioned earlier, it is not possible to eliminate Raman emission, but it will be readily detected by measuring the blank.

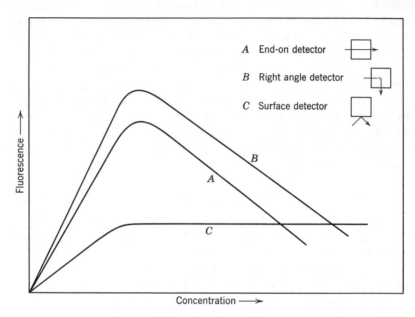

Fig. 2-2.   The effect of fluorophore concentration on the measurement of fluorescence in different arrangements (16).

The different cell geometries were mentioned briefly in the first section of this chapter. It is known that the arrangement used for illumination and detection has an effect on the calibration curve obtained. Figure 2-2 from Udenfriend (16) shows the advantage for quantitative work of using the right angle arrangement. However, for solutions with high concentrations of absorbing species, such as are frequently found in biological systems, it is often necessary to use the frontal method.

F. Inner Filter Effect

It is usually assumed that every molecule within a sample cell is illuminated with equally intense radiation, and that the emitted radiation is not affected by the presence of solute molecules. When either or both of these conditions is not fulfilled, the result is an "inner filter effect" (17). It is a decrease in fluorescence intensity caused by one of two factors: absorption of the fluorescence emission by a species in solution, or absorption of a significant fraction of the exciting radiation by some species in solution

The inner filter effect specifically does not include those processes which decrease the tendency of the molecule to emit fluorescence after it has been excited; these processes affect the quantum efficiency of the molecule and are referred to as "quenching" (4).

Inner filter effects are manifested in a variety of ways: the excitation and emission spectra may be altered, or a fluorescence vs. concentration calibration curve may be nonlinear at high concentrations. In those cases where the fluorophore is responsible for the inner filter effect, dilution of the sample is often a convenient corrective measure. A practical approach to avoiding the possible existence of an inner filter effect is that the absorption of the solution should not exceed 5% (18) when working with the right angle arrangement.

III. Chemical Problems

A. Fluorescent Reference Compounds

The use of fluorescent reference compounds for the purpose of standardization between measurements was mentioned in an earlier section. The requirements for a good reference compound are stringent. It should have a broad fluorescence spectrum, be an easily purified solid, be soluble in water and some organic solvents, and be stable to air and light. It would be helpful if a series of reference compounds could be developed which cover the visible and near ultraviolet regions of the spectrum. The reference compound used in any particular instance should have its absorption in the same region as the compound being studied, and similarly, its fluorescence should be in the same general region as the fluorescence of the compound being studied.

To date, quinine and quinine derivatives have been the most commonly used fluorescent reference compounds (4,10,19–23). Their spectral properties are known, and the absolute quantum efficiency of quinine bisulfate has been measured (21). It is a mistake, however, to think of quinine as the only reference compound, since there are regions of the spectrum where it is not usable, that is, where it does not absorb or fluoresce. Anthracene has been proposed as a reference compound (20), and fluorescein has also been used (24,25). Lippert et al. (10), as well as Argauer and White (23), have suggested the use of several additional fluorescent compounds for reference purposes. Recently, Melhuish (26) has proposed the use of plastic samples of pyrene, anthracene, 9,10-diphenylanthracene, and perylene in poly(methyl methacrylate) as fluorescent reference standards.

B. Media

Gases, liquids, and solids have all been used for fluorescence measurements. Vapor pressure limits the number of systems for which the fluorescence can be measured in the gas phase. When working in the liquid phase, the most common state for fluorescence measurements, it is important to remember that the effects caused by solvents are quite varied and complex (27). Some solvents are not particularly useful for fluorescence and phosphorescence studies due to their quenching properties; in some cases, quenching has been correlated with hydrogen-bonding properties (28).

Still another effect associated with solvents is a large shift in the frequency of emission on changing from polar to nonpolar solvents (29–32). For example, frequency changes are sometimes caused by hydrogen bonding (28,33) and by chemical reactions occurring during the lifetime of the excited state which produce new fluorescent species (34–36). Excited state dissociation has been the most thoroughly studied example of this, and it is highly solvent dependent (29). It is particularly important to differentiate between the shifts caused by excited-state reactions and those due to solvents.

Fluorescence measurements in the solid phase have been made with single crystals, in pellets, and in solvent glasses. The use of solvent glasses for both low temperature fluorescence and phosphorescence studies has been described (32,38). Van Duuren (39) has described the use of potassium bromide pellets as a dispersing medium for the fluorescing solute; sodium hydroxide pellets have also been used (40).

C. Impurities and Interferences

Fluorescent impurities in solvents often limit the sensitivity of analytical procedures. Numerous methods have been described for purifying selected solvents (41–43). Also, extra pure "fluorometric solvents" are commercially available from Matheson, Coleman, and Bell, (44) and from Harleco (45). In addition to solvents, reagent grade chemicals, adsorbents, chromatographic paper, and cleansing agents sometimes contain fluorescent impurities. A recent study has shown that stopcock greases vary greatly in their content of fluorescent impurities (46).

Due to the sensitivity of fluorometric methods and the presence of fluorescent impurities or interferences, separations often must be performed prior to analysis or characterization. Qualitatively and quantitatively, fluorescence has been applied to separation methods using paper chromatography (47,48), thin-layer chromatography (49) and to systems using ion exchange resins or impregnated papers (50). Use of the proper chromatographic paper from the standpoint of fluorescence has been discussed (47). Adsorbents and ion exchange resins must also be nonfluorescent, and must not quench the fluorescence of the compound or ion being studied.

D. Quenching

The presence of oxygen can cause a serious error by oxidation of the sample. More often, the presence of oxygen is critical because of its tendency to quench fluorescence (17,51). The fluorescence of anthracene in air-saturated ethanol as compared to a deaerated solution is reduced by 14%, but the effect of flushing with pure oxygen is almost a 50% reduction (52). Oxygen quenching of phosphorescence is even more serious, and deaeration is usually a necessity (53,54). Quenching can also be caused by other solutes or by the solvent itself.

E. Photolysis

Since intense sources are usually used for fluorescence excitation, and since the light is often in the ultraviolet or blue regions of the spectrum, photodecomposition and related complications often occur. Certain steps in instrument design can limit this source of error: a shutter, so that the sample is only irradiated when the measurements are being made, meters with fast response times, or a source of low intensity coupled with a better detector system.   The use of spectrographs equipped with high-speed photographic recording systems is also possible.

It has also been found that the concentration of the fluorescent species can have an effect on the extent of photolysis.   It is presumed that a high concentration of the fluorescent species can act as a filter. In support of this, Bowen and Wokes (18) found that very dilute solutions (1 μg/ml) were seriously affected by photolysis.

There are some cases where photodecomposition can be used to advantage, either by photoproduction of a fluorescent species from a nonfluorescent one, or by photodecomposition of a fluorescent species to remove an interference (55,56).

F. Temperature Effects

Fluorescence intensity usually decreases with increasing temperature due to higher probabilities for the other means of deactivation of the excited molecule (16,57).   Temperature coefficients are usually in the range from 1–1.2 relative fluorescence units per degree centigrade.   Since most fluorescence instrumentation makes use of high intensity sources, heating of the sample chamber or of the sample itself can readily occur.   Most instruments minimize temperature effects by providing shutter mechanisms and by insulating the sample holder.   Even under these circumstances, some heating does occur. For very precise quantitative measurements, for work with compounds that are particularly temperature sensitive, or for some kinetic studies, it is essential to have temperature regulation of the sample holder.

The effect of viscosity on fluorescence is in addition to the temperature effect.   Bowen and Sahu (58) have shown that fluorescence yields are a function of viscosity; Ewald (59) has shown that the effect of pressure on the quenching of fluorescence can be explained in terms of viscosity effects; Wilson (60–62) has studied theoretically the pressure dependence of fluorescence spectra.

G. Adsorption

The problem of adsorption has been discussed by several authors. It presents a serious error only when dealing with very dilute solutions, but these are precisely the conditions used for most fluorometric

investigations. Brodie et al. (41) studied the adsorption of quinine
onto glass surfaces, and Bird (63) has shown that different glass
surfaces adsorb quinine to different degrees. Adsorption is not
limited to alkaloids such as quinine; rather it is common to a great
many organic compounds. Fortunately, it is possible to minimize or
eliminate adsorption by a number of techniques. Minimal surface
areas should be contacted; pretreatment of glassware can often
decrease adsorption greatly (63). The solvent used also affects considerably the extent of adsorption; polar solvents often lessen
adsorption. Unfortunately, adsorption must be investigated for each
individual material being studied.

IV. Data Analysis

A. Definition of Sensitivity

The definition of fluorescence sensitivity (4,64) and the use thereof
follows directly from knowing the fluorescence quantum efficiency of
the substance. Fluorescence sensitivity is defined as $\phi_f \epsilon_\lambda$, where ϕ_f is
the quantum efficiency of fluorescence and ϵ_λ is the molar extinction
coefficient at the wavelength chosen. This entity is independent of
the instrument on which the quantum efficiency is measured.

Parker and Rees (4) extended this concept by using instead of the
molar extinction coefficient, the absorbance (optical density) per cm
for a 1 $\mu g/ml$ solution of the compound. This value is labeled D_{max}
if the absorbance at the wavelength of maximum absorption is used,
or D_{366} if the absorbance at 366 mμ is used. The product of $\phi_f D_{max}$
or $\phi_f D_{366}$ constitutes the "fluorescence sensitivity." This sensitivity
is calculated assuming that the entire fluorescence band is being
observed. If, however, one is working with a spectrofluorometer,
then only a small band of frequencies near the fluorescence peak are
usually observed, and the fluorescence sensitivity is defined as
$\phi_f D_{max}/H$, where H is the half-width of the fluorescence spectrum.
These workers (4) have given an example of how fluorescence sensitivities can be used to determine the best conditions for a determination on any given instrument.

The source, particularly if it is a mercury arc source, and the
response characteristics of the detector system, seriously affect the
overall sensitivity of an instrument. For these reasons, the sensitivity
curve and the emission characteristics of the source and of the

spectrofluorometer should be known in order to make effective use of fluorescence sensitivities.

B. Reporting of Spectral Data

The most common method of presenting emission and excitation spectra has been to plot the photomultiplier output against wavelength or wavenumber.   With this system, however, it is impossible to compare data obtained on different instruments.   Even with instruments produced by the same manufacturer, correction factors or calibration curves are likely to be very different (16).   Therefore, it has been proposed by workers in this field (65) that spectra be reported in a standard fashion and that only corrected spectra be presented (4,10,16,23,66–68).   Since there are so many wavelength-sensitive components used in most spectrofluorometers, corrected spectra (sometimes called "true spectra") are the only valid ones for comparison.   The methods of correcting the directly-recorded "apparent" spectra will be discussed later in this section.

Specifically, it has been proposed (66) that all spectra should have as their vertical axis relative quanta per frequency interval and as their horizontal axis wave number (in μ^{-1} or cm^{-1}).

The reasons for this choice have been discussed by Bowen (67) and Parker and Rees (4).   Although most instruments have a wavelength scale regardless of whether they incorporate prism or grating monochromators, wavenumber is preferable for two reasons.   First, if plotted on a wavelength scale, bands tend to be grouped in the short wavelength region of the spectrum.   On the other hand, if plotted in the recommended pattern on a wavenumber scale, the spectrum will be more easily compared with its absorption spectrum.   Relative quanta per unit frequency interval is recommended for the scale of the vertical axis since the integrated area under the curve will then be proportional to the quantum efficiency.   Some workers have also used energy per unit wavelength interval (69) or relative quanta per unit wavelength interval (23).

C. Correction of Excitation and Emission Spectra

Spectra recorded on most spectrofluorometers (except for compensating instruments) are not true emission spectra.   Due to the wavelength-sensitive components mentioned earlier, particularly monochromators and photomultiplier tubes, and due to differing light losses, it is essential that spectra be corrected before valid comparisons can be made.   Numerous authors (3,7,9,16,20,64,69–73) have discussed the various types of errors inherent in the determination of fluorescence spectra before correcting an emission spectrum.   It is usually necessary to correct for scattered light, Raman emission, fluorescence from the solvent, or fluorescence from the sample cell. This is easily accomplished by determining the background spectrum of the solvent blank.

Several methods of correcting an apparent fluorescent emission spectrum have been described (4,10,17,20,23,52,69,72).   These methods require that the spectrofluorometer be calibrated in order to determine a spectral sensitivity curve.   Parker and Rees (4) have given an excellent discussion for one method of calibration.   Drushel et al. (74) have written a computer program to facilitate the numerous calculations involved.

This method usually involves introducing a precisely measured quantity of light, having a known frequency distribution, into the monochromator–photomultiplier combination.   The intensity of the light is recorded as a function of frequency, and a correction curve for the instrument can be obtained by comparing the measured curve with the true curve for the source.   For example, with a system using a calibrated tungsten lamp, a plot of the energy per unit wavelength interval can be calculated directly from Wein's law knowing the color temperature of the lamp under specified operating conditions.

Figure 2-3 presents this procedure in graphical form.   Curve A is the known output of a calibrated tungsten lamp.   Curve B is the photomultiplier output, measured on a Jarrell-Ash Ebert scanning spectrometer (Model 82-000), 0.5 m focal length, equipped with 0.1 mm fixed slits and a RCA No. 1P28 photomultiplier tube.   The signal was amplified in a Tektronix low level preamplifier and then in an E.M.C. "lock-in" amplifier, the output of which was fed to a Leeds Northrup Model H potentiometric recorder.   The correction curve for our instrument is curve C, which was obtained by dividing curve B by curve A.

The effect of correction on an emission spectrum is shown in Figure 2-4.   The dashed line represents the corrected fluorescence emission spectrum of anthracene in methanol, while the solid line is the uncorrected spectrum.

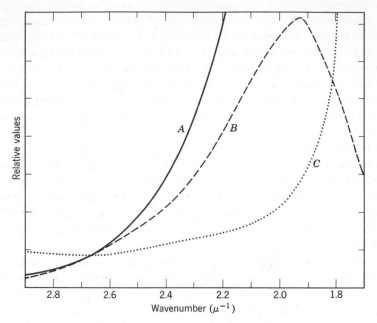

Fig. 2-3. Calculation of correction factors for a grating emission mono-chromator and a 1P28 photomultiplier tube. Curve A: output of standard tungsten lamp in relative quanta per unit frequency interval. Curve B: photo-multiplier output using fixed slit widths. Curve C: sensitivity curve (correction factors as a function of wavenumber).

Lippert (10) has suggested that fluorescent reference compounds would be more convenient as the source of reference than a tungsten lamp, provided a series of suitable reference compounds could be found. These reference compounds would have to cover the range of fluorescence emission, and their spectra would have to be known and agreed upon. Argauer and White (23) have since checked the emission spectra of the compounds suggested by Lippert on a different instrument and found they had good agreement except with one compound. An additional compound was also suggested as an emission standard (23).

The correction of excitation spectra is also necessary if comparison with absorption spectra is planned. The procedure requires that a correction curve be determined for the source–excitation mono-chromator combination to account for variations in the excitation intensity with wavelength.   Chemical actionometers (75,76) and the fluorescence of a reference compound (5,10,17) are usually used in the ultraviolet region.   The emission monochromator–photomulti- plier combination can also be used to monitor the emission of the excitation monochromator and source (23,74).   Various types of scattering materials have been used for this (8,9,74).   Recently, Argauer and White (23) have proposed the use of the aluminum chelate of 2,2-dihydroxy-1,1'-azonaphthalene-4-sulfonic acid as a fluorescence standard to calibrate the excitation source.   They found extremely good agreement between the chelate, a previously cali- brated phototube, and measurements with a thermopile.

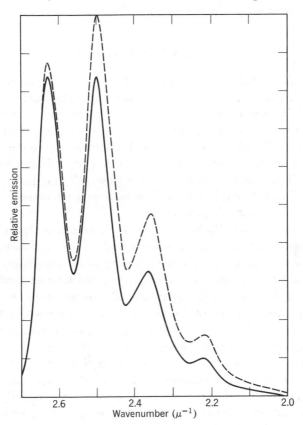

Fig. 2-4.   Comparison of uncorrected and corrected spectra of anthracene in ethanol: (—) uncorrected; (- -) corrected.

D. Calibration Curves

The application of fluorescence analysis to problems of a quantitative nature is usually approached through the use of calibration curves which are plots of fluorescence intensity vs. concentration. These calibration curves are usually linear in the region from 10^{-4} to $10^{-6}M$; at greater concentrations, the fluorescence often goes through a maximum and then decreases quite rapidly. The phenomenon has often been referred to as "concentration quenching," but the cause is usually the presence of an inner filter effect. Similarly, calibration curves can be prepared for the quantitative determination of numerous compounds by phosphorescence.

E. Quantum Efficiency

A fundamental physical entity which is often measured using a spectrofluorometer is the quantum efficiency (the number of quanta emitted divided by the number of quanta absorbed). Several techniques for measuring the quantum efficiency have been described (4,9,21,74,77–79). In one method, the fluorescence is compared to the light scattered by a glycogen solution (9). Under special conditions it is assumed that the glycogen solution has a quantum efficiency of 1.0, and it can then be used as a reference. Ludox has also been used for this purpose (8).

In their method, Parker and Rees (4) reasoned that if the total fluorescence intensities of two compounds could be measured on the same instrument with the same intensity of exciting light, and if the optical densities of the two compounds could be measured individually, then the ratio of the quantum efficiencies could be calculated. If the quantum efficiency of one compound was known from previous studies, it would then be a simple matt r to calculate the quantum efficiency of the compounds in question. This comparison method depends on a knowledge of the quantum efficiency of the reference compound and the conditions under which it was measured (as obtained from the literature or measured independently). These same conditions, particularly the temperature, must be reproduced when measuring the fluorescence quantum efficiency of the reference compound in the comparison procedure.

Parker and Rees determined the quantum efficiencies of the compounds fluorescein, eosin, Rhodamine B, thionine, and anthracene, using quinine bisulfate as their reference compound and using the value of 0.55 for its absolute quantum efficiency [obtained from the work of Melhuish (80)]. These data are listed in Table 2-1. Representative compounds for which the quantum efficiencies have been measured are also included in this table. In his more recent work, Melhuish (21,26) has used as his quantum efficiency standard $5 \times 10^{-3}M$ quinine bisulfate in $1N$ H_2SO_4 with the exciting wavelengths 313 and 366 mμ. Under these conditions and using slightly different correction factors, the quantum efficiency was found to be 0.51.

F. COMPARISON BETWEEN INSTRUMENTS

In the comparison of two instruments, it is essential to distinguish between sensitivity and resolution. When comparing the sensitivities of two instruments, the usual practice has been to speak in terms of the minimum detectable amount of a specific substance. This assumes that all variables are equal and that the detection limit is determined solely by the noise of the instruments being compared. However, in many fluorometric applications, the instrumental sensitivity is not limited by the noise but by the fluorescence blank (3). This reading will often include components of scattered and stray light, Raman emission, solvent fluorescence, or fluorescence from the sample cell. It is therefore important when comparing instruments to be certain that the fluorescence blank is minimized and that similar cells and solvents are used. A more meaningful comparison of instrumental sensitivity would be obtained by comparing the dF/dc values for different instruments under optimum conditions using the same fluorescent reference compound.

The choice of compound for comparing sensitivities is also important. Quinine sulfate is the most commonly used substance for this purpose, although other fluorescent reference compounds could be used (4,10,19–23). However, it is important to use a reference compound the absorption and fluorescence of which are in the regions where the instrument will actually be used.

The use of fluorescent reference compounds for comparing the resolution of two instruments is usually not feasible. The ability to completely resolve the Raman emission of the solvent from the excitation is one approach, or the fluorescence of a compound having a high degree of fine structure may be used.   Parker (12) has proposed that a good test of the sensitivity and resolution of a spectrofluorometer would be to measure the Raman spectrum of carbon tetrachloride.   Since the Raman band of carbon tetrachloride is displaced only 0.07 μ^{-1} from the frequency of excitation, only a highly sensitive spectrofluorometer will resolve and detect the emission.

G. Comparison with Absorption

In general, fluorometric analyses are more sensitive than corresponding spectrophotometric methods.   This is partly due to the use of more intense light sources.   However, the major gain in sensitivity

TABLE 2-1

Quantum Efficiencies of Fluorescence in Solution

Compound	Conc.[a]	Solvent	Q.E.	Ref.
Quinine bisulfate	$\to 0$	1.0N sulfuric acid	0.55	80
Quinine bisulfate	5×10^{-3}	1.0N sulfuric acid	0.51	21
Fluorescein	$\to 0$	Water, pH 7	0.65	9
Fluorescein	$\to 0$	0.1M NaOH	0.92	9
Fluorescein	$\to 0$	0.1N NaOH	0.85	4
Fluorescein	1×10^{-5}	Aq. NaOH	0.79	77
Acriflavine	$\to 0$	Water	0.54	9
Anthracene	$\to 0$	Ethanol	0.28	4
Anthracene	$\to 0$	Benzene	0.29	9
Anthracene	10^{-3}	Poly(methyl methacrylate)	0.24	26
Anthracene	2×10^{-3}	Benzene	0.241	21
9-Bromoanthracene	1.5×10^{-3}	Benzene	0.050	21
9,10-Dibromoanthracene	1.5×10^{-3}	Benzene	0.213	21
9-Cyanoanthracene	1.5×10^{-3}	Benzene	0.796	21
9,10-Diphenylanthracene	1.5×10^{-3}	Benzene	0.840	21
9,10-Diphenylanthracene	10^{-3}	Poly(methyl methacrylate)	0.83	26
Anthranilic acid	8×10^{-3}	Benzene	0.536	21
Methyl anthranilic acid	2.7×10^{-2}	Benzene	0.549	21
Benzene	0.003M	EPA (77°K)	0.16	78
Fluorobenzene	0.0032	EPA (77°K)	0.17	78
Chlorophyll a	$\to 0$	Benzene	0.26	77
Chlorophyll a	$\to 0$	Benzene	0.325	9
Chlorophyll b	$\to 0$	Methanol	0.06	34
Chlorophyll b	$\to 0$	Ethanol	0.095	9
Diphenylhexatriene	10^{-3}	Benzene	0.750	21

(continued)

TABLE 2-1 (*continued*)

Compound	Conc.[a]	Solvent	Q.E.	Ref.
Eosin	→ 0	0.1N NaOH	0.23	4
Eosin	1×10^{-5}	Water	0.12	77
Fluorene	→ 0	Ethanol	0.54	9
Indole	→ 0	Water	0.45	9
Mesoporphyrin	1×10^{-5}	Benzene	0.10	77
Naphthalene	0.001	EPA (77°K)	0.34	78
Naphthalene	→ 0	Alcohol	0.12	9
2-Naphthylamine	2.7×10^{-2}	Benzene	0.486	21
1-Dimethylamino-naphthalene-4-sulfonate	→ 0	Water	0.48	9
2-Naphthol	10^{-3}	Water, pH 10	0.21	26
Perylene	2×10^{-3}	Benzene	0.800	21
Perylene	5×10^{-4}	Poly(methyl methacrylate)	0.87	26
Phenanthrene	→ 0	Alcohol	0.10	9
Phenol	→ 0	Water	0.22	9
Pheophytin a	→ 0	Benzene	0.175	9
Pheophytin a	2.5×10^{-6}	Methanol	0.13	77
Proflavine	10^{-4}	Water, pH 4	0.27	26
Pyrene	10^{-3}	Poly(methyl methacrylate)	0.61	26
Rhodamine b	→ 0	Ethanol	0.97	9
Rhodamine b	→ 0	Ethanol	0.69	4
Riboflavin	→ 0	Water, pH 7	0.26	9
Rubrene	1×10^{-5}	n-Heptane	1.02	77
Sodium salicylate	→ 0	Water	0.28	9
Thionine	→ 0	0.1N sulfuric acid	0.024	4
Triphenylene	9×10^{-4}	EPA (77°K)	0.03	78

[a] → 0 indicates an absorbance (optical density) at the wavelength of excitation equal to or less than 0.05.

is inherent to the system. The signal resulting from the fluorescence can be amplified directly, whereas with methods of absorption or transmittance, the difference or ratio between two signals must be amplified. Fluorometers are more sensitive than the spectrofluorometers since a much broader band of frequencies is available for both excitation and emission.

The lower limit of fluorescence sensitivity is normally in the region of 0.1–0.001 mg/ml (16). A mirrored test tube has been described which provides a twofold increase in sensitivity (81). However, volume requirements are usually between 0.1 and 3 ml of solution. Some workers (82,83) have devised systems for holding even smaller samples (0.05–0.01 ml) and for combining fluorescence with microscopic techniques (84). The analysis of compounds at the submicrogram level has been discussed (85,86).

In the analysis of mixtures, fluorescence often has a unique advantage over absorption techniques. In some cases, only one species will fluoresce. Even if there are several different fluorescing species present, it is often possible to analyze just one component by taking advantage of the additional variable of selective excitation.

H. IDENTIFICATION OF COMPOUNDS USING ABSORPTION AND FLUORESCENCE

For qualitative identification of compounds, the availability of two spectra, absorption and fluorescence, can be a distinct advantage for distinguishing similar compounds. In addition, for mixtures which may contain many absorbing species, it is sometimes possible to measure the absorption of a single fluorescent species present by measuring its excitation spectrum.

V. Types of Instrumentation

A variety of luminescence instrumentation is available commercially; in addition, all types of component parts which can be used in the construction of an instrument to one's own specifications can be purchased. In Table 2-2 are listed some of the component combinations which are found in commercial instrument; the approximate price ranges are also included. Each class of instrument is discussed in more detail on the following pages and in addition, a brief description of phosphorescence instrumentation and various specialized instruments is included.

A. FILTER FLUOROMETERS

The components of a filter fluorometer can be assembled in a wide variety of ways. Some fluorometers compensate automatically for changes in the intensity of the excitation source, a feature which greatly improves their stability. Many instruments do not compensate for these fluctuations, and they comprise the simplest filter

TABLE 2-2

Components of Luminescent Instruments[a]

	Light source	Device for selecting the wavelength of excitation	Geometry	Device for selecting the wavelength of emission	Detector	Readout	Price range, $
Filter fluorometers	Hg (UV and Visible)	Filters	Right angle	Filter	PM[c]	Meter	1000–2000
Accessories for spectrophotometers	Hg Xe	Filters or monochromators[b]	Right angle or front surface	Monochromator of the spectrophotometer	PM	Strip-chart recorder	2000–4000
Spectrofluorometers	Xe	Monochromator	Right angle	Monochromator	PM	Meter and strip-chart recorder	5000–8000
Compensating spectrofluorometers	Xe	Monochromator	Right angle	Monochromator	PM	Meter and strip chart recorder	19,000–30,000

[a] The item listed is the one most frequently used.
[b] Both quartz and prism monochromators are used; the filters are sometimes used in conjunction with the monochromator.
[c] PM photomultiplier tube. The wavelength region and sensitivity of a particular instrument may be dependent on the specific photomultiplier tube used.

fluorometers available. These instruments include a source, an excitation filter, a sample holder, a fluorescence filter, and a detector. The right angle method of illumination is normally used, since it provides for the highest sensitivity. In Figure 2-5 is shown the optical diagram of one of the standard fluorometers, the Aminco Fluoro-microphotometer, in which the basic components are arranged in the normal manner. This instrument is provided with a dark current control, sensitivity attenuation up to 1000, and a method for zeroing the meter. Excitation sources are available for 255 mμ, 350 mμ, and for the region from approximately 400–550 mμ. A tungsten source is also available. Accessories include the provision for using a 20-cuvette sample changer or for measuring phosphorescence. The instrument may also be used as a colorimeter.

Other instruments which are similar in general design to the Aminco Instrument are the Photovolt Model 540, the Coleman Model 12C Photofluorometer, and the Farrand Photoelectric Fluorometer.

Table 2-3 lists the manufacturers of filter fluorometers, many of which have been discussed in recent reviews (10,44,87–89).

TABLE 2-3
Filter Fluorometers

American Instrument Company	Fluoro-microphotometer
Beckman Instruments, Inc.	Ratio Fluorometer
Coleman Instruments, Inc.	Model 12-C Photofluorometer
Farrand Optical Co., Inc.	Photoelectric Fluorometer
Hilger and Watts, Ltd.	Hilger Spekker Fluorimeter
	Hilger and Watts Fluorimeter
Hitachi, Ltd.	FPL-2 Fluorophotometer
Jarrel-Ash Co.	G-M Fluorometer
Jouan Company	Fluorometre Photoelectrique
Klett Mfg. Company	Klett Fluorimeter
Pfaltz and Bauer	Model B Fluorophotometer
Photovolt Corp.	Model 540 Fluorescence Meter
	Lumetron Model 402-EF
	Fluorescence Meter
Technicon Instruments Corp.	Technicon Fluorometer
G. K. Turner Associates	Model 110 Fluorometer
	Model 111 Fluorometer

The problems inherent to filter fluorometers are similar to the difficulties found in using a single beam instrument for absorption studies. Nonlinearity of the detector response and its lack of sensitivity in some regions are situations which can cause difficulties. Differences in lamp intensity arising from line or source variations often produce errors, but they can be compensated for with such instruments as the Beckman Ratio Fluorometer, the Photovolt Lumetron Fluorescence Meter, and the Turner Model 110 and 111 Fluorometers.

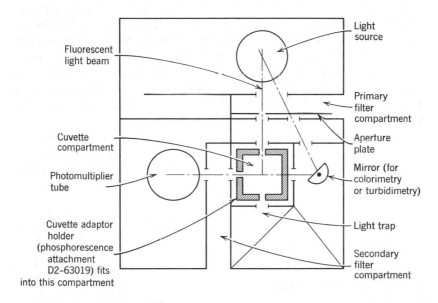

Fig. 2-5.   Placement of optical components in the fluoromicrophotometer.
(Courtesy American Instrument Company, Inc.)

The Lumetron instrument was one of the first commercial instruments to compensate for lamp fluctuations, but it has a low sensitivity. The fluorescence is detected by two barrier-layer cells. A bridge network compares their output with a reference signal derived from a photocell which "sees" a small portion of the exciting light directly. A slidewire potentiometer is used to measure the fluorescence, and a galvanometer is used to indicate the null point.

In Figure 2-6 is shown a schematic diagram of the optics of the Turner Model 110 fluorometer. The Turner fluorometer has proven to be extremely stable and very sensitive. In principle it is a double beam instrument using the calibrated rear light path as the second beam. The light interrupter permits first the fluorescence and then the calibrated rear light path to strike the photomultiplier tube. The difference between their outputs is first fed to an AC amplifier and then to a phase-sensitive detector which gives a positive signal if there is an excess of light in the sample path and a negative signal if there is an excess in the rear light path. The signal is then fed to another amplifier and to a null meter. The fluorescence is measured by turning the "fluorescence" dial which, by means of the light cam, controls the amount of light in the rear light path. The cam is so designed that each of the 100 divisions on the "fluorescence" dial represents an equal increment of light. The "blank" knob is used to balance out any fluorescence from the blank.

Effects due to line fluctuations or lamp aging are automatically cancelled out in the Turner instrument; since it is an AC system, there is no problem from dark current. Provisions are also made to

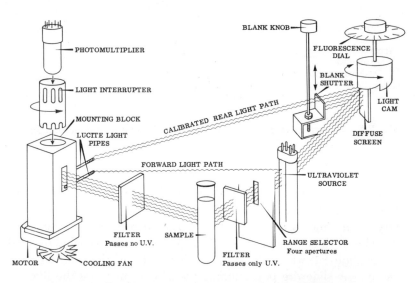

Fig. 2-6. Details of the optical design of the Turner Models 110 and 111 fluorometers. (Courtesy G. K. Turner Associates.)

eliminate any zero-point error. The instrument can be used with a special source which provides excitation at 254 mμ, provided one uses quartz cuvettes. Accessories are available for the Turner instrument which permit its use with samples in the form of pellets, paper chromatographic or electrophoretic strips, or with a continuous flow system. The Model 111, based on the design of the Model 110, is a self-balancing type fluorometer which is particularly useful for continuous monitoring; its output is for use with recording equipment.

The Beckman Ratio Fluorometer also compensates for fluctuations in the source but by a slightly different mechanism. The source is designed so that the excitation first strikes a reference solution and then strikes the sample. The instrument is adjusted so that the meter reads 100 for the reference beam, and 0 for the blank. The fluorescence of the unknown solution is read directly from the meter. Provision is made for recording the output signal also. The instrument is equipped with a turret-type sample holder which holds eight samples and provides for quick change from one sample to the next. Low wavelength excitation is possible using Vycor test tubes, which are supplied. Also available are a continuous flow cell and a device for measuring the fluorescence of a paper chromatogram.

The advantages of filter fluorometers are numerous. Generally they are of simple construction, inexpensive, and very sensitive. The instruments which compensate for fluctuations in the lamp eliminate one serious difficulty found with most fluorometers. However, filter instruments lack the versatility found in instruments where the filters are replaced by monochromators. As a logical consequence, spectrofluorometers have appeared and become very popular for research and developmental analytical work, even though the simpler filter fluorometers are still widely used for routine analyses

B. Accessories for Spectrophotometers

The first step beyond the filter instruments was the development of accessories to fit standard spectrophotometers, such as the Beckman DU (90,91), so that they could be used to measure fluorescence. Generally, these modifications involved the use of a different light source, an excitation filter, and a different arrangement for the sample holder. Currently, accessories of this type are available for the Beckman spectrophotometers, for the Cary Spectrophotometers, and for the Zeiss PMQ-II spectrophotometer.

These changes permit the recording of fluorescence spectra on a routine basis other than by spectrographic means. With this capability, the opportunity existed to study various other physical properties of the fluorescing species. This greatly increased the use of these accessories.

Interest in measuring excitation spectra necessitated the development of instruments which had monochromators in their excitation path. Some of these instruments incorporated filters for selecting the emission; but more often, instruments were used which had monochromators in both the excitation and the emission light paths. These instruments are called spectrofluorometers. They have the advantage of permitting one to measure both the fluorescence and excitation spectra.

Accessories for commercial spectrophotometers, which provide for a monochromator to select the excitation wavelength, are available from Bausch and Lomb to fit their Model 505 spectrophotometer and from Perkin-Elmer Corporation for their Model 350 spectrophotometer. With these accessories, the instruments have the same capabilities as most spectrofluorometers.

C. Spectrofluorometers

A commercial spectrofluorometer incorporating two monochromators was first produced by the American Instrument Company. Their instrument is quite similar to the one designed by Bowman et al. (92). A schematic diagram of the Aminco-Bowman Spectrophotofluorometer is shown in Figure 2-7. The source for the Aminco-Bowman instrument is normally a high pressure xenon arc which is powered by a DC power supply to provide as stable a source as possible. The output of the lamp passes through a slit and into the excitation monochromator, the grating of which is blazed at 300 mμ. This monochromator can be adjusted manually or operated by a constant speed motor through a cam. When recording, the output of a potentiometer, coupled to the wavelength cam of the monochromator, is used to determine the position of the x-axis on the oscillograph or the recorder. The emitted light from the excitation monochromator passes into the sample through a series of slits.

The fluorescence leaves the sample at right angles to the excitation path. It then enters the fluorescence monochromator which is

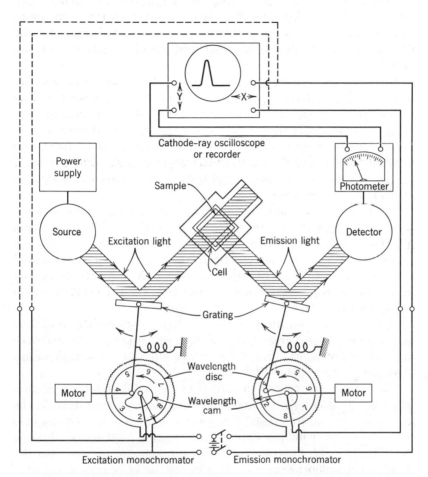

Fig. 2-7   Functional diagram of the Aminco-Bowman Spectrophotofluorometer. (Courtesy American Instrument Company, Inc.)

identical to the excitation monochromator except that its grating is blazed at 500 mμ.   For purposes of scanning the fluorescence spectrum, this monochromator is also motor driven through a wavelength cam and is coupled to a potentiometer.   The fluorescence leaving this monochromator is focused on a slit in front of the photomultiplier tube.   The output of the photomultiplier tube is fed through a resistor and the resultant voltage is amplified. The fluorescence signal can then be displayed directly on a meter, on the y axis of an oscillograph, or on an x-y recorder. A means of balancing out the dark current of the tube is provided, and sensitivity adjustments are included.

A number of accessories for the Aminco-Bowman instrument are available; adjustable slits, different photomultiplier tubes for various regions of the spectrum, an interchangeable grating for extending the range to 1200 mμ, a device for cooling the photomultiplier tube in order to lower the dark current, temperature baths, a phosphorescence accessory which includes the necessary shutter mechanism and liquid nitrogen Dewar, a polarization accessory, and a rotary turret capable of holding three samples.

The Farrand spectrofluorometer is almost identical to the Aminco-Bowman instrument in its range of applications. The only basic difference between the two instruments is the manner in which a fluorescence or excitation spectrum is recorded. In the Farrand instrument, a strip-chart recorder is used, and the spectrum is scanned at a constant rate. The time axis can then be converted to wavelength by calibration.

These two instruments were the first ones commercially available, and were used for a great many of the early studies on fluorescence and phosphorescence. Since then, three additional spectrofluorometers have been made available.

The Zeiss instrument is comprised of two prism monochromators and a 450 W xenon light source. The components are similar to the ones used in the standard Zeiss spectrophotometers. The sample holder employs a unique cuvette; the exciting light enters through the side, and the fluorescence passes through the bottom into the fluorescence monochromator. Due to the use of prisms, as opposed to the more commonly used gratings, the instrument should show higher resolution in the ultraviolet region than grating instruments. However, prisms have larger inherent light losses; this is one reason for the concomitant use of a 450 W source instead of the more normally used 150 W lamp.

Another spectrofluorometer incorporating prism monochromators has been introduced by the Schoeffel Instrument Company. It is very similar to the instruments previously discussed. It is composed of standard parts used in their spectrophotometers.

The most recently introduced spectrofluorometer is the Model SF-1 Fluorispec of Baird-Atomic, Inc. In both the excitation path and the fluorescence path, the instrument uses a double monochromator, i.e., a series arrangement of two grating monochromators with folded optics. In most other respects it is similar to other spectrofluorometers, employing a xenon source and a photomultiplier tube for detection. Both solid and liquid samples can be studied, and an accessory is available for microsamples. Readout is to a recorder, a meter, or an oscillograph.

All of these instruments present uncorrected spectra. They are essentially single beam devices, and to obtain a true or corrected spectrum, either instrumental modifications must be incorporated, or the spectra obtained must be corrected. The methods of correction were discussed earlier.

D. Compensating Spectrofluorometers

Two compensating spectrofluorometers are available commercially. With these instruments, a "true" fluorescence spectrum is recorded directly, rather than having to correct an apparent fluorescence spectrum which is obtained when using one of the instruments previously discussed. Both the reasons for presenting data as "true" fluorescence spectra and the means of correcting apparent fluorescence spectra were discussed earlier (see Section IV-C).

The Perkin-Elmer Model 195 linear energy spectrofluorometer has been described by Slavin (93). It is composed of two Perkin-Elmer Model 198 monochromators with silica prisms. A small portion of the light leaving the excitation monochromator is separated by a beam-splitter and falls upon a thermocouple, which measures the energy striking it regardless of wavelength. By using the signal from the thermocouple in conjunction with a slit servomechanism, the energy striking the thermocouple is kept constant. This is easily converted to quanta if necessary. Differences in the response of the photomultiplier tube and other wavelength-dependent variables are corrected by using a second servo-actuated slit which operates on the fluorescence monochromator and is controlled by an adjustable electrical cam. Since prism monochromators are used, the spectrum obtained is linear in frequency, a result favored by some workers. The range of excitation is from 200–700 mμ and the fluorescence can be scanned over the same region.   Fluorescence of longer wavelength, as high as 1 μ, can be measured with some modifications.

G. K. Turner Associates' Model 210 "Spectro" is described as "An Absolute Spectrofluorometer" in an excellent paper by Turner (94). It has three basic modes of operation. (1) Excitation spectra under conditions of constant excitation energy can be measured from 2000–11,000 A.   By the simple procedure of dividing by the wavelength, the measured excitation spectrum will coincide with the absorption spectrum. (2) Emission spectra are recorded directly in relative quanta per unit bandwidth (i.e., "corrected") over the range from 2000–6500 A.   Emission spectra can be recorded in the region from 6500–11,000 A., but they are not energy compensated. (3) Absorption can be recorded in the range from 1900–11,000 A. with elimination of fluorescence artifacts.

Figure 2-8 indicates the techniques which make these possible. Specifically, the bolometer compares the transmitted light from the sample with the reference lamp; the reference lamp is then adjusted to provide the identical energy.   Another beam from the reference lamp is focused through an attenuator on to the photomultiplier during one phase.   This signal is therefore proportional to the energy hitting the sample.   In a second phase, the fluorescence output, which has passed through the fluorescence monochromator, goes to the photomultiplier tube.   The ratio of the fluorescence signal to the reference signal is then amplified and recorded.   The attenuator mentioned above provides for the compensation necessitated by the nonlinear response of the emission monochromator and photomultiplier tube combination.   The attenuator, an optical density wedge, controls the reference signal striking the photomultiplier tube and is actuated by a cam which is cut so that the spectral response of the emission monochromator and the photomultiplier tube are compensated for.

The compensating spectrophotofluorometers now provide what was only possible previously by correction of apparent spectra or by building one's own instrument to incorporate these features.   These instruments should provide the type of instrumentation needed to study many of the fundamental physical and chemical problems of luminescence.   The ability to measure quantum efficiencies directly from the recorded spectra should be particularly useful.

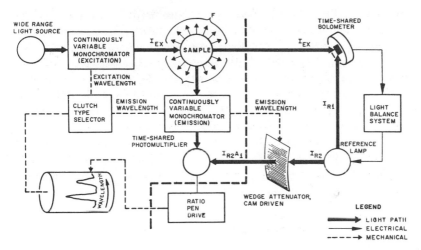

Fig. 2-8. Schematic representation of the Turner Model 210 "Spectro," an absolute spectrofluorometer manufactured by G. K. Turner Associates (94). (Courtesy G. K. Turner Associates.)

E. Phosphorescence Instrumentation

The instrumentation used to measure phosphorescence or phosphorescence spectra is quite similar to that used for the corresponding fluorescence measurement. The major differences arise because of the longer lifetime of the phosphorescence. For instance, although phosphorescence has been detected in liquid solution from dyes (54,95), normally the sample to be studied must be present in a rigid matrix. This is usually accomplished by the use of solvent glasses; a large number of which are available (37,38). Plastics (26) have also been used for phosphorescence measurements, and various crystal systems have been studied. With most systems used to measure phosphorescence, a device is used which alternately excites the sample, and then during the phase when the sample is not being excited, scans the sample for phosphorescence. This is in contrast to fluorescence, where the excitation and scanning are carried out simultaneously.

The difference in phosphorescence lifetimes from compound to compound provides an additional variable which can be utilized for identification and analysis. This should be particularly useful for the analysis of mixtures without prior separation.

Kiers et al. (96) were the first to use phosphorescence for analytical purposes. Currently, the American Instrument Company manufactures an accessory for their Aminco-Bowman Spectrophotofluorometer which permits both phosphorescence analysis and the measurement of phosphorescence spectra. The accessory contains a liquid nitrogen Dewar within which is placed the sample cell. The part of the Dewar containing the sample is then placed inside a rotating shutter driven by a variable speed motor. The accessory and the previously available Aminco-Kiers Spectrophosphorimeter have found widespread application. In addition, many of the available filter fluorometers and spectrofluorometers can be modified quite easily to measure phosphorescence.

F. Specialized Instruments

Individual investigators have often designed instruments for their own purposes. Udenfriend (16) discusses several such instruments, including many of the early compensating spectrofluorometers. The instruments designed by Parker (5) and Lipsett (70) are examples. More recently a versatile high resolution spectrofluorometer has been described (97), and a double beam spectrofluorometer which provides for the direct measurement of excitation spectra has been designed using the Aminco-Kiers spectrophosphorimeter (98). A vertical axis filter fluorometer for use with solutions has been described (99). An instrument has been designed which corrects automatically for any light source variations by means of an automatic gain control amplifier (100).

Fluorescence instrumentation has been adapted for biological purposes (16). The instrument designed by French (101) is elaborate but highly functional for its purpose of measuring fluorescence of intact cells and protoplasts. Duysens and Amesz (102) designed an instrument for fluorescence measurement in the near ultraviolet and visible regions; it was later modified by Olson (103) to permit the measurement of excitation spectra of intact cells and particles. Chance and Legallis (104) described a differential microfluorometer which permits the detection and comparison of fluorescence in two separated portions of a cell. A flow cell has been designed to accompany this instrument (105). A versatile microspectrofluorometer has been developed by Olson (86). Chance, Legallis, and Schoener (106) have recently described a combined fluorescence and double beam spectrophotometer for reflectance measurements.

A recently described technique (107) provides a unique tool to distinguish closely related substances. Using oscillographic recording and some intricate electronics, it has been possible to record simultaneously the excitation and emission spectra. These spectra are presented on the vertical and horizontal scales of an oscilloscope, respectively; the resulting trace, when photographed with Polaroid film, is called a "fluorograph." Further electronic development permits recording only if the fluorescence intensity exceeds a preset minimum. Using these three parameters, "stereofluorographs" can be constructed which portray the excitation wavelength, the emission wavelength, and the emission intensity.

Instrumentation designed specifically to measure fluorescence lifetimes by a variety of techniques (108–113) has been described. Burton et al. (114) have recently developed a special mercury hydrogen lamp which produces high intensity pulses of 0.5×10^{-9} s duration. This should permit direct experimental studies of a variety of excited state reactions, as well as fluorescence life-times Additional specialized instrumentation continues to be developed. Hengge (115) has described a "universal" fluorescence spectrophotometer for optically opaque samples, and a spectrofluorophosphorimeter has been described (116). Flexible light pipes (117) and a simple photomultiplier cooling apparatus (118) have also been described. The biannual reviews of fluorometric analysis by White (87–89) provide a comprehensive coverage of recent luminescence instrumentation.

This investigation was supported in part by Public Health Service Research Grant GM 10805 from the National Institutes of Health and from the Central University Research Fund of the University of New Hampshire.

General References

P. F. Lott, *J. Chem. Educ.*, *41*, A327, A457 (1964).

C. A. Parker and W. T. Rees, *Analyst*, *87*, 83 (1962).

S. Udenfriend, *Fluorescence Assay in Biology and Medicine*, Academic Press, New York, 1962.

C. E. White and A. Weissler, *Anal. Chem.*, *34*, 81R (1962); *36*, 116R (1964).

References

1. N. Z. Searle, P. Giesecke, R. Kinmonth, and R. C. Hirt, *Appl. Opt.*, *3*, 923 (1964).
2. C. M. Doede and C. A. Walker, *Chem. Eng.*, *62*, 159 (1955).
3. C. A. Parker and W. T. Rees, *Analyst*, *87*, 83 (1962).
4. C. A. Parker and W. T. Rees, *Analyst*, *85*, 587 (1960).
5. C. A. Parker, *Nature*, *182*, 1002 (1958).
6. Ultra-Violet Products, Inc., San Gabriel, California.
7. H. Sprince and G. R. Rowley, *Science*, *125*, 25 (1957).
8. D. M. Hercules and H. Frankel, *Science*, *131*, 1611 (1960).
9. G. Weber and F. W. J. Teale, *Trans. Faraday Soc.*, *53*, 646 (1957).
10. E. Lippert, W. Nägle, I. Seibold-Blankenstein, U. Staiger, and W. Voss, *Z. Anal. Chem.*, *170*, 1 (1959).
11. R. M. King and D. M. Hercules, *Anal. Chem.*, *35*, 1099 (1963).
12. C. A. Parker, *Analyst*, *84*, 446 (1959).
13. F. B. Huke, R. H. Heidel, and V. A. Fassel, *J. Opt. Soc. Am.*, *43*, 400 (1953).
14. H. E. Bennett and W. R. McBride, *Appl. Opt.*, *3*, 919 (1964).
15. J. M. Price, M. Kaihara, and H. K. Howerton, *Appl. Opt.*, *1*, 521 (1962).
16. S. Udenfriend, *Fluorescence Assay in Biology and Medicine*, Academic Press, New York, 1962.
17. C. A. Parker and W. J. Barnes, *Analyst*, *82*, 606 (1957).
18. E. J. Bowen and F. Wokes, *Fluorescence of Solutions*, Longmans, Green, London, 1953.
19. J. W. Collat and L. B. Rogers, *Anal. Chem.*, *27*, 961 (1955).
20. W. H. Melhuish, *J. Phys. Chem.*, *64*, 762 (1960).
21. W. H. Melhuish, *J. Phys. Chem.*, *65*, 229 (1961).
22. V. A. Stephen, *J. Council. Sci. Ind. Research*, *21*, 355 (1948).
23. R. J. Argauer and C. E. White, *Anal. Chem.*, *36*, 368 (1964).
24. G. D. Miller, J. A. Johnson, and B. S. Miller, *Anal. Chem.*, *28*, 884 (1956).
25. H. S. Strickler, R. C. Grauer, and M. R. Caughey, *Anal. Chem.*, *28*, 1240 (1956).
26. W. H. Melhuish, *J. Opt. Soc. Am.*, *54*, 183 (1964).
27. B. L. Van Duuren, *Chem. Rev.*, *63*, 325 (1963).
28. N. Mataga, Y. Torihashi, and Y. Kaifu, *Z. Physik. Chem. (Frankfurt)*, *34*, 379 (1962).
29. D. W. Ellis and L. B. Rogers, paper presented at the 144th Meeting, American Chemical Society, Los Angeles, Calif., April, 1963.
30. E. Lippert, *Z. Physik. Chem. (Frankfurt)*, *2*, 328 (1954).
31. N. Mataga, Y. Kaifu, and M. Koizumi, *Bull. Chem. Soc. Japan*, *29*, 465 (1956).
32. N. Mataga, *Bull. Chem. Soc. Japan*, *31*, 481 (1958).
33. N. Mataga and Y. Kaifu, *J. Chem. Phys.*, *36*, 2804 (1962).
34. D. W. Ellis and L. B. Rogers, *Spectrochim. Acta*, *18*, 265 (1962); *20*, 1709 (1964).
35. Th. Förster, *Z. Elektrochem.*, *54*, 42 (1950).
36. A. Weller, "Fast Reactions of Excited Molecules," in G. Porter, Ed., *Progress in Reaction Kinetics*, Vol. 1, Pergamon Press, New York, 1961.

37. D. R. Scott and J. B. Allison, *J. Phys. Chem.*, *66*, 561 (1962).
38. J. D. Winefordner and P. A. St. John, *Anal. Chem.*, *35*, 2211 (1963).
39. B. L. Van Duuren and C. E. Bardi, *Anal. Chem.*, *35*, 2198 (1963).
40. R. Abraham and H. Staudinger, *Z. Naturforsch.*, *186*, 421 (1963).
41. B. B. Brodie, S. Udenfriend, and J. E. Baer, *J. Biol. Chem.*, *168*, 299 (1947).
42. D. E. Duggan, *Arch. Biochem. Biophys.*, *84*, 116 (1959).
43. S. M. Hess, P. A. Shore, and B. B. Brodie, *J. Pharmacol. Exptl. Therap.*, *118*, 84 (1956).
44. Matheson, Coleman, and Bell, E. Rutherford, N. J.
45. Hartman-Leddon Company, Inc., Philadelphia 43, Pa.
46. J. T. Dubois and F. Wilkinson, *Appl. Spectry.*, *18*, 27 (1964).
47. W. H. Wadman, G. J. Thomas, and A. B. Pardee, *Anal. Chem.*, *26*, 1192 (1954).
48. G. Alberti and M. A. Massucci, *J. Chromatogr.*, *11*, 394 (1963).
49. D. F. Bender, E. Sawicki, and R. M. Wilson, *Anal. Chem.*, *36*, 1011 (1964).
50. P. A. Hedin, *Agr. Food Chem.*, *11*, 343 (1963).
51. W. R. Ware, *J. Phys. Chem.*, *66*, 455 (1962).
52. C. A. Parker, *Anal. Chem* , *34*, 502 (1962).
53. G. Jackson, R. Livingston, and A. C. Pugh, *Trans. Faraday Soc.*, *56*, 1635 (1960).
54. C. A. Parker and C. G. Hatchard, *Trans. Faraday Soc.*, *57*, 1894 (1961).
55. B. B. Brodie, S. Udenfriend, W. Dill, and T. Chenkin, *J. Biol. Chem.*, *168*, 319 (1947).
56. D. M. Hercules and J. J. Surash, *Spectrochim. Acta*, *19*, 788 (1963).
57. E. J. Bowen and D. Seaman in H. P. Kallman and G. M. Spruch, Eds., *Luminescence of Organic and Inorganic Materials*, Wiley, New York, 1962.
58. E. J. Bowen and J. Sahu, *J. Phys. Chem.*, *63*, 4 (1959).
59. A. H. Ewald, *J. Phys. Chem.*, *67*, 1727 (1963).
60. D. J. Wilson, B. Noble, and B. Lee, *J. Chem. Phys.*, *34*, 1392 (1961).
61. D. J. Wilson, *J. Chem. Phys.*, *36*, 1293 (1962).
62. J. W. Brauner and D. J. Wilson, *J. Chem. Phys.*, *36*, 2547 (1962).
63. L. H. Bird, *New Zealand J. Sci. Technol.*, *30B*, 334 (1949).
64. C. A. Parker, *Photoelec. Spectrometry Group Bull.*, *No. 13*, 334 (1961).
65. Anon., *Photoelec. Spectrometry Group Bull.*, *No. 14*, 378 (1962).
66. J. H. Chapman, Th. Förster, G. Kortüm, C. A. Parker, E. Lippert, W. H. Melhuish, and G. Nebbia, *Appl. Spectry.*, *17*, 171 (1963).
67. E. J. Bowen, *Photoelec. Spectrometry Group Bull.*, *No. 13*, 311 (1961).
68. G. Nebbia, in E. R. Lippincott and M. Margoshes, Eds., *Proceedings of the Xth Colloquium Spectroscopicum Internationale*, Spartan Books, Washington, D. C., 1963.
69. C. E. White, M. Ho, and E. Q. Weimer, *Anal. Chem.*, *32*, 438 (1960).
70. F. R. Lipsett, *J. Opt. Soc. Am.*, *49*, 673 (1959).
71. P. F. Lott, *J. Chem. Educ.*, *41*, A327, A421 (1964).
72. W. H. Melhuish, *J. Opt. Soc. Am.*, *52*, 1256 (1962).
73. D. M. Hercules, *Science*, *125*, 1242 (1957).
74. H. V. Drushel, A. L. Sommers, and R. C. Cox, *Anal. Chem.*, *35*, 2166 (1963).
75. C. A. Parker, *Proc. Roy. Soc. (London)*, *A220*, 104 (1953).

76. C. G. Hatchard and C. A. Parker, *Proc. Roy. Soc. (London)*, *A235*, 518 (1956).

77. L. S. Forster and R. Livingston, *J. Chem. Phys.*, *20*, 1315 (1952).

78. E. H. Gilmore, G. E. Gibson, and D. S. McClure, *J. Chem. Phys.*, *20*, 829 (1952).

79. V. G. Shore and A. B. Pardee, *Arch. Biochem. Biophys.*, *60*, 100 (1956).

80. W. H. Melhuish, *New Zealand J. Sci. Technol.*, *37B*, 142 (1955).

81. M. Laikin, *Appl. Spectry.*, *17*, 26 (1963).

82. D. Glick and D. Redlich, *Anal. Biochem.*, *6*, 471 (1963).

83. O. H. Lowry, N. R. Roberts, K. Y. Leiner, M. L. Wu, and A. L. Farr, *Biol. Chem.*, *207*, 1 (1954).

84. O. H. Lowry, *J. Histochem. Cytochem.*, *1*, 420 (1953).

85. R. L. Bowman, *Microchem. J. Symp. Ser.*, *1961*, 355.

86. R. A. Olson, *Rev. Sci. Inst.*, *31*, 844 (1960).

87. C. E. White, *Anal. Chem.*, *32*, 37R (1960).

88. C. E. White and A. Weissler, *Anal. Chem.*, *34*, 814 (1962).

89. C. E. White and A. Weissler, *Anal. Chem.*, *36*, 116R (1964).

90. M. H. Fletcher, C. E. White, and M. S. Sheftel, *Ind. Eng. Chem. Anal. Ed.*, *18*, 179 (1946).

91. R. A. Burdett and L. D. Jones, *J. Opt. Soc. Am.*, *37*, 554 (1947).

92. R. L. Bowman, P. A. Caulfield, and S. Udenfriend, *Science*, *122*, 32 (1955).

93. W. Slavin, R. W. Mooney, and D. T. Palumbo, *J. Opt. Soc. Am.*, *51*, 93 (1961).

94. G. K. Turner, *Science*, *146*, No. 3641, 183–189 (1964).

95. C. A. Parker and C. G. Hatchard, *Analyst*, *87*, 664 (1962).

96. R. J. Kiers, R. D. Britt, Jr., and W. E. Wentworth, *Anal. Chem.*, *29*, 202 (1957).

97. R. H. Rehwoldt, R. M. King, and D. M. Hercules, *Anal. Chem.*, *33*, 1362 (1961).

98. W. H. Melhuish and R. H. Murashige, *Rev. Sci. Instr.*, *33*, 1213 (1962).

99. M. H. Fletcher, *Anal. Chem.*, *35*, 288 (1963).

100. L. Eisenberg, P. Rosen, and G. M. Edelman, *Rev. Sci. Instr.*, *33*, 1435 (1962).

101. C. S. French, in F. H. Johnson, Ed., *The Luminescence of Biological Systems*, American Association for the Advancement of Science, Washington, D. C., 1955.

102. L. N. M. Duysens and J. Amesz, *Biochim. Biophys. Acta*, *24*, 19 (1957).

103. J. M. Olson and J. Amesz, *Biochim. Biophys. Acta*, *37*, 14 (1960).

104. B. Chance and V. Legallis, *Rev. Sci. Instr.*, *30*, 732 (1959).

105. E. Kohen, *Biochim. Biophys. Acta*, *75*, 139 (1963).

106. B. Chance, V. Legallis, and B. Schoener, *Rev. Sci. Instr.*, *34*, 1307 (1963).

107. M. M. Schachter and E. O. Haenni, *Anal. Chem.*, *36*, 2045 (1964).

108. E. A. Bailey, Jr. and G. K. Rollefson, *J. Chem. Phys.*, *21*, 1315 (1953).

109. R. G. Bennett, *Rev. Sci. Instr.*, *31*, 1275 (1960).

110. L. Brewer, C. G. James, R. G. Brewer, F. E. Stafford, R. A. Berg and G. M. Rosenblatt, *Rev. Sci. Instr.*, *33*, 1450 (1962).

111. G. C. Brown, Jr., *Rev. Sci. Instr.*, *34*, 414 (1963).

112. F. P. Schäfer and K. Röllig, *Z. Physik. Chem. (Frankfurt)*, *40*, 199 (1964).
113. G. B. Zarowin, *Rev. Sci. Instr.*, *34*, 1051 (1963).
114. J. T. D'Alessio, P. K. Ludwig, and M. Burton, *Rev. Sci. Instr.*, *35*, 1015 (1964).
115. E. Hengge, H. G. Kruger, and H. Kubsa, *Chem.-Ingr.-Tech.*, *32*, 355 (1960).
116. G. P. Haugen and R. J. Marcus, *Appl. Opt.*, *3*, 1049 (1964).
117. N. W. Reay and L. M. Preston, *Rev. Sci Instr.*, *35*, 519 (1964).
118. H. W. Gandy and J. F. Weller, *Rev. Sci. Instr.*, *35*, 413 (1964).

chapter 3

Fluorescence and Phosphorescence of Organic Molecules

E. L. Wehry* and L. B. Rogers

Department of Chemistry,
Purdue University, Lafayette, Indiana

I. Introduction

Many organic compounds fluoresce and/or phosphoresce, and these properties of organic compounds have been widely used for analysis. The study of luminescence processes in organic molecules has also received widespread attention from physical chemists and physicists, but many of the results from such studies appear to have escaped the attention of analytical chemists. It is evident that an understanding of the basic aspects of the luminescence of organic compounds can greatly enhance its efficacy as an analytical tool. It is the purpose of this chapter to discuss, from a relatively fundamental viewpoint, the fluorescence and phosphorescence behavior of organic molecules, and to point out the analytical implications of some studies that have been performed. In this chapter, familiarity with the concepts and terminology of Chapter 1 will be assumed. This chapter will concentrate principally on results published since 1955; for coverage of earlier work, the excellent review of West (1) should be consulted.

II. Photoluminescence and the Structure of Organic Molecules

Fluorescence and phosphorescence spectroscopy are not broadly useful methods for determining molecular structure in the same way that, for example, infrared or microwave spectroscopy are. Nonetheless, significant qualitative (and occasionally quantitative) information concerning molecular structure can be obtained from fluores-

---

* Present address: Department of Chemistry, Indiana University, Bloomington, Indiana.

cence studies.   Of the large number of known organic compounds, relatively few exhibit intense luminescence.   Therefore, the mere fact that an organic molecule does luminesce can constitute significant information regarding its structure.   In this section, the structural characteristics which tend to enhance or repress luminescence will be discussed with reference to particular classes of compounds.

A. Aliphatic Compounds

Relatively few aliphatic or alicyclic compounds exhibit true fluorescence in the ultraviolet or visible region.   Aliphatic compounds often do not strongly absorb in the ultraviolet or visible region, and, since strong absorption is usually a prerequisite for intense emission, such compounds generally do not fluoresce.   Of the aliphatic compounds which do absorb strongly, a large majority absorb in the short-wavelength (ca. 200 mμ) ultraviolet region.   The absorption of this high-energy radiation may lead to direct photodecomposition of the molecule, in which case the absorbed energy is utilized to break one or more bonds in the molecule and cannot reappear as emitted energy.   Examples of direct photodecomposition are not uncommon; as will be discussed below, photodecomposition of aliphatic ketones has led to difficulty in the interpretation of the luminescence of these compounds.

Even if direct photodecomposition does not occur in the high energy ultraviolet, a phenomenon known as "predissociation" may take place (2).   In this process, a molecule absorbs a photon and is raised to an excited state which is stable to decomposition.   From the stable excited state, the molecule then undergoes a radiationless transition to another, unstable, excited state.   The absorbed energy is then dissipated via the breaking of bonds in the unstable excited state.   Predissociation processes (in particular, the radiationless transition between the stable and unstable excited states) are not completely understood, but they appear to provide important mechanisms for the dissipation of excitation energy in saturated compounds.   Predissociation has been invoked to rationalize the observed fact that a number of aliphatic compounds (especially those containing nitro and iodo groups) do not fluoresce, even though they absorb at fairly long wavelengths, and that photodecomposition often occurs in such compounds despite the fact that the absorbed energy is below that of any bond in the molecule. As an example, the vapors of many aliphatic amines, alcohols, and carboxylic acids luminesce when exposed to short-wavelength ultraviolet. The luminescence does *not*, however, originate from the excited molecules themselves, but from excited NH_2 and OH radicals which are decomposition products of the original molecule. This type of phenomenon is responsible for the ostensible "fluorescence" of many other aliphatic compounds.

Aliphatic and alicyclic aldehydes and ketones, however, do exhibit true molecular luminescence. The isolated carbonyl group shows a characteristic absorption band having a maximum at about 280 mμ. Exposure of aliphatic carbonyl compounds to radiation of this wavelength frequently results in visible luminescence; however, the origin of this luminescence is not always obvious.

The emission properties of biacetyl (2,3-butanedione) have been studied extensively. This molecule is of great interest because it is one of the very few organic species to exhibit phosphorescence in liquid solutions (3). In fact, the quantum efficiency of biacetyl phosphorescence is greater than that for fluorescence, even in fluid solution. Dubois and Wilkinson found the quantum-yield ratio of phosphorescence to fluorescence to be 64 in the vapor state, "very large" in glassy EPA (a solvent mixture of 8 parts diethyl ether, 3 parts isopentane, and 5 parts ethanol by volume), and 7.5 in EPA at room temperature (4). Triplet state emission can be distinguished from fluorescence due to the fact that, in the vapor state, triplet emission is strongly quenched by oxygen, while singlet emission is not (3,5). Biacetyl also exhibits very interesting and useful energy-transfer behavior. It has been postulated (6) that many of the unusual characteristics of this compound are due to photochemical enolizations:

$$H_3C—C—C—CH_3 \rightleftharpoons H_3C—C—C=CH_2 \tag{3-1}$$

The luminescence of acetone has received much study. Exposure of acetone vapor to 254 or 313 mμ radiation results in a visible luminescence containing a blue and a green component. At least a portion of the green component is due to biacetyl formed by a photochemical reaction of acetone (7). The intrinsic luminescence of acetone has been shown (8) to consist of both fluorescence and phosphorescence. The luminescence appears between 380 and 470 mμ and is quite weak ($\Phi_F = 2 \times 10^{-3}$) (9). A number of acetone derivatives (especially halogenated acetones) and other aliphatic ketones exhibit similar luminescence in the gas phase (10). Acetaldehyde vapor, likewise, shows an emission from 338–500 mμ (maximum between 405 and 420 mμ) which consists of both triplet- and singlet-state components (11–13). Again, the green biacetyl phosphorescence occurs as a result of photodecomposition, and the separation of this luminescence from the acetaldehyde emission can be an arduous task. Similar behavior is observed for other aliphatic aldehydes.

While many aliphatic carbonyl compounds do luminesce, emission is usually a minor means of energy dissipation and such weak emission is of little analytical significance. Furthermore, most experimental studies have been performed on gas-phase aldehydes and ketones. However, the difficulties involved in the interpretation of the luminescence of these compounds are vividly demonstrated by the fact that the luminescence of acetone has been studied for at least 20 years and still does not appear to be fully understood. This illustrates an important fact: the absorber and the emitter are not always the same molecular species. Even if the two species are identical, the emission does not necessarily result from a simple transition from the excited to the ground state. Such complexities are often manifested in one of the following ways:

1. The emission intensity may vary with time.
2. The emission intensity may show unusual concentration dependences.
3. There may be an abnormally large displacement between the absorption and the emission maxima.
4. The quantum efficiency of emission may vary with wavelength. [In theory, the quantum efficiency should be approximately the same over all wavelengths at which the compound absorbs (14).]

B. Aromatic Compounds

A great majority of the organic compounds which exhibit intense analytically-useful fluorescence possess cyclic, conjugated structures. However, the fact that a molecule possesses these structural characteristics does not guarantee that the species will fluoresce. This section discusses the fluorescence characteristics of the different classes of aromatic and heterocyclic compounds, and some of the effects of molecular structure upon the luminescence of such compounds.

1. Aromatic Hydrocarbons

In liquid solution, most unsubstituted aromatic hydrocarbons exhibit fluorescence, either in the visible or ultraviolet. In general, the greater the number of condensed rings in an aromatic hydrocarbon, the lower will be the energy of emission. Thus, benzene and naphthalene fluoresce in the ultraviolet, anthracene exhibits blue fluorescence, naphthacene fluoresces green, and pentacene exhibits a red emission (1). Various aromatic hydrocarbons may fluoresce at widely differing frequencies, a fact which is of considerable analytical importance. In that regard, the work of Thommes and Leininger (15) is illustrative. Solutions of the aromatic hydrocarbons anthracene, phenanthrene, and fluorene fluoresce as shown in Figure 3-1. Note that the three spectra do not overlap completely; it is therefore possible, by careful choice of exciting and emitting wavelengths, to determine each hydrocarbon quantitatively in the presence of the other two (15). One can often analyze mixtures of two or three aromatic hydrocarbons, without prior separation, by selective choice of excitation and emission wavelengths. Of course, such a procedure will fail if the fluorescence spectra of the various components of the mixture coincide or if certain types of energy transfer occur (*vide infra*).

Two major difficulties are encountered in the measurement of the room-temperature fluorescence of aromatic hydrocarbons. First, the fluorescence of many polynuclear aromatic hydrocarbons is extremely sensitive to oxygen quenching (16); thus, solutions of aromatic hydrocarbons should be carefully purged of oxygen before fluorescence intensities are measured. Second, the fluorescence of solutions of condensed-ring aromatic hydrocarbons is often extraordinarily sensitive to the presence of small concentrations of impurities. For example, the fluorescence usually reported for fluorene is, in fact, due to small amounts of an impurity, carbazole, which is often present in commercial preparations of fluorene. Therefore, it is necessary to use carefully purified solutes and solvents when investigating the fluorescence properties of aromatic hydrocarbons.

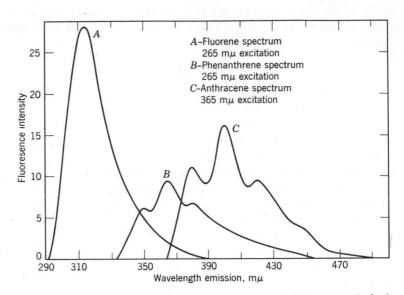

Fig. 3-1. Room-temperature fluorescence spectra of three aromatic hydrocarbons in methanol. Note that the spectra do not overlap completely, which facilitates the fluorometric determination of any one hydrocarbon in the presence of the other two. From Thommes and Leininger (15).

Kasha (17) has pointed out that, in many aromatic hydrocarbons, absorption from the ground state to the first excited singlet is forbidden; thus, the mean lifetime of fluorescence from the first excited singlet is quite long. This means that intersystem crossing (see Chapter 1) can compete with fluorescence; accordingly, many aromatic hydrocarbons exhibit phosphorescence in rigid glassy solutions at low temperature. Figure 3-2 shows three low-temperature fluorescence and phosphorescence spectra of aromatic hydrocarbons. Note especially the high resolution of vibrational fine structure which can be obtained. In a number of cases, such "total emission" spectra have been useful in augmenting vibrational frequencies obtained from infrared and Raman spectra (18,19).

Detailed study of the origin of the phosphorescence of unsubstituted aromatic compounds has been the subject of several investigations. Krishna and Goodman (20) have pointed out that some sort of spin–orbit coupling (see Chapter 1) is necessary for this phosphorescence to occur. They have concluded, from studies of polarized phosphorescence, that mixing of π,π^* triplet states with π,σ^* singlets, and mixing of π,σ^* triplets with the ground state, are the major sources of phosphorescence in aromatic hydrocarbons. Mixing of π,π^* singlets and triplets is held to be relatively unimportant (20). Similar conclusions have been indicated by El-Sayed, who also noted the somewhat surprising result that phosphorescence

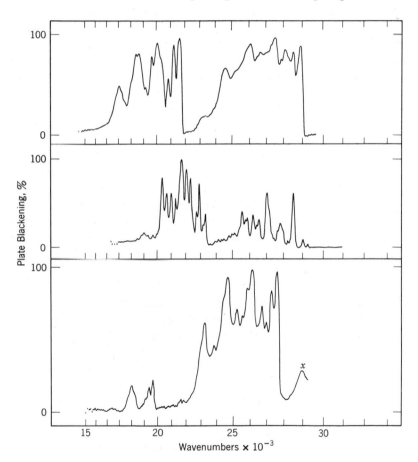

Fig. 3-2. Total emission spectra of three aromatic hydrocarbons in EPA glass at 77°K. *Upper*, phenanthrene; *middle*, triphenylene; *lower*, chrysene. Fluorescence is at higher frequencies, phosphorescence at lower frequencies. From Kasha (17).

spectra of aromatic hydrocarbons are rather *insensitive* to molecular symmetry, geometry, and structure (21).

Crystalline aromatic hydrocarbons exhibit interesting and useful electronic emission behavior. The luminescence of aromatic hydrocarbons in the vapor state, or in liquid or glassy solutions, is a true molecular property; in crystals, however, it is possible to observe emission which is a property of the *crystal as a whole*. Such emission cannot be regarded as a molecular phenomenon because the energy levels involved are not those of a single molecule but those of the crystal lattice. A discussion of the nature of "crystal luminescence" is beyond the scope of this chapter; McClure (22) and Hochstrasser (23) have reviewed some aspects of this subject. In a number of cases, however, molecular luminescence from crystals of aromatic compounds can be observed (24); it is then generally noted that intermolecular forces within the crystal cause shifts of the fluorescence to frequencies lower than those found for the hydrocarbon vapor. Stevens (25) has shown that the fluorescence of aromatic hydrocarbon crystals is a function of the lattice structure of the crystal and may thus be a useful adjunct to x-ray crystallography.

Crystals of aromatic hydrocarbons exhibit extraordinary energy-transfer effects, and have been used as scintillators for the detection of ionizing radiation. This aspect of the luminescence of aromatic hydrocarbons is discussed more fully in Section III.

2. Substituted Aromatic Hydrocarbons

Certain functional groups on an aromatic ring exert definite, predictable influences upon both the energy and intensity of emission. These substituent effects are listed in Table 3-1, and a few of them are discussed briefly below.

a. Alkyl Groups. In general, addition of alkyl groups of an aromatic nucleus has little influence upon the energy or intensity of emission, unless steric factors are involved. In a number of aromatic compounds, substitution of methyl or ethyl groups causes substantial increases in the phosphorescence-to-fluorescence intensity ratio (26).

b. Halogens. McClure (27) noted, for halogen-substituted naphthalenes, that as the series F, Cl, Br, I was traversed, the fluorescence diminished in intensity while the phosphorescence efficiency increased. This effect is very dramatically illustrated in Figure 3-3; it is generally termed the "intramolecular heavy-atom effect." Thus, bromo- or iodo-substituted aromatics exhibit intense phosphorescence, but only very weak fluorescence (if any). Furthermore, many iodo-substituted aromatic compounds are subject to predissociation or photodissociation in liquid solution, rendering the observation of any fluorescence even less probable.

In a study of the mechanism of the heavy-atom effect, it has been indicated that the halogen substituent enhances the spin–orbit coupling mechanism of the aromatic hydrocarbon and, in addition, introduces a new spin–orbit coupling process of its own (28).

The heavy atom need *not* be a constituent of the emitting molecule in order to manifest this perturbation; a heavy-atom-containing *solvent* will also quench the fluorescence (while enhancing the phosphorescence) of the solute. This interesting effect is discussed in the section on fluorescence quenching.

c. Nitro Groups. As a general rule, nitro-substituted aromatics may exhibit phosphorescence, but do not fluoresce. It appears that heavy-atom effects and predissociation are both involved in the quenching of fluorescence by nitro groups. Some dyes containing nitro groups, which absorb at very long wavelengths, do emit fluorescence (1). Generally speaking, however, nitro compounds can be analyzed by fluorimetric techniques only after conversion to a fluorescent compound, such as the corresponding amine.

TABLE 3-1

Effects of Substituents upon the Fluorescence of Aromatics

Substituent	Effect on frequency of emission	Effect on intensity
Alkyl	None	Very slight increase or decrease
OH, OCH$_3$, OC$_2$H$_5$	Decrease	Increase
CO$_2$H	Decrease	Large decrease
NH$_2$, NHR, NR$_2$	Decrease	Increase
NO$_2$, NO	—	Total quenching
CN	None	Increase
SH	Decrease	Decrease
F Cl Br I	Decrease ↓	Decrease ↓
SO$_3$H	None	None

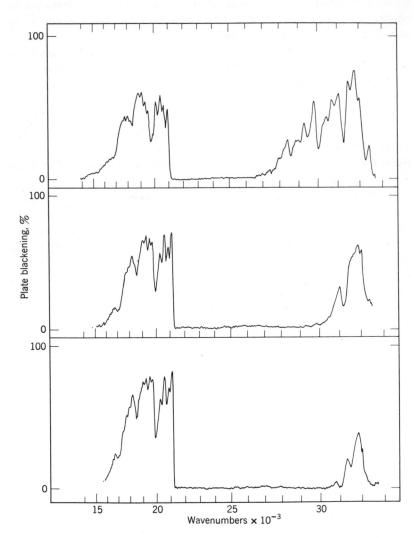

Fig. 3-3. The heavy-atom effect in intersystem crossing. Total emission spectra of halogenated naphthalenes in EPA at 77°K. *Upper*, 2-chloronaphthalene; *middle*, 2-bromonaphthalene; *lower*, 2-iodonaphthalene. Fluorescence is at higher frequencies, phosphorescence at lower frequencies. After Kasha (17).

d. Hydroxyl and Amino Groups. These groups are mainly of interest due to the unusual acid–base dissociation properties of excited organic compounds. These phenomena are examined in Section IV-C.

A summary of the influence of various substituent groups upon the emission of naphthalene is given in Table 3-2.

TABLE 3-2

Effect of Substituents on the Fluorescence and Phosphorescence
of Naphthalene (29)

Compound	Φ_p/Φ_F	$\bar{\nu}$, fluor., cm^{-1}	$\bar{\nu}$, phosphor., cm^{-1}
Naphthalene	0.093	31750	21250
1-Fluoronaphthalene	0.068	31600	21150
1-Chloronaphthalene	5.2	31360	20700
1-Bromonaphthalene	16.4	31280	20650
1-Iodonaphthalene	>1000	—	20500
1-Methylnaphthalene	0.053	31450	21000
1-Naphthaldehyde	>200	—	19750
1-Nitronaphthalene	>1000	—	19250

3. Aromatic Carbonyl Compounds

The electronic emission spectroscopy of aromatic ketones, aldehydes, and carboxylic acids is quite different from that of most aromatic compounds. In most aromatic carbonyls the lowest energy electronic transition is of n,π^* character, whereas that in most aromatics is π,π^*. As discussed in Chapter 1, molecules having low-lying n,π^* singlet states *usually* do not fluoresce, but may exhibit phosphorescence. In fact, such aromatic carbonyls as benzophenone, acetophenone, and anthraquinone exhibit intense phosphorescence but no measurable fluorescence (17).

Aromatic aldehydes or ketones containing substituents capable of hydrogen-bonding with the carbonyl oxygen (e.g., OH, NH$_2$) may fluoresce, presumably because the hydrogen bond "ties up" the non-bonding electrons on the oxygen, thereby removing their perturbing influence. Thus, anthraquinone is nonfluorescent while 1,4-dihydroxyanthraquinone fluoresces. Similarly, benzoic acid does not fluoresce, but hydroxybenzoic acids do (30). In some cases, aldehydes and ketones which do not fluoresce in nonpolar solvents exhibit fluorescence in very polar, hydrogen-bonding solvents. Such behavior is exhibited by pyrene-3-aldehyde (31). Similar effects are noted in the fluorescence of nitrogen heterocycles.

4. Nitrogen Heterocycles

Despite widespread study of these compounds, many aspects of their spectroscopic behavior are presently somewhat unclear. In most unsaturated N-heterocycles, the lowest energy electronic transition is n,π^*; accordingly, we should expect such compounds to phosphoresce but not fluoresce.

The role of n,π^* transitions in the spectroscopy of nitrogen heterocycles has been reviewed by Kasha (32), who has given a list of diagnostic criteria for use in deciding whether or not an observed electronic transition is of n,π^* character. One of these criteria is the absence of fluorescence emanating from the transition. If the influence of the lone pair on the nitrogen atom can be negated in some way, fluorescence of nitrogen heterocycles can be observed. Quinoline is nonfluorescent in neutral aqueous solutions, but fluoresces with moderate intensity in acidic solutions, presumably due to protonation of the lone electron pair on the nitrogen atom (33).

The emission properties of compounds possessing low-lying n,π^* singlet states are quite sensitive to the nature of the solvent. As the solvent polarity is increased, n,π^* transitions shift to higher energies, while π,π^* transitions shift to lower energies (34). If the n,π^* and π,π^* states lie very close in energy, the order of the states may interchange if a sufficiently polar solvent is used. Thus, in polar solvents, fluorescence of nitrogen heterocycles may be observed (17,35) because the lowest singlet state is π,π^*, rather than n,π^*. Similar effects have been noted in aromatic aldehydes.

There is evidence that all nitrogen heterocyclics do not exhibit a long wavelength n,π^* transition, even in the absence of solvent perturbations. It appears that the lowest electronic transition in acridine (the heterocyclic analog of anthracene) is of π,π^* character, and this compound appears to exhibit an intrinsic fluorescence (36). Also, some nitrogen heterocycles appear to exhibit $\pi^* \rightarrow n$ fluorescence, such as 9,10-diazaphenanthrene (37) and 1,2,4,5-tetrazine (38). The reasons why a few N-heterocycles exhibit this strange behavior, while others do not, is a subject of current interest (38,39). Suffice it to say that the nature of the emission (if any) from nitrogen hetercycles cannot presently be predicted with certainty, and, in several cases, the origin of the observed luminescence is not understood. This fact, together with the extreme sensitivity of the emission of nitrogen heterocycles to solvent effects, has retarded the use of fluorescence and phosphorescence for determinations of these compounds.

5. Other Heterocyclic Compounds

Fluorescence and phosphorescence of oxygen, sulfur, and silicon heterocycles is just beginning to be investigated systematically; heterocycles containing other elements (e.g., B, P, As, Se) have apparently not been investigated to any extent. A number of phenyl-substituted oxazoles have been used in liquid scintillation counting; for example, 2,5-diphenyloxazole is the well-known scintillator, "PPO." These are discussed more thoroughly in Section III. Oxygen heterocycles generally do not appear to fluoresce unless the oxygen-containing ring is fused to at least one aromatic ring, as in coumarin,

The same can be said for sulfur heterocycles. Thiophene does not appear to fluoresce or phosphoresce, but dibenzothiophene and other condensed sulfur heterocycles are known to phosphoresce (40).

Some recent work has been concerned with the emission of various silicon heterocycles (41); as yet, however, no general statements regarding the fluorescence properties of such compounds can be made.

It is not surprising to note that the intramolecular heavy-atom effect holds for heterocyclic compounds. Fluorene and three heterocyclic analogs (dibenzofuran, carbazole, and dibenzothiophene) have been investigated recently (42). As one carbon atom of fluorene is replaced, respectively, by oxygen, nitrogen, and sulfur, the quantum yield of fluorescence decreases while that of phosphorescence increases. It therefore appears that heterocycles containing atoms heavier than nitrogen will be even less prone to exhibit fluorescence than nitrogen heterocycles, but may, in turn, exhibit quite intense phosphorescence. With the development of phosphorimetry as an analytical tool (Chapter 6), the hitherto-unstudied phosphorescence of heavy-atom-containing heterocycles should make possible interesting analytical applications.

6. Organic Polymers

Despite the importance of synthetic polymers to chemical industry, relatively few careful studies of polymer fluorescence have been performed. Much of the reported work is of limited value because the fluorescence intensities and wavelengths were only visually estimated, and a very broad band of ultraviolet was used for excitation. With the appearance of spectrofluorometers, more definitive work has commenced to appear. Investigations of luminescent solutes in a plastic matrix have been numerous and, in some cases, it makes possible the observation of room-temperature phosphorescence of organic solutes (43). However, phosphorescence spectra obtained at room temperature in plastic matrices are often quite sensitive to the method of preparation of the matrix, and they usually contain less fine structure than those obtained at liquid nitrogen temperature. For the study of phosphorescence, there is presently no adequate substitute for glasses at liquid nitrogen temperature. Luminescent organic molecules embedded in polymeric matrices have been successfully used as scintillators (cf. Section III). It appears that the luminescence characteristics of solutes in plastics may often be determined by chemical bonding of the solute with the matrix material (44).

Fluorescence spectrometry of organic molecules in plastic matrices has recently been utilized for analytical purposes by Drushel and Sommers (45), who determined inhibitors added to polymers to retard oxidation. Such methods appear promising and their use should grow in importance.

The fluorescence of solid polymers themselves (rather than that of a fluorescent material "dissolved" in the polymer) has received surprisingly little investigation. A wide variety of polymers exhibit fluorescence; polystyrenes, polyacrylonitriles, and poly(methyl methacrylates) all appear to exhibit blue luminescence (46). The fluorescence maxima often decrease, both in energy and intensity, as the molecular weight of the polymer is increased. The concentration of residual monomer in a polymer sample also influences the characteristics of the emission (47).   The use of fluorescence as a technique for polymer characterization may deserve further study, since definite relationships appear to exist between the luminescence and structure of solid polymers (46,48).

Luminescence of *solutions* of polymers has received attention (49–51).   Fluorescence polarization methods have been developed for study of the internal structure of dissolved, molten, and solid polymers.   Viscosity effects and rotational relaxation times of dissolved polymeric species can be investigated in this manner, and some very interesting results have been obtained (49).

It would appear that the use of fluorescence as a tool for polymer characterization has received less attention than it warrants, and further work in this area should be of interest.

7. Dyes

There are many classes of dyes, and no attempt will be made to consider the fluorescence of each type.   Only the more prominent features of dye luminescence are discussed here.   Because virtually all dyes are intensely colored, they can be excited by absorbing radiation of much lower frequency than simpler organic compounds and, consequently, dye fluorescence will also be of relatively low frequency.   Accordingly, it is not unusual to observe dye fluorescence in the red, or even the near infrared, region of the spectrum.   The low absorption and emission energies of dyes often enable them to fluoresce, even if they contain substituents which quench fluorescence in simpler molecules *via* dissociative mechanisms (e.g., I, NO_2).   For example, some iodinated fluorescein dyes exhibit fluorescence (52), whereas virtually all iodo derivatives of simple aromatic compounds are nonfluorescent, due to the photochemical lability of carbon–iodine bonds.

The molecular structures of most dyes are quite complex.   Many of them possess more than one dissociable proton, so that a variety of partially-ionized species can exist in different pH ranges, each characterized by different absorption and fluorescence spectra.   This fact, of course, is the basis of the use of certain dyes as pH indicators, but it can be burdensome in a study of dye luminescence, where it is desirable to limit the number of major ground-state species in the solution to one.   Furthermore, dyes exhibit a pronounced tendency to aggregate into dimers or higher polymeric forms.   Presumably, this tendency is due to the high electronic polarizability of most dyes, so that aggregation can occur as a result of London force-interactions (17). Millich and Oster (53) reported that some acridine dyes underwent self-quenching of fluorescence, due to dimer formation, at concentrations as low as $10^{-6}M$. However, more recent data indicate that the observed self-quenching was due to self-absorption of the fluorescent radiation and did not require the postulation of dimerization at micromolar concentrations (54). Nonetheless, aggregation usually becomes important at concentrations greater than $10^{-4}M$. Clearly, great care must be exercised in studies of dye luminescence to ensure that only one ground-state species is present under a given set of solution conditions.

The effect of concentration upon dye fluorescence can be noted in Figure 3-4, in which fluorescence of both monomer and dimer are observed. Similar aggregation effects occur in the absorption spectra of dyes, indicating that the dyes form stable dimers in the ground state. This is in sharp contrast to the behavior of simpler aromatic compounds, most of which tend to form so-called "excimers" at high solute concentrations (cf. Section IV-A). The "excimers" are dimers stable *only* in electronically excited states. Such species are seldom, if ever, observed with dyes, due to the great tendency of ground-state dye molecules to aggregate.

Aggregation of dye molecules affects the efficiency of their luminescence. For many classes of dyes, dimerization reduces the fluorescence intensity while causing enhancement of phosphorescence (55). McRae and Kasha (56) contend that this effect should be of general importance in dye luminescence, and they have advanced explanations for the increased phosphorescence efficiency produced by aggregation of dyes.

Most dyes are structurally complex, so that it is reasonable to expect isomerism to be prevalent. Different geometric isomers of the same dye sometimes exhibit quite different luminescence characteristics. For example, in thioindigo dyes, the *trans* isomers have tightly-held, rigid, coplanar structures and exhibit fluorescence; the *cis* isomers are usually noncoplanar and nonfluorescent (57). Similar phenomena prevail in cyanine dyes. Cyanine dyes which are sterically hindered exhibit very low efficiencies of luminescence, while those not possessing crowded structures are intensely fluorescent (17). This exemplifies the general principle, discussed further in Section

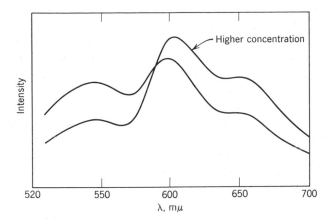

Fig. 3-4. Fluorescence spectra of the dye 1,1'-diethyl-2,2'-pyridocyanine iodide at two different concentrations. The monomer emission maximum is ca. 600 mμ; the dimer emission maximum is ca. 650 mμ. From Levinson, Simpson, and Curtis (55).

II-D, that rigid, noncrowded, planar structures are conducive to intense fluorescence.

Further support for this statement can be found in the studies of Oster and co-workers (58,59). Certain dyes (such as triphenyl-methane dyes, diphenylmethane dyes, some stilbene derivatives, and some of the fluorescein dyes) are nonfluorescent or only very weakly fluorescent in water or organic solvents. The fluorescence intensity is significantly increased, however, in very viscous media, such as glycerol. The fluorescence also increases if the dyes are bound to high polymers in solution. This indicates that internal conversion, due to intramolecular rotations, is the cause of the low emission efficiency in nonviscous media; binding of the dye to a polymer or its dissolution in a viscous solvent will tend to retard intramolecular twisting, and thus enhance fluorescence.

Heavy-atom effects have been observed in dyes. We have seen (Section II-C-2) that, in aromatic hydrocarbons, heavy-atom-containing substituents enhance intersystem crossing from the first excited singlet to the lowest triplet state, thereby enhancing phos-phorescence at the expense of fluorescence. This does *not* appear to be the case for fluorescein dyes, where heavy-atom substitution causes a reduction in fluorescence but *no* concomitant enhancement of phosphorescence (52). It has been concluded that heavy-atom effects in fluorescein dyes operate not by enhancing intersystem crossing, but rather by fostering internal conversion from the excited singlet to the ground state (52,60). Reasons for the apparently different heavy-atom perturbations in dyes compared to simpler aromatic compounds do not appear to have been advanced.

Solutions of dyes exhibit unusual energy-transfer processes. A discussion of these phenomena is beyond the scope of this chapter, but it appears that concentrated solutions of dyes exhibit intermolecular energy-transfer processes not unlike exciton migration phenomena in crystals of aromatic hydrocarbons (61).

C. EFFECTS OF MOLECULAR GEOMETRY UPON LUMINESCENCE OF ORGANIC COMPOUNDS

From the foregoing discussion, it is clear that all members of a given class of aromatic or heterocyclic compounds will exhibit reasonably similar electronic emission spectra, with only relatively minor variations caused by changes in the finer details of molecular structure. As a result, fluorescence and phosphorescence spectroscopy are not broadly useful tools for the determination of molecular structure. Nonetheless, there are a number of instances in which the influence of molecular geometry can be clearly observed in fluorescence spectra, and a few of these are mentioned below.

Many intensely fluorescent organic molecules are characterized by highly rigid, planar structures. For example, fluorescein exhibits very intense fluorescence in solution, whereas phenolphthalein does not, although it is structurally similar to fluorescein.

Fluorescein   Phenolphthalein

The only structural difference between the two compounds is an oxygen bridge in fluorescein, absent in phenolphthalein. In phenolphthalein, rotations and vibrations of the aromatic rings with respect to one another are presumably facile, so that electronic excitation can be easily dissipated internally, without leading to emission. Vibrational dissipation of electronic energy is considerably more difficult in a rigid structure, such as that of fluorescein. Generally, therefore, the efficiency of luminescence increases greatly with the *rigidity* of molecular structure.

Internal dissipation of excitation energy is also facilitated by *steric crowding*. Thus, steric hindrance decreases fluorescence intensity (17). As pointed out in the discussion of substituent effects, alkyl groups generally exert little effect upon the emission of an aromatic nucleus. This statement is vitiated if the alkyl groups are bulky and interfere sterically with one another or with another portion of the molecule. Steric hindrance of rings or substituents can cause marked decreases in emission intensity; examples of such effects are common in cyanine dyes and are discussed more fully by Kasha (17).

It has often been noted that many of the most intensely fluorescent organic molecules are *planar*, presumably because coplanarity is usually considered to be a requirement for effective π-electron delocalization. Often, an aromatic molecule in which different π-electron systems are distorted greatly from planarity exhibits unusual electronic emission. A good example is hexahelicene (phenanthro[3, 4c]phenanthrene). Unlike most catacondensed aromatic hydrocarbons, hexahelicene is not planar; its principal structural feature is a high degree of helicity. In its fluorescence and phosphorescence properties, this compound behaves very much like two weakly-interacting phenanthrene molecules (62), presumably as a result of distortion from planarity. A similar conclusion holds for 1,1-binaphthyl, which is apparently nonplanar, undergoes intramolecular twisting, and exhibits low-temperature luminescence characteristic of two non-interacting naphthalene molecules (63).

In some cases, fluorescence spectrometry is a useful tool for the study of geometric isomers. A number of aromatic compounds exhibit *cis–trans* isomerism; often *cis* isomers are nonfluorescent, while the *trans* species exhibit rather intense fluorescence, as in the case of stilbene and its derivatives (64,65). Presumably *cis*-stilbene is nonplanar due to steric interference of the *ortho*-hydrogens of the two aromatic rings (65). Occasionally, both *cis* and *trans* isomers fluoresce, but the spectra are different, as in the case for 2-vinylanthracene (66).

Fluorescence has also been used as a tool to study *photochemical* isomerizations. Dyck and McClure (67) have performed an extensive study of the photochemical *cis–trans* isomerization of stilbene. The work of Hammond et al. (68,69) also illustrates the use of fluorescence and phosphorescence in the investigation of excited-state isomerizations. For example, the phosphorescence spectrum of 2-naphthil,

exhibits two sub-spectra which can be understood only by assuming that *two* triplet-state species are present. Presumably, these two triplets are *cis*- and *trans*-isomeric triplet states of the compound (68). With the known propensity of organic compounds to photoisomerize, it will not be surprising if other examples of stereoisomeric triplet states manifest themselves.

Another aspect of fluorimetry relating to molecular structure is the so-called "mirror image" rule (1). Generally, the fluorescence spectrum of an organic molecule is very similar to a mirror image of the ultraviolet absorption spectrum of the compound. The *lack* of such a relation between absorption and fluorescence spectra has been interpreted as indicating a large change in the nuclear configuration of the molecule upon electronic excitation (70). Thus, distortions of the intensity distribution of a fluorescence spectrum may be of interest in studying changes in molecular structure upon electronic excitation.

III. Fluorescence Quenching and Energy Transfer in Organic Compounds

The sum of the quantum yields of fluorescence and phosphorescence of many organic molecules is less than unity. As a result, the question, "What happens to the remaining energy?" becomes of interest. In this section, certain of the more important aspects of energy transfer and fluorescence quenching in organic systems will be discussed in a qualitative fashion. (For a more thorough treatment of the theoretical aspects of these topics, the reader is referred to Chapter 1.)

A. Transfer of Singlet and Triplet Excitation Energy

The transfer of *singlet* excitation energy from one organic molecule to another is a subject of intense research activity at the present time. The most obvious mechanism by which an excited organic molecule, $^1A^*$, can transfer energy to a ground-state molecule of another species, Q, is by fluorescence of $^1A^*$ followed by absorption of the emitted quantum by Q:

$$^1A^* \rightarrow A + h\nu \tag{3-2}$$

$$Q + h\nu \rightarrow {}^1Q^* \tag{3-3}$$

Since this process involves emission and re-absorption of radiant energy, it is commonly called "radiative energy transfer." Radiative transfer is an easy process to visualize and is often referred to in the literature as a "trivial" process. While it may be trivial in its theoretical aspects, the practical implications of radiative transfer should not be lost upon the analytical chemist. If a solution contains the solute of interest, A, and an additional solute, B, and if the ultraviolet absorption spectrum of B overlaps the fluorescence spectrum of A, the fluorescence of A may be quenched to an appreciable extent. Before fluorometric analysis of a mixture of compounds is attempted, the absorption and fluorescence spectra of each species should be determined separately in order to ascertain if spectral overlap will be a serious factor. If the answer to this question is affirmative, as much as possible of the offending compound(s) should be removed from the test solution before making a measurement.

Most important energy-transfer processes in liquid solution, however, do *not* involve emission and re-absorption of photons; instead, they proceed with no observable intermediate emission or absorption. Consequently, they are referred to as *nonradiative* transfer mechanisms. There appear to be several distinct means by which this type of transfer can occur.

In some cases, nonradiative energy transfer from one solute to another is strongly dependent upon the viscosity of the solution, and it behaves much as a diffusion-controlled chemical reaction (71). However, nonradiative energy transfer can also occur *without* close approach of the donor and acceptor; Förster (72,73) has noted that energy transfer can occur between two molecules separated by distances as large as 60 A. Such long-range transfer is highly probable only if there is partial overlap of the absorption spectrum of the energy acceptor with the fluorescence spectrum of the donor. For a more complete discussion of nonradiative transfer of electronic excitation energy, Chapter 1 should be consulted.

In summary, there are at least three distinct mechanisms by which singlet excitation energy of organic molecules can be transferred in liquid solution:

1. Radiative transfer (fluorescence followed by absorption).
2. Diffusion-controlled nonradiative transfer.
3. Long-range dipole–dipole resonance interactions.

Regardless of the detailed mechanism, singlet–singlet energy transfer is responsible for the process of "sensitized fluorescence," wherein emission is observed from a species which does not absorb the incident energy:

$$A + h\nu \rightarrow {}^1A^* \tag{3-4}$$

$$^1A^* + Q \rightarrow {}^1Q^* + A \tag{3-5}$$

$$^1Q^* \rightarrow Q + h\nu' \tag{3-6}$$

Sensitized fluorescence is especially common in solutions containing several polycyclic aromatic hydrocarbons, and a number of examples have been discussed by Bowen (74). Singlet energy transfer can also manifest itself by causing quenching of the fluorescence of organic compounds; this is discussed in Section III-D.

The occurrence of singlet–singlet energy transfer has been known for many years, principally due to early observations of sensitized fluorescence. More recently, it has been noted that aromatic aldehydes and ketones can sensitize the *phosphorescence* of aromatic hydrocarbons (75). The observation of sensitized phosphorescence was of great interest because it demonstrated that energy-transfer phenomena are not restricted to singlet states, but can also drastically affect the phosphorescence of organic molecules. In addition to energy transfer between two triplet-state molecules, singlet–triplet and triplet–singlet transfer have been observed in organic systems (76,77). The mechanisms of these processes are discussed in Chapter 1.

Triplet–triplet energy transfer can, of course, lead to quenching and sensitization of phosphorescence, but most triplet energy migration processes are diffusion-controlled (78–80). It is expected, therefore, that energy-transfer phenomena may exert less severe effects upon low-temperature phosphorescence than room-temperature fluorescence. Nonetheless, the fact that sensitized phosphorescence can be observed in rigid matrices should make the analytical chemist cautious about assuming that energy transfer in rigid media is never appreciable.

Of course, the implications of triplet–triplet energy transfer in liquid-state photochemistry are sizable. Hammond and co-workers (81,82) have pointed out that the effect offers attractive possibilities for the preparation of triplet states of organic molecules whose triplet levels cannot be populated directly by excitation. Aromatic carbonyl compounds are especially useful as donors of triplet energy.

B. ENERGY TRANSFER IN ORGANIC CRYSTALS

There have been recent reviews of energy-transfer effects in crystalline aromatic compounds (22,23,83). An example which illustrates the almost unbelievable efficiency of crystal energy transfer is the anthracene–naphthacene system. When very small concentrations of naphthacene are dissolved in crystalline anthracene, the anthracene can transfer its excitation energy to naphthacene molecules, causing the fluorescence of both species to be observed even though only anthracene is absorbing the incident energy. The ratio of fluorescence of naphthacene to anthracene reaches unity (84) at a mole fraction of naphthacene of only 10^{-6}! The extreme sensitivity of organic crystal luminescence to traces of impurities has hampered fundamental studies. For example, it is almost prohibitively difficult to prepare naphthalene crystals in which the luminescence of a persistent impurity, 2-methylnaphthalene, is not also observed (85).

Ganguly and Chaudhury (83) have pointed out that at least four different energy migration mechanisms may be operative in organic crystals:

1. *Photon emission and reabsorption.* This radiative transfer process is probable only if there exists considerable overlap between the emission spectrum of the energy donor and the absorption spectrum of the acceptor, and if the system has a high absorption efficiency in the region of overlap (86).

2. *Resonance Transfer.* This is a resonance phenomenon between allowed electric dipole transitions in donor and acceptor. The mechanism has been discussed quantitatively by Förster (72).

It is analogous to the long-range resonance transfer which can occur in liquid solutions (Chapter 1). The process is highly probable only if the emission spectrum of the donor overlaps the absorption spectrum of the acceptor, similar to radiative transfer, but no emission or absorption occurs as such.

3. *Exciton Migration.* Frenkel (87) introduced the term "exciton" to refer to the rapid transfer of excitation energy from one constituent to another of a crystal lattice. An exciton is, in essence, an "excitation wave." No attempt will be made to provide a detailed discussion of exciton theory; suffice it to say that such phenomena appear to be of considerable significance in organic crystals. Further aspects of exciton processes are discussed in detail by Heller and Marcus (88), Hochstrasser (23), Rice (89), and Davydov (90).

4. *Electron and Hole Migration.* It was first proposed by Mott and Gurney (91) that electronic excitation energy could be transferred through a crystal by means of the production of electrons and positive holes, freed from one another, which migrated through the crystal. Such processes are significant in photoconductive inorganic solids, but it is not clear to what extent they occur in organic crystals.

Much remains to be learned about the details of energy migration in the organic solid state. The necessity of using very pure materials in investigations of crystalline organic phosphors cannot be over-emphasized.

C. Intramolecular Energy Transfer

Thus far, we have considered energy transfer between two different molecular species, or between two different molecules of the same species. Energy transfer *within a single molecule* can also be observed, particularly if the molecule possesses two independent systems of conjugated double bonds (14). In such compounds, excitation of one chromophore can lead to fluorescence from the other, so that the quantum yield of fluorescence will not be constant as the exciting frequency is altered (Section II-A).   An example of a compound in which intramolecular energy transfer can occur is

This compound contains two independent aromatic systems, and excitation energy can be transferred from one to the other. It is presumed that energy transfer between the two absorbing systems occurs by means of a resonance coupling of oscillators (14).   It appears that intramolecular energy transfer is of greater importance in large biological molecules and lanthanide chelates than in simple organic molecules.

D. QUENCHING OF FLUORESCENCE IN LIQUID SOLUTION

Having presented the fundamental aspects of electronic energy transfer in a qualitative fashion, we now turn our attention to the influence of energy-transfer processes upon various subjects of analytical interest.   One phenomenon of which the analytical chemist cannot remain unaware is fluorescence quenching. *Quenching* of fluorescence is defined (92) as any process that results in a decrease in the *true* fluorescence efficiency of a molecule; quenching processes divert the absorbed energy into channels other than fluorescence. Therefore, events which cause changes in the ground-state concentration of the fluorescent species (e.g., association, decomposition) or which cause the fluorescence emission to be reabsorbed ("inner-filter effects") are not quenching processes *per se*.   One very important mechanism by which true quenching can occur is energy transfer from the excited solute to another molecule in solution; the reader is referred to Chapter 1 for a detailed description of this process.

Frequently, the concentration of quenching agent in a solution will be sufficiently small that quenching can be reduced by suitable dilution, provided, of course, that the initial concentration of fluorescent species is not too small.   An apparent exception to this general rule is quenching by gaseous oxygen.   As a result of the presence of oxygen in unpurged solvents, dilution of a solution usually effects little change in the oxygen concentration.   The quenching action of oxygen can only be negated by purging the solution with another gas (such as nitrogen) or by preparing all solutions in a vacuum system. Unfortunately, oxygen quenching is a very general phenomenon; very few electronically excited organic molecules can withstand more than one or two collisions with molecular oxygen without being deactivated (93).   In some cases, oxygen decreases the fluorescence intensity of an organic compound by oxidizing it; more often, however, there is no obvious chemical reaction between the compound and oxygen. Quenching by oxygen often behaves as a diffusion-controlled process (94).   Oxygen and other paramagnetic gases (e.g., NO) are believed to quench fluorescence of an excited molecule, $^1A^*$, by promoting intersystem crossing of $^1A^*$ to its triplet state.   The actual intersystem crossing process appears (95) to occur *via* formation of a transitory complex of pronounced charge transfer character between the excited solute and molecular oxygen:

$$^1A^* + {}^3O_2 \rightarrow (A^+O_2^-)^* \rightarrow {}^3A^* + {}^3O_2 \qquad (3\text{-}7)$$

In room-temperature solution, of course, no phosphorescence from $^3A^*$ can be observed.

Effects of oxygen quenching are most serious for solutions of aromatic hydrocarbons, but the fluorescence of virtually all organic compounds is quenched, at least slightly, by oxygen.   Deaeration of solutions is therefore a routine step in the preparation of samples for fluorometric analysis.

Although it is recognized that extraneous organic solutes can quench fluorescence of a given organic compound by means of intermolecular energy transfer, the fact that fluorescence of an organic molecule can also be quenched by other molecules of the same species is less widely appreciated.   Particularly if a solute is present in high concentration ($10^{-3}M$ or greater), an excited organic molecule can form a transient dimer with a ground-state molecule of the same species:

$$^1A^* + A \rightarrow (AA)^* \qquad (3\text{-}8)$$

The dimeric species (AA)* is called an "excimer." Excimers are capable of characteristic emission; the formation of an excimer which emits and then decomposes after emission, to yield two ground-state A molecules, clearly tends to quench the fluorescence of ^{1}A* (96). The principles of excimer formation are discussed in more detail in Section IV-A. It should be noted that "mixed excimers" can also be formed between two *different* molecules (97). Thus, a second solute, Q, can quench the fluorescence of ^{1}A* by forming a mixed excimer, (AQ)*, even if no energy-transfer process (in the usual sense) takes place. Obviously, high concentrations of the solute of interest or of extraneous materials are to be avoided when possible. In addition to excimer interactions, "inner-filter effects," such as self-absorption of fluorescence, can cause apparent decreases in fluorescence efficiency at high concentrations.

Quenching effects can also be produced by the solvent even if no extraneous solutes are present in the solution. Usually, the quantum efficiency of fluorescence of an organic compound varies with the solvent. Bowen and co-workers (98,99) have proposed a mechanism for solvent quenching of fluorescence which involves chemical inter-action between the solvent and excited solute, leading to formation of an encounter complex:

$$A + h\nu \rightarrow {}^1A* \qquad (3\text{-}9)$$

$$^1A* + S \rightarrow (A^-S^+)^\ddagger \rightarrow A + S \qquad (3\text{-}10)$$

In this scheme, S represents the solvent and, as usual, A is the fluorescent solute. It appears that most, if not all, of the energy degradation involved in solvent quenching occurs through the triplet level of A (100). Therefore, the encounter complex in process (3–10) is represented as (A$^-$S$^+$), to indicate transfer of an electron from the solvent to the excited solute, the species "A$^-$" being a triplet. Solvent quenching occurs to an appreciable extent even in nonpolar solvents, such as saturated hydrocarbons, but it becomes much more serious for polar solute–solvent pairs. The stronger the interaction between the solvent and excited solute, the greater the energy lost through solvent quenching. This fact should be borne in mind when choosing solvents for fluorometric analysis.

Certain solvents decrease the intensities of fluorescence of organic molecules in a somewhat different manner. It was pointed out in Section II-C that the presence of heavy-atom-containing substituents in an organic molecule can induce enhancement of phosphorescence at the expense of fluorescence. Kasha (101) noted that this effect can occur even if the heavy atom is *not* a constituent of the emitting molecule. It is found, for example, that addition of ethyl iodide to solutions of aromatic hydrocarbons enhances their phosphorescence/ fluorescence ratios (102). The "external heavy-atom effect," which results from the addition of heavy-atom-containing solvents (or solutes) to a fluorescent solution, causes an increase in the rate constant for intersystem crossing; the mechanism is believed to be charge-transfer in nature (103,104). McGlynn et al. (105) have proposed that a weak charge-transfer complex is formed between the emitting and perturbing molecules, thereby facilitating intersystem crossing. Earlier, Kasha (101) had proposed that the effect was caused by energetic collisions between the excited solute and perturbing molecule. (It should be noted that the formation of weak charge-transfer complexes is assumed to occur in both solvent quenching and the external heavy-atom effect.)

It should, therefore, be clear that solvents such as nitromethane, carbon tetrabromide, and ethyl iodide are not suitable for sensitive fluorometric analyses. On the other hand, these solvents may be quite useful for enhancing the sensitivity of phosphorescence analysis. Also, heavy-atom-containing solvents have been used to obtain singlet–triplet absorption spectra in liquid solution (106,107); normally, this absorption cannot be observed without utilizing flash excitation. Thus, under certain circumstances, the external heavy-atom effect may be quite valuable to the analytical chemist.

It should not be inferred that fluorescence quenching is *always* an analytically undesirable occurrence. It is possible to determine fluorimetrically an organic compound which quenches the fluorescence of another material by measuring the extent of quenching. The basis of such analyses is clearly contained in the Stern-Volmer quenching expression, eq. (1-8). For example, oxygen can be determined by its quenching action on the fluorescence or phosphorescence of the dye, trypaflavine (108). The full analytical potentialities of fluorescence quenching have not been appreciated; quenching measurements should be useful in the sensitive fluorometric determination of compounds which do not fluoresce, and may also be useful in enhancing the specificity and selectivity of fluorometric analysis (109).

E. ORGANIC LIQUID SCINTILLATORS

Energy-transfer phenomena are of great importance in the action of organic scintillators for the detection of high-energy radiation. No attempt will be made to discuss this subject exhaustively; reference should be made to several recent monographs and reviews of the subject (110–113).

In *liquid* organic scintillators, a solution is prepared which usually contains a single fluorescent solute. The incident energy produces ionization and electronic excitation of solvent molecules. The solvent ions thus produced may decompose, transfer their charge to another solvent (or solute) molecule, or may be neutralized to yield highly excited singlet or triplet states which then internally convert to lower singlet states (114). These excited solvent molecules may transfer electronic energy to solute molecules, which then fluoresce. Although the preponderance of excitation processes affect the *solvent*, emission of the *solute* is observed. Clearly, then, high energy-transfer efficiencies are necessary for useful scintillation properties.

Energy transfer from solvent to solute should be rapid, efficient, and irreversible. The first important consideration in this regard is the nature of the solvent. For high scintillation efficiency, the solvent must have a large excitation coefficient and must transfer a large fraction of its excitation energy irreversibly to the fluorescent solute. Furst and Kallmann (115) reported that, when the fluorescence of a given solute was tested in different solvents, nearly equal intensities were found under ultraviolet excitation but large differences were observed under high-energy irradiation. A proposed scintillation mixture must therefore be tested under high-energy irradiation in order to effectively gage its scintillation efficiency. Most of the "good" scintillation solvents are unsaturated; examples are benzene, toluene, and the xylenes. Dioxane, although saturated, is an effective scintillation solvent. Solvents with "poor" scintillation properties include acetone, chloroform, ethanol, hexane, and diethyl ether. Unfortunately, many of the "good" scintillation solvents do not dissolve a wide range of materials. If solubility poses a problem, it is often possible to dissolve the solute in a "poor" solvent and then add as much "good" solvent as possible.

The nature of the solute is also important. According to Heller (116), the most effective scintillation solutes are molecules which do *not* possess highly rigid structures (for example, terphenyl and diphenyloxazole). This seems somewhat unusual, because, as pointed out in Section II, many of the most highly-fluorescent organic molecules have quite rigid nuclear configurations. Apparently a nonrigid scintillation solute leads to high efficiency, however, because it facilitates irreversible energy transfer. If the solute, under electronic excitation, undergoes a conformational change, energy transfer from solvent to solute will tend to be irreversible and equipartition of excitation energy between solvent and solute will be prevented. Conformational changes upon excitation are, of course, more likely if the molecular structure of the solute is not rigid.

The prospective scintillation solute must exhibit intense fluorescence in a region of the spectrum convenient to measure, such as the visible or near ultraviolet. Some representative classes of organic scintillation solutes are:

1. *p*-Oligophenylenes:

2. Oxazole and oxadiazole derivatives; for example, the common scintillation solute "PPO" is 2,5-diphenyloxazole:

$$C_6H_5 \qquad\qquad C_6H_5$$

3. Other ring systems, such as benzene, naphthalene, pyridine, pyrrole, or indole.

Of the possible substituents, CH_3, OCH_3, F, and Cl do not adversely affect scintillator efficacy, but as expected, NO_2, Br, and I should be avoided.

It is sometimes desirable to add a second solute to the scintillator solution. This secondary solute is called a "wavelength shifter"; its purpose is to receive excitation energy from the primary solute and emit its own characteristic fluorescence (117). Wavelength shifters are utilized to lower self-absorption of fluorescence or to obtain more efficient matching of the emission frequency with the sensitivity curve of the detector.

The actual energy-transfer processes in liquid scintillator solutions have not been completely established. Both nonradiative and radiative mechanisms can be important. Melhuish (118) has derived an equation for scintillator efficiency which includes contributions from both modes of transfer. Long-range resonance radiationless transfer usually is not significant in practical liquid scintillator systems because the necessary overlap of absorption and fluorescence spectra (See Chapter 1) is minimized so as to limit self-absorption of fluorescence. Nonradiative transfer processes occurring in scintillation solutions usually involve diffusion of the accepting and transferring molecules (119).

Lipsky and Burton (120) contend that to speak of excitation of single solvent molecules in the scintillation process is inaccurate; they prefer the concept of "solvent domains," in which the excitation moves very rapidly through exciton states of the entire solvent domain. While there are certain attractive features of this picture, it has not been well defined and no attempt has been made to quantitatively describe these domains.

Liquid scintillator solutions are quite susceptible to poisoning by miniscule amounts of impurities, especially organic sulfur and halogen compounds (121). They are often subject to oxygen quenching and require careful deaeration; oxygen concentrations as low as $10^{-3}M$ can cause considerable losses in efficiency (112,122). Despite these difficulties, liquid scintillators are extremely versatile and have won widespread acceptance for the detection of ionizing radiation.

F. ORGANIC PLASTIC SCINTILLATORS

Plastics containing dissolved scintillating chemicals have been used for detection of high-energy radiation. While the mode of action of scintillator plastics is not completely understood, it appears that the fluorescence process is initiated principally by excitation of the polymer molecules, which then transfer energy to the fluorescent solute. Since plastics are heterogeneous mixtures of long-chain molecules, it is possible that intramolecular energy transfer can occur along the polymer chain. If the solute molecules can attach themselves in some manner to the polymer chain, the energy may be transferred to the solute, the fluorescence of which will then be observed. In some plastics, the scintillation efficiency depends upon the molecular weight of the polymer; the efficiency increases sharply with molecular weight up to a certain value and then levels off (123). This has led several authors to the conclusion that chemical bonding of the solute with the polymer matrix is important in the scintillation process (44,123). The work of Weinreb and Avivi (124), however, indicates that energy transfer is not related to possible bonding of the polymer with the solute. The influence of such bonding may vary with changes in polymeric matrix or solute. Thus, the mode of energy transfer between the plastic and the fluorescent compound remains something of a mystery. It has been suggested that both radiative and nonradiative transfer can occur in plastic scintillators but, in most practical plastic scintillators, nonradiative transfer appears to predominate (125,126).

Many of the solutes used in liquid scintillators are also used in plastics (113). Purity of solute is a very important consideration, as is the method of preparation of the plastic matrix. The plastic may absorb a large portion of the solute fluorescence unless it is prepared from very pure monomer under conditions carefully controlled to preclude oxidation. Many oxidation inhibitors quench scintillator fluorescence and consequently cannot be added to scintillation plastics. Scintillation efficiency can also be markedly affected by small changes in the polymerization temperature (123).

Recently, a novel application of plastic scintillators has been reported. Scintillating ion-exchange resins have been prepared by suspension polymerization of a plastic bead containing both a fluorescent solute and a wavelength shifter (127,128). The beads act as anion- or cation-exchange resins which can be used to simultaneously concentrate and count very dilute solutions containing radioactive biochemicals or organic solutes. The counting efficiencies of the scintillating resins are quite high, and the method is nondestructive. It appears that scintillating ion-exchangers should find use in research concerned with nucleic acids, carbohydrates, and other radioactive biological molecules occurring in dilute solutions.

G. Organic Crystal Scintillators

Very pure organic crystals can also be used as scintillators. The energy-transfer processes which occur in organic crystals have been previously discussed. In general, energy transfer from the host material to another molecular species present in the crystal is *not* desirable, and purity of the crystalline materials thus becomes a crucial factor, due to the very high efficiency of energy transfer in the organic solid state. The most effective scintillating crystals are characterized by large π-electron systems, high molecular symmetry, and the absence of appreciable steric hindrance (24). Crystalline aromatic hydrocarbons (especially anthracene) are widely used. The choice of suitable compounds to serve as crystal scintillators is much more limited than for plastic or liquid scintillators.

H. Summary

Intermolecular transfer of electronic excitation energy is quite prevalent in organic systems. Since energy transfer phenomena are often responsible for quenching or sensitization of fluorescence, such processes affect analytical applications of fluorometry. The high efficiency of energy migration from one molecular species to another has limited the use of fluorometry as a method for analyzing complex mixtures of organic compounds without prior separation and purification steps. Many fundamental studies of fluorescence in organic materials have also been rendered of questionable value by the presence of minute concentrations of impurities, and great precautions must usually be exercised in this regard.

Energy-transfer effects are also responsible for the action of certain solutions, plastics, and organic crystals which are used as scintillators for the detection of high-energy radiation. The search for new, more effective, scintillation systems is hampered by lack of understanding of the complex energy-migration phenomena involved. Much effort is presently being expended to untangle the web of energy transfer; due to the importance of energy transfer in biochemical processes, this phenomenon probably will continue to occupy the attention of many investigators.

IV. Special Effects in the Luminescence of Organic Molecules

A. "Excimer" Fluorescence

The study of so-called "excimer" fluorescence represents an interesting application of luminescence techniques to the study of fast reactions of organic molecules in excited states. This effect was first observed by Förster and Kasper (96), who noted that dilute solutions of pyrene, a polycyclic aromatic hydrocarbon, fluoresced in the violet. The violet fluorescence contained some fine structure and obeyed the mirror-image law (cf. Section II-D). As the pyrene concentration of the solutions was increased above about $10^{-4}M$, the fluorescence intensity of the violet band decreased, while a new, broad, structureless, blue emission appeared. The intensity of the blue fluorescence was proportional to the square of the pyrene concentration. Förster and Kasper interpreted the results by postulating that the species responsible for the broad, structureless fluorescence was a dimer, formed by combination of an electronically excited pyrene molecule with a pyrene molecule in its ground state. The structured, violet emission was attributed to pyrene monomer. The dimer responsible for the broad emission band could not have been formed from two ground-state pyrene molecules, because (a) no change in the form of the pyrene absorption spectrum occurred upon increasing the concentration of the solutions, and (b) cryoscopic measurements indicated no association of pyrene molecules in the ground state, even in very concentrated solutions. Therefore, pyrene existed as a stable dimer *only* in an excited state. Stevens and Hutton (129) have proposed the name "excimer" for an excited dimer of this type, in order to distinguish this species from an excited state of a dimer which is *stable* in its ground state. Förster (145) has discussed the nature of excimer forces and the energy-level requirements for excimer formation.

Initially, excimer fluorescence appeared to be restricted to pyrene and its derivatives. However, many aromatic hydrocarbons and their alkyl derivatives are now known to exhibit this behavior. Birks and Christophorou (130,131) have prepared an extensive compilation of the compounds for which excimer fluorescence has been observed in solution; they include, among others, benzene, toluene (132), naphthalene (133), pyrene (96), and a large number of anthracene derivatives (131). Furthermore, the phenomenon is not restricted to aromatic hydrocarbons. Lehrer and Fasman (134) have expressed the belief that certain polymerized amino acids, which contain aromatic groups, can exhibit conformation-dependent excimer fluorescence. Solutions of isotactic polystyrene polymers exhibit fluorescence behavior which resembles excimer fluorescence (51). The only heterocyclic compound for which excimer emission has been observed is 2,5-diphenyloxazole, the organic scintillator known as "PPO" (135).

The intensity of excimer fluorescence usually increases as the square of the solute concentration. Therefore, one would expect pure organic liquids to display intense excimer emission. This is indeed true for certain naphthalene derivatives which are liquids at room temperature and for others which must be melted.   The observation of excimer fluorescence from molten aromatic hydrocarbons and their derivatives constitutes an exception to a generalization that aromatic compounds are not fluorescent in the pure liquid or molten state. (This "rule" is often rationalized (138) on the basis of concentration quenching; obviously, the concentration of emitting species is quite high in a melt.)   On the other hand, if the temperature of a melt exhibiting excimer fluorescence is sufficiently high, the excimer, if formed, decomposes before it can emit, and the resulting fluorescence will be that of the monomer (137).

In all the cases discussed thus far, both "halves" of the excimer were the same molecule, except that one monomer was electronically excited while the other was not.   Birks and Christophorou (97) have postulated the existence of "mixed excimers," formed by the processes

$$A^* + B \rightarrow (AB)^* \qquad (3\text{-}11)$$

or

$$A + B^* \rightarrow (AB)^* \qquad (3\text{-}12)$$

where A and B are *not* the same molecular species.   This phenomenon can produce concentration quenching of one organic solute by high concentrations of another compound in solution (148).

The formation of excimers in solution is thought to be a diffusion-controlled collision process, in which a surprisingly large fraction of the collisions between excited and unexcited monomers are effective (139,140).   If the process is diffusion-controlled, one would not expect to observe intense excimer fluorescence in low-temperature rigid glasses.   The fact that excimer emission is not observed for a given solute at room temperature does not necessarily signify that excimers are not formed by that species.   If the "excimer inter-action" is very weak, thermal decomposition of most of the excimers will occur before emission can take place, since the radiative lifetimes of excimers are usually quite long.   If this is the case, lowering the temperature of the solution should cause an increase in the excimer fluorescence intensity, so long as the solvent remains sufficiently fluid at lower temperatures so as not to inhibit the diffusion-controlled excimer formation process.   This type of behavior has been observed in naphthalene solutions (133).

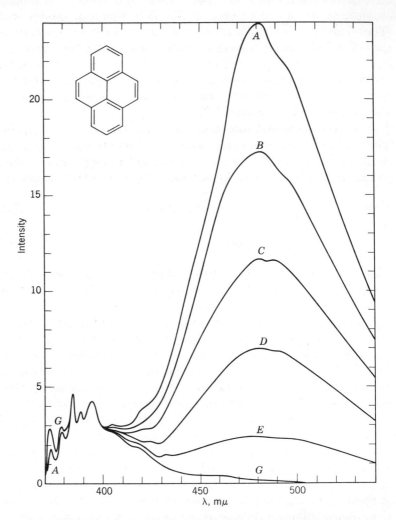

Fig. 3-5. Fluorescence of pyrene in cyclohexane at several concentrations. $A = 10^{-2}M$, $B = 7.75 \times 10^{-3}M$, $C = 5.5 \times 10^{-3}M$, $D = 3.25 \times 10^{-3}M$, $E = 10^{-3}M$, $G = 10^{-4}M$. The excimer band has its maximum at 482 mμ. From Birks (232).

The properties of excimers of aromatic hydrocarbon derivatives are determined primarily by the nature of the parent hydrocarbon, and substitution (even by large, bulky alkyl groups) usually has little effect upon the spectral properties of the excimers (139). However, an exception to this statement can occur if the formation of excimers is inhibited for steric reasons. p-Xylene and a number of 9,10-disubstituted anthracene derivatives do not appear to form excimers, presumably due to steric hindrance by the substituents (131).

Just as a weak "excimer interaction" can result in weak excimer fluorescence, a very strong interaction can have the same effect. The monomer–monomer attractive forces may be so strong that chemical combination takes place, resulting in the formation of stable photodimers. This occurs in anthracene and some of its derivatives (141, 142), many of which form stable photodimers, and do not exhibit excimer fluorescence. The compound 9-methylanthracene appears to form *both* stable photodimers and metastable excimers under ultraviolet irradiation; this is attributed to partial steric hindrance to stable dimer formation by the methyl group (143). The polycyclic aromatic hydrocarbons tetracene and pentacene also form stable dimers rather than excimers (144).

Excimer fluorescence bands characteristically lack fine structure (cf. Fig. 3-5). This is reasonable when it is considered that, by definition, the excimer does not exist in its ground state, but dissociates after emission. It is also noteworthy that excimer emission does not show concentration quenching, whereas monomer fluorescence bands are quite susceptible to self-quenching (137). If excimer emission is essential to concentration quenching of monomer fluorescent (See Section III-D), then, by analogy, self-quenching of excimer fluorescence should involve interaction of the excimer with an "unexcited excimer," a species which does not exist.

Excimer formation is not restricted to the liquid state; the phenomenon has also been observed in organic crystals (25,146,147). Stevens (25) has pointed out that, in the crystalline state, the diffusional process $A + A^* \rightarrow (AA)^*$ is improbable. Nonetheless, some crystalline aromatic hydrocarbons exhibit a structureless emission very similar to the excimer fluorescence shown by the same compounds in solution, whereas others do not. This is due to the fact that aromatic hydrocarbons crystallize in one of two distinct types of lattice. In one type of crystal (that of anthracene, naphthalene, phenanthrene, and chrysene), the π-orbital overlap of adjacent parallel molecules is small, so that these crystals do not show the excimer-type luminescence. However, molecules such as perylene, coronene, pyrene, 3,4-benzpyrene, and ovalene assume a second type of lattice structure, in which the lattice unit is a pair of overlapping parallel molecules. These crystals do exhibit an excimer-type fluorescence band. In Figure 3-6, the analogy between the solution and crystal fluorescence spectra of pyrene can be seen. Note the apparent excimer emission in the crystalline phase. Stevens (25) has shown that this property can be utilized to complement x-ray analysis in the assignment of lattice structures to aromatic hydrocarbon crystals.

Hochstrasser (147) has reported *mixed* dimer emission in pyrene crystals containing perylene. The mixed dimer emission band is indicated in Figure 3-7. This phenomenon is believed to occur whenever there are impurities in a crystal which has a sandwich-type lattice structure and represents a sensitive criterion for purity of aromatic crystals. Thus, the formation of "mixed excimers" can apparently occur in both the liquid and solid states.

The implications of excimer formation and fluorescence are more extensive than is initially evident. As discussed in Section III, the mechanism of "self-quenching" involves the formation of molecular aggregates in the excited state. The apparent formation of "mixed excimers" suggests that a high concentration of one solute can cause concentration quenching of other fluorescent species present in solution, and this has actually been observed (148). The apparent widespread occurrence of excimer fluorescence suggests that anomalous fluorescence behavior of organic compounds, especially at high solution concentration, may be frequently rationalized (although not necessarily correctly!) by this mechanism. The dependence of the degree of excimer formation in crystals upon the lattice structure and impurity content of the crystal has interesting analytical implications. Finally, excimer formation is an important step in one mechanism for "delayed fluorescence," which is discussed in the following section.

B. Delayed Fluorescence

The term "delayed fluorescence" refers to fluorescent emission which possesses the same spectral characteristics as "ordinary"

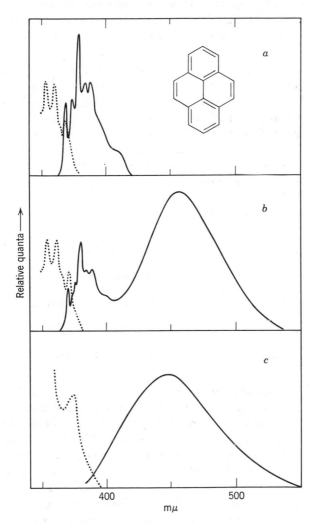

Fig. 3-6.   Absorption (. .) and fluorescence (—) spectra of pyrene; (*a*) $10^{-4}M$ in ethanol; (*b*) $10^{-2}M$ in ethanol; (*c*) crystalline pyrene.   Note the excimer band in both the $10^{-2}M$ ethanolic solution and in the crystalline state.   From Stevens (25).

fluorescence, but which has an unusually long lifetime.   Most fluorescent organic molecules have radiative lifetimes on the order of 10^{-8} or 10^{-9} s.   Some molecules exhibit the short-lived fluorescence and, in addition, a spectrally identical emission with a lifetime on the order of milliseconds.   The latter can be observed separately from the "prompt" fluorescence through the use of a rotating-shutter phosphorimeter.

There are several distinct mechanisms for delayed fluorescence. One of these was discussed originally by Lewis, Lipkin, and Magel (149), who termed the delayed emission "alpha-phosphorescence." In the mechanism of alpha-phosphorescence, a molecule is excited from its ground state to the first excited singlet, then undergoes intersystem crossing to the lowest triplet, which has a relatively long radiative lifetime.   The molecule is then excited *thermally* from the triplet back to the excited singlet state, from which it emits fluorescence, thereby reverting to the ground state.   This process may be represented stepwise as follows:

Step	Description	
$A + h\nu_A \rightarrow {}^1A^*$	Absorption	(3-13)
${}^1A^* \rightsquigarrow {}^3A^*$	Intersystem crossing	(3-14)
${}^3A^* + kT \rightarrow {}^1A^*$	Thermal excitation	(3-15)
${}^1A^* \rightarrow A + h\nu_F$	Delayed fluorescence	(3-16)

Clearly, alpha-phosphorescence should occur only in media in which collisions between molecules are sufficiently frequent and energetic to provide the necessary thermal energy for eq. (3-15).   Evidently, alpha-phosphorescence should occur only with molecules in which the energy spacing between the excited singlet and lowest triplet states is relatively small.   Since the lifetime of the delayed fluorescence is determined by the lifetime of the triplet molecule produced in eq. (3-14), the radiative lifetimes for phosphorescence and delayed fluorescence should be virtually identical for any given molecule (150). Alpha-phosphorescence has been observed in liquid solutions of eosin (151) and proflavine hydrochloride (152), and in room-temperature boric acid glasses containing fluorescein (149).

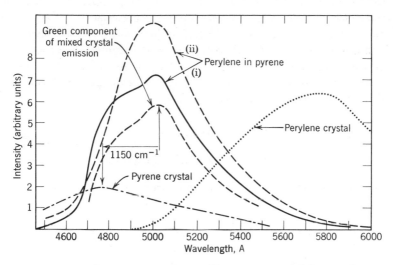

Fig. 3-7. Fluorescence spectra of crystalline pyrene containing perylene as a contaminant. Concentration of perylene in pyrene: (i) 10^{-4} moles/mole; (ii) 10^{-3} moles/mole. Spectra for pure pyrene and perylene crystals are also given. The green emission is thought to arise from mixed pyrene–perylene dimers. From Hochstrasser (147).

However, the alpha-phosphorescence mechanism is not general and cannot account for the characteristics of most of the delayed fluorescence which has been observed. Delayed fluorescence has been observed in vapors, liquid solution, room-temperature rigid glasses, low-temperature glasses, and organic crystals. Obviously, delayed fluorescence in rigid glasses at 77°K or in crystals at 4.2°K cannot be rationalized by the alpha-phosphorescence (thermal excitation) process. Furthermore, the delayed fluorescence exhibited by most organic molecules is "biphotonic," i.e., *two* photons are absorbed initially for each delayed fluorescence photon which is emitted. The intensity of biphotonic delayed fluorescence varies as the square of the incident light intensity (150–152). There is nothing in the alpha-phosphorescence mechanism to account for this fact. Additionally, most organic molecules exhibit delayed fluorescence with a lifetime *not* equal to that for the phosphorescence of the molecule. Thus, there must be at least two distinct "types" of delayed fluorescence; Parker (153) has proposed that alpha-phosphorescence be called "E-type delayed fluorescence," while the two-photon delayed fluorescence be termed "P-type delayed fluorescence." We shall discuss several proposed mechanisms for the P-type delayed emission.

Williams (154) has noted that vapors of the aromatic hydrocarbons anthracene, phenanthrene, pyrene, and perylene show a biphotonic delayed fluorescence component. This is attributed to the formation of excimers (cf. Section IV-A):

$$A + h\nu_A \rightarrow {}^1A^* \qquad \text{Absorption} \qquad (3\text{-}17)$$

$$^1A^* + A \rightarrow A_2^* \qquad \text{Excimer formation} \qquad (3\text{-}18)$$

$$A_2^* \rightarrow {}^1A^* + A \qquad \text{Dissociation (nonradiative)}$$
$$\text{of excimer} \qquad (3\text{-}19)$$

$$^1A^* \rightarrow A + h\nu_F \qquad \text{Delayed fluorescence} \qquad (3\text{-}20)$$

P-type delayed fluorescence can also be observed in liquid solutions of certain organic molecules. Parker and Hatchard (152) have reported that solutions of phenanthrene and anthracene exhibit biphotonic delayed fluorescence, as do pyrene solutions (155). They have proposed a mechanism (156) based upon the following considerations. The long lifetime of the delayed fluorescence suggests the involvement in the process of long-lived triplet molecules; further, the biphotonic nature of the slow fluorescence implies that *two* triplet molecules must be involved for each delayed-fluorescence photon emitted. Putting these together, Parker and Hatchard (156) postulate that P-type delayed emission involves a triplet–triplet annihilation step as discussed in Chapter 1 [eqs. (1-13) through (1-16)].

Delayed fluorescence has also been observed in rigid glass solutions of organic molecules. The pioneering studies of alpha-phosphorescence in room-temperature boric acid glasses by Lewis and co-workers (149) have already been mentioned. More recent studies have been concerned with delayed fluorescence in rigid glasses at liquid-nitrogen temperature, where alpha-phosphorescence cannot be important. Azumi and McGlynn (150,157) have observed delayed fluorescence from rigid glasses (77°K) containing the following aromatic hydrocarbons: naphthalene, phenanthrene, hexahelicene(phenanthro[3, 4c]phenanthrene), triphenylene, or biphenyl. Delayed fluorescence has not been observed from rigid glassy solutions of anthracene,

1,2-benzanthracene, pyrene, or chrysene. However, delayed fluorescence and delayed excimer fluorescence have both been observed
from pure EPA glasses of pyrene "perturbed" by the addition of small
amounts of water (158). Figure 3-8 shows the delayed fluorescence,
delayed excimer fluorescence, and phosphorescence observed from the
"perturbed" pyrene glasses. The figure also indicates that delayed
fluorescence is apparently biphotonic, but delayed *excimer* fluorescence is not. That the delayed monomer emission is biphotonic
suggests that triplet–triplet annihilation processes and excimer
formation are probably involved in the process. However, because
the delayed excimer fluorescence is not biphotonic, the excimer must
be formed by combination of a singlet ground-state molecule with a
singlet excited state species produced by single-photon light-absorp-
tion, rather than by the triplet–triplet aninhilation processes described in the mechanisms of Parker and Hatchard (156). Therefore,
it is possible that the very long lifetime of the delayed excimer
fluorescence is not necessarily due to triplet-state involvement in the
formation of the excimer, but may merely reflect the inherently
forbidden character of excimer emission. Azumi and McGlynn (150)
contend that the triplet–triplet interaction, which apparently *does*
occur in connection with the biphotonic delayed monomer fluorescence, may involve direct resonance interactions between triplet
molecules, rather than excimer formation or other excited state
reactions.

A *third* type of process in which delayed luminescence occurs is by
photochemical processes in rigid glasses. In this case, both delayed
fluorescence and delayed phosphorescence can be observed. Lewis
and co-workers (159,160) showed that photochemical processes in
rigid glasses could lead to the appearance of phosphorescence emission
of unusually long lifetime. Linschitz, Berry, and Schweitzer (161)
demonstrated that this slow phosphorescence was spectrally identical
with the normal phosphorescence of the molecule. It has been concluded (161,162) that the delayed phosphorescence is due to triplet
molecules formed by the recombination of radicals and trapped
electrons produced initially by photooxidation of the molecule. That
this process actually occurs is indicated by the observation (163) that
photoconductivity occurs in a rigid glass solution known to exhibit
delayed phosphorescence. Similar behavior is observed for a number
of organic dyes, many of which possess complex molecular structures
and which are notorious for their complicated photochemistry.

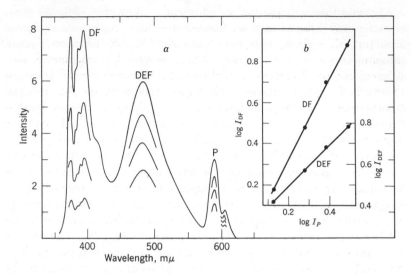

Fig. 3-8.   (a) Emission spectra of a $2 \times 10^{-3}M$ solution of pyrene in "perturbed" isopentane glass at 77°K.   DF is delayed fluorescence, DEF is delayed excimer fluorescence, and P is phosphorescence.   (b) Logarithmic plots of phosphorescence intensity vs. that of delayed fluorescence and delayed excimer fluorescence, indicating that the former is biphotonic while the latter is not. From Azumi and McGlynn (158).

Delayed fluorescence can also occur in rigid glasses by a similar process.   Lim (164,165) has observed delayed fluorescence in glassy solutions of the dye acriflavine (3,6-diamino-10-methylacridinium chloride), which he interprets as being due to excited singlets formed by recombination of ions and trapped electrons produced by prior photooxidation of dye molecules.   A similar explanation has been advanced for the observed delayed fluorescence of polymethinecyanine dyes (166).

Aromatic hydrocarbon crystals exhibit delayed fluorescence at low temperatures.   Crystals of naphthalene, anthracene, phenanthrene, chrysene, pyrene, and perylene exhibit delayed fluorescence at liquid-helium temperatures (167,168).   It has been suggested that the long-lived fluorescence from crystals of aromatic hydrocarbons involves exciton–exciton annihilation processes, presumably involving triplet states (150,169).

Clearly, delayed fluorescence can occur in aromatic compounds in a variety of physical states by a number of mechanisms. Currently, this is a very active research area, and further clarification of the processes involved in delayed luminescence of organic molecules should be expected.

C. EFFECTS OF pH ON FLUORESCENCE: EXCITED-STATE DISSOCIATION

As discussed briefly in Chapter 1, the effects of pH upon the fluorescence spectrum of an organic molecule often are different from those on the absorption spectrum. In 1931, Weber (170) noted a puzzling effect: the fluorescence of 1-naphthylamine-4-sulfonate changed color as the pH of the solution was altered, while no corresponding change was observed in the absorption spectrum. This phenomenon was first explained by Förster (171), who found that a similar effect occurred in the fluorescence of 3-hydroxypyrene-5,8,10-trisulfonate. The hydroxyl group of this molecule has an approximate pK_a of 7.3, but Förster noted that the compound exhibited fluorescence characteristic of the phenolate anion in solutions which were much too acidic for this species to exist in the ground state. He suggested that phenols must be much stronger acids when electronically excited than in their ground states (171). Verification of this hypothesis was obtained by means of a series of elegant flash-photolysis experiments (172). Similar changes in acidity upon electronic excitation have since been observed for a wide variety of ionizable organic compounds.

The fact that such acidity differences can be observed by fluorescence measurements indicates that the protolytic dissociation reaction must be more rapid than the decay period for fluorescence, a time on the order of 10^{-8} s. In some cases, the dissociation reaction is so rapid that a state of equilibrium is attained in the very short interval between the absorption and emission of light. Quite often, however, the dissociation reaction is not sufficiently fast to allow attainment of equilibrium before fluorescence occurs. In the latter cases, the change from one excited-state species to another (as determined from the different fluorescence spectra of the two forms) will be spread out over as much as 5 or 6 pH units, whereas, if equilibrium is established very rapidly, the change from one species to the other, as a function of pH, will be more abrupt, analogous to the changes usually found in ultraviolet absorption studies. Weller (173) has performed a number of experiments concerned with the kinetics of protolytic dissociation of excited organic molecules.

In order to compare the acidity of a molecule in its ground and excited states, it is necessary to estimate the pK_a of the excited species. Two methods for obtaining the pK_a of the first excited singlet level of an organic molecule from fluorescence measurements are discussed by Weller (173). The first method is easily applicable only if the dissociation reaction reaches equilibrium before fluorescence occurs; it consists merely of a series of measurements of relative intensities of the fluorescence of the acidic and basic forms of the compound as a function of pH as indicated above.

A second method for determining the excited-singlet-state dissociation constant, pK_a*, is a thermodynamic calculation based on the cycle (174) shown in Figure 3-9. From the thermochemistry of the system, it is evident that

$$\Delta E + E_d* = \Delta E' + E_d \qquad (3\text{-}21)$$

where ΔE and $\Delta E'$ are the energy changes for the transition from the ground electronic state to the first singlet level of the acid and anion, respectively. The dissociation energies, E_d and E_d*, can be expressed as

$$E_d - E_d* = (\Delta G_i + T\Delta S_i) - (\Delta G_i* + T\Delta S_i*) \qquad (3\text{-}22)$$

If we assume

$$\Delta S_i = \Delta S_i* \qquad (3\text{-}23)$$

then,

$$\Delta G_i - \Delta G_i* = -RT(\ln K_a - \ln K_a*) = \Delta E - \Delta E' \qquad (3\text{-}24)$$

So that

$$pK_a - pK_a* = (\Delta E - \Delta E')/2.303RT = [hc(\Delta \bar{\nu})]/2.303kT \qquad (3\text{-}25)$$

where $\Delta \bar{\nu}$ is the difference in the electronic transition frequencies (in cm^{-1}) of the acid and conjugate base. A good estimate of the energy just necessary to produce excitation from the ground to the first electronically excited state, with no additional vibrational excitation (i.e., the "0-0" band), can be obtained (180) by averaging the frequencies of the fluorescence excitation and emission maxima (or the ultraviolet absorption and fluorescence maxima).

It should be noted that the thermodynamic calculation assumes approximate equality of the entropy of ionization in the ground and excited states. This may not always be a safe assumption; however, the results from the thermodynamic calculation agree with those obtained from the "titration curve" method for virtually all compounds which have been studied (173). The thermodynamic method is experimentally more facile than the study of relative fluorescence intensities as a function of pH, particularly if the break in the "titration curve" is not abrupt or if one (or both) of the prototropic species is unstable.

Calculations of pK_a^* values have been performed for a number of aromatic hydroxyl compounds, and a selection of the results is provided in Table 3-3. We note that the increase in acidity brought about by electronic excitation may amount to six or more orders of magnitude.

TABLE 3-3

Ground-State and Excited-Singlet-State Acidities of Some Aromatic Alcohols

Compound	pK_a	pK_a^*	Reference
1-Naphthol	9.23	2.0	177
		2.5	174
		2.7	178
2-Naphthol	9.46	2.5	177
		2.8	174
		3.1	179
Phenol	9.97	5.7	180
		5.1	181
p-Cresol	10.27	4.3	181
1,2-Naphthalenediol	8.11	2.4	178
1,7-Naphthalenediol	10.29	3.1	178
2,3-Naphthalenediol	9.87	3.2	178
2-Naphthol-5-sulfonic acid	9.18	1.4	174
3-Hydroxypyrene-5,8,10-trisulfonate	7.30	1.0	177

Hercules and Rogers (175) have reported an interesting aspect of the excited-state dissociation behavior of aromatic alcohols. Reference to Table 3-3 shows that 1-naphthol and 2-naphthol are of roughly equal acidity in the ground state, but that 1-naphthol appears to be significantly more acidic than 2-naphthol in the excited state.

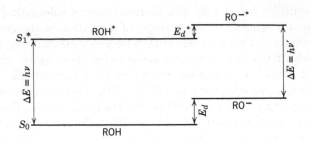

Fig. 3-9. Schematic thermochemical diagram for the dissociation reactions ArOH $\rightleftarrows$ ArO$^-$ + H$^+$ in the ground state; ArOH* $\rightleftarrows$ ArO^{-*} + H$^+$ in the first excited singlet state. After Bartok, Lucchesi, and Snider (180).

Because the compound 1,6-naphthalenediol contains one hydroxyl in the alpha position and one on the beta position, its singly-charged anion can exist in two different excited states:

These two excited states are characterized by different basicities, and fluorescence measurements have been used to study interconversions between them.

In contrast to the alcohols, aromatic carboxylic acids exhibit a *decrease* in acidity in the first excited singlet state relative to the ground state. Benzoic acid is a very weak base, with a ground state pK$_a$ of -7.3, corresponding to the equilibrium

$$C_6H_5C \underset{\diagdown OH}{\overset{\diagup O}{}} + H^+ \rightleftarrows C_6H_5C \underset{\diagdown OH}{\overset{\diagup \overset{\oplus}{OH}}{}} \qquad (3\text{-}26)$$

However, in the excited state, pK$_a$* for benzoic acid is approximately zero, indicating that the carbonyl oxygen is much more basic in the excited singlet state (176). Similar results have been reported for other carboxylic acids (176), as well as the aromatic ketones acridone (182) and acetophenone (176).

The acid–base properties of excited aromatic amines have also been investigated. Generally, aromatic amines are more basic in their ground states than in their first excited singlet levels (173,183,184). In other words, the protonated amine, $ArNH_3^+$, is a stronger acid in its excited state than in the ground state. For example, Jackson and Porter (184) have shown that pK_a for the 2-naphthylammonium cation is 4.1, while its pK_a^* is -2. Neutral amines ($ArNH_2$) can also ionize in the excited state. It is possible to form excited 2-naphthylamide anions ($C_{10}H_7NH^-$) in aqueous solution by the reaction sequence:

$$C_{10}H_7NH_2 \underset{h\nu}{\rightarrow} [C_{10}H_7NH_2]^* \rightarrow [C_{10}H_7NH^{\ominus}]^* + H^{\oplus} \qquad (3\text{-}27)$$

Anionic fluorescence can be detected at appropriate pH values, despite the fact that the ground-state anion does *not* exist at any pH in aqueous solution (183). This again indicates the reduction in basicity of amines which takes place upon electronic excitation.

In contrast to amine nitrogens, heterocyclic nitrogens are *more* basic in the excited state than in the ground state by several orders of magnitude. For example, pK_a^* for the acridinium cation is 10.3, while the ground state pK_a is only 5.45 (186). Consequently, the acridinium cation is a weaker acid (and acridine a stronger base) in the excited state by five orders of magnitude.

We may thus conclude, with Weller (173), that aromatic acids fall into two distinct classes. Acids belonging to group I:

$$\text{ArOH; Ar—N—R; Ar—N—H}^{\oplus}\text{ ; and ArSH}$$

with substituents R' and H on the nitrogen atoms

have $pK_a^* < pK_a$; their acidity is enhanced by electronic excitation. Acids belonging to class II:

$$\text{ArCO}_2\text{H; Ar—C=OH}^{\oplus}\text{ ; ArNH}^{\oplus}$$

with substituent R

have $pK_a^* > pK_a$, and are thus stronger bases in the excited than in the ground state.

Acidity is thought to be a sensitive function of molecular electron distribution, both in the ground and excited states. Hence, the above trends in excited-state acidities can be understood in terms of the electronic charge densities in the excited and unexcited molecules. Consider, as an example, phenol. The charge densities on the substituted carbon and the phenolic oxygen calculated by molecular orbital methods (187) are given below:

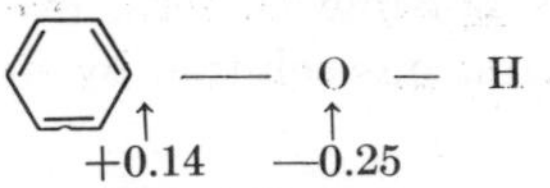

+0.14 —0.25	+0.16 +0.03
(Ground state)	(First excited singlet state)

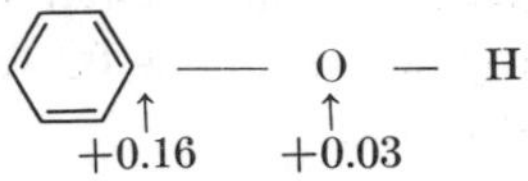

Because the phenolic oxygen is more positive in the excited state, it will attract the proton less in the excited state than in the ground state. Consequently, excited phenol should be more acidic than the ground-state molecule, a fact which, as we have noted, is quite true. Similar calculations (188) indicate that, upon excitation, electronic charge migrates *from* the nitrogen atom in amines, but *toward* heterocyclic nitrogen atoms. This rationalizes the observed trends in excited-state basicities for amine and heterocyclic nitrogens discussed above. It would, therefore, appear that studies of excited-state protolytic dissociation should prove useful in estimating charge distributions in electronically excited molecules.

Recently, the behavior of molecules containing both acidic and basic functional groups has been investigated. Ellis and Rogers (189,190) studied several isomeric aminonaphthols and noted the absorption characteristics of three distinct species as a function of pH: the neutral molecule, the naphtholammonium ion in very acidic solutions, and the aminonaphtholate anion in very basic media. For some of the aminonaphthols, the presence of a fourth excited-state species was indicated from fluorescence measurements. It was postulated (189) that this species was a zwitterion:

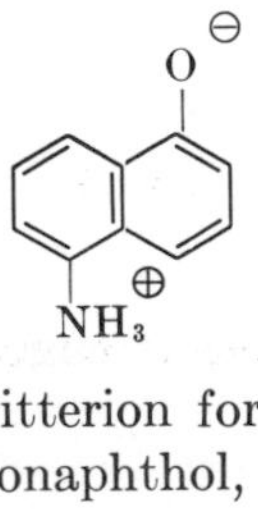

It should be noted that zwitterion formation apparently can take place for 1,5- and 2,7-aminonaphthol, where intramolecular proton transfer is unlikely, due to the large distance between the two functional groups. In addition, proton transfer by means of dimeric intermediates was shown not to occur (190). This result is quite interesting in that it implies that each substituent acts more or less independently in transferring protons from or to nearby solvent molecules. In effect, it appears that *both* excited-state dissociation and protonation can occur in the same molecule, at least over limited pH ranges.

The concept of zwitterion formation in the excited state has received corroboration from the work of Haylock, Mason, and Smith (191), who postulated excited-state zwitterion formation in 3-hydroxyquinoline. The ring nitrogen becomes more basic, and the hydroxyl more acidic, upon electronic excitation. By analogy with the aminonaphthols, 3-hydroxyquinoline forms four species in the excited state as the pH is changed; pK_a^* values for each of the five possible equilibria between these four species have been obtained.

The studies discussed above have concerned the transfer of protons to or from solvent molecules by a fluorescent organic species. Proton shifts *within* an excited molecule have also been observed. Weller (192) encountered unusually large Stokes displacements in salicylic acid and its esters, while ethers of salicylic acid exhibited smaller, more nearly normal, frequency shifts. The unusual pattern of Stokes displacements can be rationalized by assuming an excited-state proton transfer. Upon excitation, a hydroxyl group becomes more acidic while a carbonyl group becomes more basic. When these acidity changes are sufficiently dramatic, the proton can shift from the phenolic oxygen to the carbonyl oxygen:

$$(3-28)$$

The unusual Stokes shifts in salicylic acid and its derivatives are associated with the internal hydrogen bond in these molecules, as indicated by the fact that the *meta* and *para* isomers of salicylic acid do not exhibit this behavior. Similar intramolecular proton transfers have been reported for several hydroxynaphthoic acids (193).

Since excited singlet-state acidity constants can be determined from fluorescence spectra, triplet-state acidities should be obtainable from phosphorescence studies. The pioneering work in this area is that of Jackson and Porter (184), who verified the triplet pK_a values (hereafter denoted $pK_a{}^T$) obtained from phosphorescence spectra by flash-photolysis studies. From their results, summarized in Table 3-4, we note that $pK_a{}^T$ is not greatly different from the ground-state pK_a, whereas $pK_a{}^*$ is quite different. These results are consistent with theory, as discussed by Jackson and Porter (184) and Murrell (194). A more recent study of triplet-state acidity has been performed with o-phenanthroline, which is a somewhat stronger base in its triplet state than in its ground state (195). This is consistent with the results for quinoline (184), another nitrogen heterocycle. The heterocycles are weaker bases in their triplet states than in their first excited singlet states.

TABLE 3-4

Comparison of Singlet and Triplet Acidity Constants
for Some Organic Molecules (184)

Compound	pK_a	$pK_a{}^*$	$pK_a{}^T$ (flash spectros-copy)	$pK_a{}^T$ (phospho-rescence)
2-Naphthol	9.5	3.1	8.1	7.7
2-Naphthoic acid	4.2	10–12	4.0	4.2
1-Naphthoic acid	3.7	10–12	3.8	4.6
Acridine	5.5	10.6	5.6	—
Quinoline	5.1	—	6.0	5.8
2-Naphthylamine	4.1	−2	3.3	3.1
N,N-Dimethyl-1-naphthylamine	4.9	—	2.7	2.9

The effect of substituents upon $pK_a{}^*$ has been the subject of some preliminary investigations. Bartok, Lucchesi, and Snider (180) reported that $pK_a{}^*$ values obtained for para-substituted phenols could not be correlated with the Hammett sigma constants for the substituents. More recently, however, Bartok (196) has rescinded this conclusion and has indicated that the excited pK_a's can be correlated with Hammett substituent constants. The question of whether or not electronically excited aromatic compounds obey a linear free energy relationship has not been conclusively settled (181, 197).

In three recent communications (197–199), the shortcomings of fluorescence techniques as applied to the study of excited pK_a's have been discussed. A particular difficulty is that, since fluorescence occurs only from the lowest excited singlet state and phosphorescence only from the lowest triplet level, only two excited-state pK_a values can be obtained. Also, the pK_a* values obtained from fluorescence data are not valid if the transitions leading to fluorescence in the two prototropic species are not corresponding, and establishment of such correspondence may be difficult. It is said to be possible to study acidities of excited states using only ultraviolet absorption data (198). The method of calculating pK_a* values solely from absorption spectral data only uses eq. (3-25) but "$\Delta\bar{v}$" is taken to be the difference in the absorption *maxima* of the ionized and un-ionized species. Thus, it is claimed (197–199) that the use of absorption spectra can yield a pK_a* for each transition present in the absorption spectra, so that it is possible to obtain five or more excited pK_a's for a single compound.†
One can also calculate pK_a* for substances which do not fluoresce; since many organic acids and bases are nonfluorescent, this could constitute a significant advantage.

Several comments may be made in regard to the above arguments. First, the use of absorption *maxima* to find excited-state acidities is not rigorously consistent with the thermodynamic cycle because the frequency at an absorption maximum does *not* correspond to ΔE in the cycle, simply because the energy of the O—O band cannot be evaluated from an absorption maximum; this quantity is obtained from the long-wavelength limit of absorption. Where fluorescence spectra are used to calculate pK_a*, an estimate of the energy of the O—O band is made, and this method is therefore not inconsistent with the thermodynamic cycle. It appears that pK_a* values calculated

---

† **Editor's Note:** Some question can be raised concerning the validity of calculating pK_a* values for excited states other than the lowest excited singlet state, or the lowest triplet state. Generally it is considered that internal conversion to the lowest excited state of a system is fast (10^{-13} to 10^{-11} s) relative to processes such as spontaneous emission (10^{-9} to 10^{-7} s), intersystem crossing (10^{-8} s), and diffusion-controlled reactions (10^{-9} s). Because acid–base reactions in solution are diffusion controlled, the probability of a molecule undergoing ionization while in a higher excited state is quite low, internal conversion to the lowest excited state being much more probable. Therefore, any calculated value for a pK_a* of a higher state is probably without physical reality, and such numbers should be used with a great deal of caution.

by both methods may disagree seriously (181), possibly due to excited-state solvation phenomena which affect fluorescence (but not absorption) spectra.

It is admittedly not always easy to establish whether or not the fluorescence of an acid and its conjugate base originate in the corresponding excited states, but it is also often difficult to show that absorption maxima for an acid and base originate in the same transition. We conclude that both methods are useful in characterizing the acidities of excited organic molecules, but that the fluorescence methods have more merits than Jaffé et al. (197–199) have indicated.

1. Analytical Implications

Some conclusions regarding the significance of excited-state dissociation to analytical chemists are in order. If the fluorescence of a substance undergoes a sudden change at some specified pH, it is possible to utilize the compound as a fluorescent indicator for acidimetry and alkalimetry (200). For example, the fluorescence intensity of 1-naphthol-4-sulfonic acid in the visible region increases abruptly with pH at pH = 8.2, so that this compound can be used as an indicator for acid–base titrations. Because such a titration must usually be carried out in the dark, the titration vessel being illuminated with ultraviolet, this technique has never achieved widespread popularity. Other acid–base fluorescent indicators are discussed by Kolthoff and Stenger (200). Clearly, only compounds undergoing very rapid excited-state dissociation would be suitable for this purpose.

The use of fluorescent indicators has never become widespread, but the analysis, by fluorometry, of dissociable compounds has. Thus, the analytical chemist should be aware of the changes in acidity which occur when an organic acid or base absorbs ultraviolet. "Slow" excited-state dissociation is especially nettlesome, since the fluorescence of both the acidic and basic species persists over a range of several pH units; obviously, this is not a desirable situation and pH values should be chosen for analysis such that only one fluorescent species is present. Since the fluorescence efficiencies of an acid and its conjugate base may be quite different, advantage may be taken of the dissociation to obtain the most strongly-fluorescent species for analytical use. For example, Thommes and Leininger have utilized excited-state dissociation in the fluorometric determination of mixtures of hydroxybenzoic acids (30).

While the use of excited-state dissociation studies in the elucidation of the properties of excited states of molecules is not analytical chemistry *per se*, the results obtained from such investigations may well be of interest to analytical chemists. It is expected that the nature of excited organic acids and bases will continue to be an active area of inquiry for some years to come.

D. Solvent Effects: Hydrogen Bonding

It is known that fluorescence spectra of organic molecules in solution depend upon the nature of the solvent. Solvent effects have recently been reviewed in detail by Van Duuren (201); for that reason, they are discussed below only briefly.

The influence of solvent upon fluorescence or phosphorescence spectra may be quite different from that observed for the ultraviolet absorption spectrum of the same solute. To understand why this is true, we must invoke the Franck-Condon principle, which asserts that electronic transitions occur much more rapidly than nuclear motions. Because electronic charge distributions in excited organic molecules are often quite different from those in the ground-state species, the equilibrium arrangement of solvent molecules about an excited solute may be quite different from that for the ground state. Thus, after electronic excitation has taken place, solvent reorientation will occur. There may exist a transitory excited state, in which electronic excitation has occurred but solvent reorientation has not. This transitory excited state is often called a "Franck-Condon" state; after the solvent has reoriented, an "equilibrium excited state" is present. The "equilibrium" excited state is the one from which fluorescence originates in room-temperature solution. By analogy, after fluorescence, there is a "Franck-Condon ground state," which persists until the solvent molecules rearrange to the equilibrium orientation for the ground state. These states are shown in Figure 3-10. We can therefore represent ultraviolet absorption of a solute A as

$$(A)_{eq.} \xrightarrow[h\nu]{} (A^*)_{F-C} \tag{3-29}$$

while room-temperature fluorescence can be represented as

$$(A)_{F-C} \leftarrow (A^*)_{eq.} \tag{3-30}$$

Clearly, the excited and ground states of interest in absorption and emission spectra are different. It is not surprising, therefore, that solvent effects on absorption and fluorescence spectra may not be parallel.

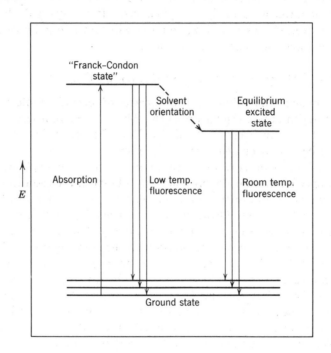

Fig. 3-10. Energy-level diagram showing the "blue shift" in fluorescence spectra at very low temperatures. Note the energy difference between the "Franck-Condon" and "equilibrium" excited states, due to solvent reorientation after electronic excitation. From Hercules and Rogers (224).

The solvent can affect fluorescence spectra in several distinct ways. In *polarization shifts*, the energy of the fluorescence maximum shifts to higher or lower energy as a function of the polarity or polarizability of the solvent. *Hydrogen bonding* can affect fluorescence if the solute and solvent can engage in intermolecular hydrogen bonding. Certain solvents can *quench* the fluorescence of a solute; the *temperature* of the medium can also affect the efficiency and energy of fluorescence.

1. Polarization Shifts

Provided that specific solute–solvent interactions, such as hydrogen bonding, do not take place, changes in fluorescence energy with solvent can often be related to the dielectric constant of the solvent. Bayliss and McRae (202,203) termed these energy changes "polarization shifts" and ascribed them to polarization of solvent molecules induced by the transition dipole of the solute. In addition to induced dipole interactions, permanent dipole–dipole forces may be important. Electrostatic effects upon fluorescence energies have been studied carefully by Lippert and co-workers (204–206). An appreciation for the magnitude of these electrostatic effects may be had by consulting the work of Van Duuren (207), Veljković (208), Löber (209), and Kawski (210).

Studies of electrostatic shifts of fluorescence maxima indicate that many organic molecules become considerably more polar when electronically excited. Lippert (204,211) and Mataga et al. (212) have shown that the magnitude of the frequency shifts observed upon changing solvent can be used to calculate dipole moments of excited organic molecules. From the data presented in Table 3-5, one can see that the increases in polarity are quite striking. Czekalla and co-workers (213,214) have shown that excited-state dipole moments can also be calculated from changes in the degree of polarization of the fluorescence of an organic compound irradiated in a strong electric field.

TABLE 3-5

Dipole Moments of Excited Organic Molecules (211,214)

Compound	μ, Ground state (Debye units)	μ, Excited state
2-Amino-7-nitrofluorene	7	17.8
4-Dimethylamino-4'-nitrostilbene	7.6	32
4-Dimethylamino-4'-cyanostilbene	6.1	29
p-Amino-p'-nitrobiphenyl	6.0	22.2
p-Dimethylamino-p'-nitrobiphenyl	6.6	23.1
p-Amino-p'-cyanobiphenyl	6.0	15.3
p-Dimethylamino-m-nitrostyrene	7.7	17.8

An interesting analogy has been drawn between dissolution of an organic molecule in a very polar solvent and adsorption of the same species on an adsorbent (e.g., activated alumina). The energy shift of the emission spectrum of an adsorbed fluorescent compound is in the same direction as the shift observed when the compound is dissolved in an extremely polar solvent (215).

The high polarity of many excited organic molecules and the magnitudes of the resulting frequency shifts are clearly significant to the analytical chemist. It is not uncommon to note extrapolations in the literature of the fluorescence of a compound from one solvent system to another; such extrapolations are, at best, extremely risky. In fluorometric analysis, the solvent cannot be changed at random. However, polarization shifts of the type discussed above are frequently obscured by more specific solute–solvent interactions.

2. Hydrogen Bonding

One very specific solvent–solute interaction is hydrogen bonding. The effects of hydrogen bonding upon fluorescence spectra are often difficult to predict in advance, and a *caveat* might well be addressed to the analytical chemist utilizing fluorescence: avoid hydrogen-bonding situations wherever possible! In the following paragraphs, the influence of hydrogen bonding on fluorescence specrta will be discussed.†

An extensive study of hydrogen-bonding effects upon fluorescence has been carried out by Mataga and co-workers (216,217). Hydrogen bonding can cause either red or blue fluorescence shifts. For example, with naphthylamines in alcohol solvents, bonding of an amine hydrogen with an oxygen atom of the solvent produced a decrease in the fluorescence frequency, while bonding of a solvent hydrogen with the amine nitrogen caused an increase in the frequency of the naphthylamine fluorescence. Prediction of the type of hydrogen bonding that will predominate in the fluorescence spectrum is difficult, since hydrogen-bonding abilities of organic solutes are often markedly different in electronically excited states and in the ground state. It is often possible to predict that hydrogen-bonding

---

† One important hydrogen-bonding interaction has already been considered: the protonation effect upon n,π^* transitions in heterocycles and carbonyl compounds; cf. Section II-C.

effects will occur in a given system, but it is considerably more difficult to predict the magnitude, or even the sign, of the wavelength shifts.

It has been reported that hydrogen bonding of a fluorescent solute with the solvent (or another solute) can cause significant changes in the emission efficiency of the solute. It has been noted (218) that phenol, aniline, and pyrrole severely quench the fluorescence of nitrogen heterocyclics, while pyridine has no quenching effect. Similarly, the fluorescence of naphthols and naphthylamines is quenched by pyridine, whereas phenol and aniline have little or no effect. It appears that hydrogen bonding produces fluorescence quenching if the hydrogen bond is intimately related with the π-electron system of the proton donor, and the π-electron systems of the donor and acceptor are conjugated. If, however, the hydrogen bond is isolated from the π-electron system of the proton donor by a sigma bond, fluorescence is enhanced by hydrogen bonding. Mataga (216,218) concluded that these quenching processes occur by means of delocalization of π electrons through the hydrogen bond, the charge transfer being followed by vibronic energy dissipation. Miwa and Koizumi (219) have, however, questioned some of Mataga's conclusions. Furthermore, it appears that, with some proton donor–acceptor pairs, dipole interactions of the type discussed earlier in this section are more important than hydrogen-bonding action. For a given solute whose fluorescence is observed in a variety of solvents, there may be no correlation between the fluorescence efficiency of the solute and the hydrogen-bonding ability of the solvent, even if all the solvents are capable of hydrogen bonding (220).

Mataga (216) has shown that fluorescence spectrometry is useful in calculating equilibrium constants for hydrogen bonding in excited states of organic compounds, and this is of considerable theoretical interest. However, it should be clear that it is often preferable to avoid hydrogen bonding, if possible, in analytical applications of fluorescence.

3. Temperature Effects

Much better resolution of vibrational fine structure is obtained for fluorescence spectra observed in low-temperature glasses, rather than in room-temperature solution. An example of the detail which can be observed is provided in Figure 3-2. Low temperatures are, of course, indispensable to the observation of phosphorescence.   A number of workers, particularly in the Soviet Union, have used low-temperature electronic emission spectra to supplement vibrational assignments obtained from infrared or Raman spectroscopy (18,19, 221,222).

Fluorescence quantum efficiency in liquid solution is usually a function of temperature (99,223).   As the temperature is decreased, the fluorescence efficiency of an organic compound usually (but not always) increases; the increase in fluorescence with decreasing temperature is either quite sharp or very gradual.   This is believed to be due to the fact that there are two radiationless processes by which deactivation of an excited state can occur.   One of these is intersystem crossing to the lowest triplet state; this process is essentially independent of temperature.   The other process, internal conversion, is strongly temperature-dependent (223).   Therefore, if decreasing the temperature of a solution of an aromatic molecule causes a sharp increase in the fluorescence, internal conversion is presumably the dominant mode of radiationless decay of the excited singlet; if the increase in fluorescence is very gradual, intersystem crossing probably predominates over internal conversion.   Therefore, temperature effects can serve as a useful tool in the study of radiationless processes.

In addition to changes in efficiency, frequency shifts also occur when the temperature of a fluorescent solution is changed.   Fluorescence maxima shift to lower frequency (longer wavelength) as the temperature is raised from liquid nitrogen temperature to room temperature.   Table 3-6 illustrates the effect for some hydroxynaphthalenes (224).   Similar effects have been noted by Lippert et al. (225) and Bhaumik and Hardwick (226).

The reason for the frequency shifts is related to the solvent reorientation processes discussed in Section IV-D.   Solvent reorientation normally is quite facile at room temperature but becomes considerably more difficult at low temperatures.   The emission energy is lower from the equilibrium excited state to the ground state, than from the Franck-Condon excited state to ground (See Fig. 3-10).   Therefore, if solvent reorientation cannot occur (as is the case in low-temperature glasses), the fluorescence energy will be considerably higher than if solvent rearrangement had taken place.   Therefore, the blue shift which occurs at very low temperatures is understandable.   The effect appears to be principally due to the increased viscosity of the rigid glassy solutions (226).

TABLE 3-6

Temperature Effect on Fluorescence Maxima of Hydroxynaphthalenes (224)

Compound	Form	$\bar{\nu}$, Room temp. (cm^{-1})	$\bar{\nu}$, 77°K	Difference
1-Naphthol	Molecular	27400	29000	1600
	Ionic	20600	23900	3300
2-Naphthol	Molecular	27700	28200	500
	Ionic	23000	25300	2300
1,3-Naphthalenediol	Molecular	26400	26850	450
	Hemi-ionic	23000	24100	1100
1,6-Naphthalenediol	Molecular	27350	27550	200
	Hemi-ionic	23000	25500	2500
2,3-Naphthalenediol	Molecular	29500	29600	100
	Hemi-ionic	25050	27250	2200

4. Solvent Quenching

The fluorescence efficiencies of organic compounds are commonly greater in the vapor phase than in liquid solution. The efficiency in liquid solution is a function of the particular solvent used, and some solvents exhibit unusual quenching effects. Solvent quenching is considered in Section III-D.

5. Conclusion: Analytical Implications

The solvent is a very important variable in fluorometric analysis. Some obvious conclusions apply to the choice of a solvent: the solvent should not absorb or fluoresce in the frequency region of interest, and it should, of course, dissolve the solutes under study. In addition, it is usually desirable to avoid solvent–solute pairs which exhibit pronounced hydrogen-bonding tendencies. It is clear that fluorescence data obtained in one solvent at a given temperature should not be assumed to apply to another solvent or another temperature. Despite a number of fundamental studies, correlations between macroscopic properties of solvents and the fluorescence energy and efficiency of a given solute are often tenuous.

It is occasionally possible for a solvent to form charge–transfer complexes with the solute. This problem is particularly acute with ether and dioxane, both of which tend to decompose to peroxides. Ladner and Becker (36) noticed that the fluorescence spectrum of acridine in ethyl ether changed with age of the ether; they attributed this to the formation of an acridine–peroxide complex. Solvents which tend to decompose (even very slightly) upon aging are perhaps best avoided in analytical work. The presence of trace impurities, from any source, in the solvent can also lead to anomalous results.

E. Stimulated Emission from Organic Compounds

It has been proposed that "laser action" (stimulated emission) may be observed in organic systems under proper conditions (227–229). There are many intriguing potentialities in the preparation of "organic lasers," but three significant difficulties have retarded progress in this field. First, both the absorption and fluorescence (or phosphorescence) intensities of the electronic transition under study must be large. Second, population inversion must be attained, usually by means of flash excitation; the organic compound must therefore be able to withstand intense flashes of energy without undergoing photodecomposition. Third, and most important, the emission bands of most organic compounds are fairly broad, even in the crystalline state. This decreases the homogeneity of the emitted energy, relative to that usually obtained from inorganic lasers.

The principal advantage which might accrue from the use of organic lasers would be the wide range of possible emission frequencies. It may be feasible to "tailor-make" lasers of virtually any frequency in the near ultraviolet or visible region of the spectrum, owing to the large number of fluorescent organic compounds. "Fine tuning" could perhaps be obtained by varying substituents and by utilizing solvent shifts of electronic emission spectra (229).

Preliminary reports (228) have appeared that claim the observation of stimulated emission from several organic compounds, including acetophenone, pyrazine, 1-bromonaphthalene, and naphthalene, but few (if any) really successful organic lasers have yet been reported. Complexes of lanthanides with conjugated ligands have been proposed as laser systems (230,231) because they combine the intense absorption of the ligand with the narrow line-like emission of the metal ion (See Chapter 4). It is clear that the study of organometallic and organic compounds as lasers has only begun, and the potentialities of such studies are indeed exciting.

V. Conclusion

In this chapter, we have examined some aspects of the fluorescence and phosphorescence of organic molecules. We have noted that analytically-useful fluorescence is restricted to aromatic and heterocyclic compounds, and have indicated some of the special effects which may affect the observation of fluorescence of various classes of organic compounds. The influence of the medium in which the fluorescence is measured has been emphasized as an important variable in fluorometric analysis.

An attempt has been made to indicate the current state of knowledge concerning the mechanisms of emission and energy transfer in organic systems. This is presently a very active research area. As more becomes known about the finer details of fluorescence and phosphorescence of organic compounds, it should be expected that analytical fluorometry will become less of a "trial and error" method. While the analytical chemist need not be an expert spectroscopist to utilize fluorescence, awareness of the types of behavior which organic molecules exhibit when exposed to ultraviolet is highly desirable.

References

1. W. West, Ed., in *Chemical Applications of Spectroscopy*, (Technique of Organic Chemistry, Vol. 9) Interscience, New York, 1956, Chap. 6.
2. W. Kauzmann, *Quantum Chemistry*, Academic Press, New York, 1957, p. 542–544.
3. J. W. Sidman and D. S. McClure, *J. Am. Chem. Soc.*, *77*, 6461 (1955).
4. J. T. Dubois and F. Wilkinson, *J. Chem. Phys.*, *39*, 899 (1963).
5. W. A. Noyes, Jr., G. B. Porter, and J. E. Jolley, *Chem. Rev.*, *56*, 49 (1956).
6. D. S. Weir, *J. Chem. Phys.*, *36*, 1113 (1962).
7. J. Heicklen and W. A. Noyes, Jr., *J. Am. Chem. Soc.*, *81*, 3858 (1959).
8. J. Heicklen, *J. Am. Chem. Soc.*, *81*, 3863 (1959).
9. G. W. Luckey and W. A. Noyes, Jr., *J. Chem. Phys.*, *19*, 227 (1951).
10. P. Ausloos and E. Murad, *J. Phys. Chem.*, *65*, 1519 (1961).
11. E. Murad, *J. Phys. Chem.*, *64*, 942 (1960).
12. P. Longin, *Compt. Rend.*, *251*, 2499 (1960).
13. C. S. Parmenter and W. A. Noyes, Jr., *J. Am. Chem. Soc.*, *85*, 416 (1963).
14. G. Weber and F. W. J. Teale, *Trans. Faraday Soc.*, *54*, 640 (1958).
15. G. A. Thommes and E. Leininger, *Talanta*, *7*, 181 (1961).
16. E. J. Bowen, *Trans. Faraday Soc.*, *50*, 97 (1954).
17. M. Kasha, *Radiation Res. Suppl.*, *2*, 243 (1960).
18. R. Griswold, Ph.D. Thesis, Massachusetts Institute of Technology, 1960.

19. E. V. Shpol'skii, *Soviet Phys. Usp.* (*English Transl.*), *3*, 372 (1960).
20. V. G. Krishna and L. Goodman, *J. Chem. Phys.*, *37*, 912 (1962).
21. M. A. El-Sayed, *Nature*, *197*, 481 (1963).
22. D. S. McClure, *Solid State Phys.*, *8*, 1 (1959).
23. R. M. Hochstrasser, *Rev. Mod. Phys.*, *34*, 531 (1962).
24. R. C. Sangster and J. W. Irvine, Jr., *J. Chem. Phys.*, *24*, 670 (1956).
25. B. Stevens, *Spectrochem. Acta*, *18*, 439 (1962).
26. V. V. Zelinskii, V. P. Kolobkov, and I. I. Reznikova, *Dokl. Akad. Nauk SSSR*, *121*, 315 (1958).
27. D. S. McClure, *J. Chem. Phys.*, *17*, 905 (1949).
28. T. Pavlopoulos and M. A. El-Sayed, *J. Chem. Phys.*, *41*, 1082 (1964).
29. V. L. Ermolaev and K. K. Svitashev, *Optics and Spectroscopy*, *7*, 399 (1959).
30. G. A. Thommes and E. Leininger, *Anal. Chem.*, *30*, 1361 (1958).
31. K. Bredereck, T. Förster, and H.-G. Oesterlin, in H. Kallmann and G. M. Spruch, Eds., *Luminescence of Organic and Inorganic Materials*, Wiley, New York, 1962, p. 161.
32. M. Kasha, in W. D. McElroy and B. Glass, Eds., *Light and Life*, Johns Hopkins Press, Baltimore, 1961, p. 31.
33. N. Mataga and S. Tsuno, *Bull. Chem. Soc. Japan*, *30*, 368 (1957).
34. G. J. Brealey and M. Kasha, *J. Am. Chem. Soc.*, *77*, 4462 (1955).
35. M. A. El-Sayed and M. Kasha, *Spectrochim. Acta*, *15*, 758 (1959).
36. S. J. Ladner and R. S. Becker, *J. Phys. Chem.*, *67*, 2481 (1963).
37. H. Sponer and Y. Kanda, *J. Chem. Phys.*, *40*, 778 (1964).
38. M. Chowdhury and L. Goodman, *J. Chem. Phys.*, *38*, 2979 (1963).
39. M. A. El-Sayed, *J. Chem. Phys.*, *38*, 2834 (1963).
40. R. C. Heckman, *J. Mol. Spectry.*, *2*, 27 (1958).
41. E. Hengge and H. Grupe, *Chem. Ber.*, *97*, 1783 (1964).
42. F. Dörr, H. Gropper, and N. Mika, *Angew. Chem.* (*Intern. Ed. English*), *3*, 387 (1964).
43. G. Oster, N. Geacintov, and A. U. Khan, *Nature*, *196*, 1089 (1962).
44. C. F. Forster and E. F. Rickard, *Nature*, *197*, 1199 (1963).
45. H. V. Drushel and A. L. Sommers, *Anal. Chem.*, *36*, 836 (1964).
46. V. F. Gachkovskii, *J. Struct. Chem.* (*USSR*) (*English Transl.*), *4*, 386 (1963).
47. L. J. Basile, *J. Chem. Phys.*, *36*, 2204 (1962).
48. K. F. Plitt and S. D. Toner, *J. Appl. Polymer Sci.*, *5*, 534 (1961).
49. Y. Nishijima, in H. Kallmann and G. M. Spruch, Eds., *Luminescence of Organic and Inorganic Materials*, Wiley, New York, 1962, p. 235.
50. P. Wahl, *J. Polymer Sci.*, *29*, 375 (1958).
51. S. S. Yanari, F. A. Bovey, and R. Lumry, *Nature*, *200*, 242 (1963).
52. L. S. Forster and D. Dudley, *J. Phys. Chem.*, *66*, 838 (1962).
53. F. Millich and G. Oster, *J. Am. Chem. Soc.*, *81*, 1357 (1959).
54. G. Weill and M. Calvin, *Biopolymers*, *1*, 401 (1963).
55. G. S. Levinson, W. T. Simpson, and W. Curtis, *J. Am. Chem. Soc.*, *79*, 4314 (1957).
56. E. G. McRae and M. Kasha, *J. Chem. Phys.*, *28*, 721 (1958).
57. D. A. Rogers, J. D. Margerum, and G. M. Wyman, *J. Am. Chem. Soc.*, *79*, 2464 (1957).

58. J. S. Bellin and G. Oster, *J. Am. Chem. Soc.*, *79*, 2461 (1957).
59. G. Oster and G. K. Oster, in H. Kallmann and G. M. Spruch, Eds., *Luminescence of Organic and Inorganic Materials*, Wiley, New York, 1962, p. 186.
60. A. Adelman and G. Oster, *J. Am. Chem. Soc.*, *78*, 3977 (1956).
61. L. I. Al'perovich, *Opt. Spectry.*, *(USSR)* *(English Transl.)*, *14*, 400 (1963).
62. W. Rhodes and M. A. El-Sayed, *J. Mol. Spectry.*, *9*, 42 (1962).
63. R. M. Hochstrasser, *Can. J. Chem.*, *39*, 459 (1961).
64. Y. Hirschberg and F. Bergmann, *J. Am. Chem. Soc.*, *72*, 5118 (1950).
65. G. N. Lewis, T. T. Magel, and D. Lipkin, *J. Am. Chem. Soc.*, *62*, 2973 (1940).
66. A. S. Cherkasov, *Dokl. Akad. Nauk SSSR*, *146*, 716 (1962).
67. R. H. Dyck and D. S. McClure, *J. Chem. Phys.*, *36*, 2326 (1962).
68. W. G. Herkstroeter, J. Saltiel, and G. S. Hammond, *J. Am. Chem. Soc.*, *85*, 482 (1963).
69. G. S. Hammond, J. Saltiel, A. A. Lamola, N. J. Turro, J. S. Bradshaw, D. O. Cowan, R. C. Counsell, V. Vogt, and C. Dalton, *J. Am. Chem. Soc.*, *86*, 3197 (1964).
70. J. B. Birks and D. J. Dyson, *Proc. Roy. Soc.* *(London)*, *A275*, 135 (1963).
71. W. H. Melhuish, *J. Phys. Chem.*, *67*, 1681 (1963).
72. T. Förster, *Ann. Physik*, *2*, 55 (1948).
73. T. Förster, *Discussions Faraday Soc.*, *27*, 7 (1959).
74. E. J. Bowen, in W. A. Noyes, Jr., G. S. Hammond, and J. N. Pitts, Jr., Eds., *Advances in Photochemistry*, Vol. 1, Interscience, 1963, p. 23.
75. A. Terenin and V. L. Ermolaev, *Trans. Faraday Soc.*, *52*, 1042 (1956).
76. R. G. Bennett, R. P. Schwenker, and R. E. Kellogg, *J. Chem. Phys.*, *41*, 3040 (1964).
77. R. G. Bennett, *J. Chem. Phys.*, *41*, 3048 (1964).
78. G. Porter and F. Wilkinson, *Proc. Roy. Soc.* *(London)*, *A264*, 1 (1961).
79. S. Kusuhara and R. Hardwick, *J. Chem. Phys.*, *41*, 3943 (1964).
80. M. L. Bhaumik and M. A. El-Sayed, *J. Phys. Chem.*, *69*, 275 (1965).
81. G. S. Hammond, N. J. Turro, and P. J. Leermakers, *J. Phys. Chem.*, *66*, 1144 (1962).
82. G. S. Hammond and N. J. Turro, *Science*, *142*, 1541 (1963).
83. S. C. Ganguly and N. K. Chaudhury, *Rev. Mod. Phys.*, *31*, 990 (1959).
84. F. R. Lipsett and A. Dekker, *Can. J. Phys.*, *30*, 165 (1951).
85. C. W. Reed and F. R. Lipsett, *J. Mol. Spectry.*, *11*, 139 (1963).
86. J. B. Birks, *Phys. Rev.*, *94*, 1957 (1954).
87. J. Frenkel, *Phys. Rev.*, *37*, 1276 (1931).
88. W. R. Heller and R. A. Marcus, *Phys. Rev.*, *84*, 809 (1951).
89. S. A. Rice, J. Jortner, J. L. Katz, and S.-I. Choi, *J. Chem. Phys.*, *39*, 1896 (1963).
90. A. V. Davydov, *Theory of Molecular Excitons*, translated by M. Kasha and M. Oppenheimer, Jr., McGraw-Hill, New York, 1962.
91. N. F. Mott and R. W. Gurney, *Electronic Processes in Ionic Crystals*, Oxford, New York, 1949.
92. C. A. Parker and W. T. Rees, *Analyst*, *87*, 83 (1962).
93. B. L. Funt and E. Neparko, *J. Phys. Chem.*, *60*, 257 (1956).

94. W. R. Ware, *J. Phys. Chem.*, *66*, 455 (1962).
95. B. Stevens and J. T. Dubois, *Trans. Faraday Soc.*, *59*, 2813 (1963).
96. T. Förster and K. Kasper, *Z. Elektrochem.*, *59*, 976 (1955).
97. J. B. Birks and L. G. Christophorou, *Nature*, *196*, 33 (1962).
98. E. J. Bowen and R. J. Cook, *J. Chem. Soc.*, *1953*, 3059.
99. E. J. Bowen and K. West, *J. Chem. Soc.*, *1955*, 4394.
100. G. Porter and M. W. Windsor, *Discussions Faraday Soc.*, *17*, 178 (1954).
101. M. Kasha, *J. Chem. Phys.*, *20*, 71 (1952).
102. I. J. Graham-Bryce and J. M. Corkill, *Nature*, *186*, 965 (1960).
103. S. P. McGlynn, R. Sunseri, and N. D. Christodouleas, *J. Chem. Phys.*, *37*, 1818 (1962).
104. S. P. McGlynn, J. Daigre, and F. J. Smith, *J. Chem. Phys.*, *39*, 675 (1963).
105. S. P. McGlynn, M. J. Reynolds, G. W. Daigre, and N. D. Christodouleas, *J. Phys. Chem.*, *66*, 2499 (1962).
106. S. P McGlynn, T. Azumi, and M. Kasha, *J. Chem. Phys.*, *40*, 507 (1964).
107. D. F. Evans, *J. Chem. Soc.*, *1957*, 1351.
108. L. J. Tolmach, *Arch. Biochem. Biophys.*, *33*, 120 (1951).
109. E. Sawicki, T. W. Stanley, and H. Johnson, 148th Meeting, American Chemical Society, Chicago, Ill., September, 1964.
110. J. B. Birks, *Scintillation Counters*, Pergamon Press, London, 1953.
111. F. D. Brooks, *Progr. Nucl. Phys.*, *5*, 252 (1956).
112. H. Kallmann and M. Furst, in G. C. Bell and F. N. Hayes, Eds., *Liquid Scintillation Counting*, Pergamon Press, London, 1958, p. 3.
113. E. Schram, *Organic Scintillation Detectors*, Amsterdam, Elsevier, 1963.
114. J. Yguerabide and M. Burton, *J. Chem. Phys.*, *37*, 1757 (1962).
115. M. Furst and H. Kallmann, *J. Chem. Phys.*, *23*, 607 (1955).
116. A. Heller, *J. Chem. Phys.*, *35*, 1980 (1961).
117. H. Kallmann and M. Furst, *Phys. Rev.*, *87*, 853 (1951).
118. W. H. Melhuish, *J. Chem. Phys.*, *40*, 1369 (1964).
119. F. H. Brown, M. Furst, and H. Kallmann, in H. Kallmann and G. M. Spruch, Eds., *Luminescence of Organic and Inorganic Materials*, Wiley, New York, 1962, p. 100.
120. S. Lipsky and M. Burton, *J. Chem. Phys.*, *31*, 1221 (1959).
121. R. K. Swank, *Ann. Rev. Nucl. Sci.*, *4*, 111 (1954).
122. V. Bar and A. Weinreb, *J. Chem. Phys.*, *29*, 1142 (1958).
123. B. L. Funt and A. Hetherington, *Intern. J. Appl. Radiation Isotopes*, *4*, 189 (1959).
124. A. Weinreb and P. Avivi, in G. C. Bell and F. N. Hayes, Eds., *Liquid Scintillation Counting*, Pergamon Press, London, 1958, p. 270.
125. L. J. Basile, *J. Chem. Phys.*, *27*, 801 (1957).
126. R. K. Swank, *Nucleonics*, *12*, No. 3, 14 (1954).
127. A. H. Heimbuch, H. Gee, and H. Bould, 144th Meeting, American Chemical Society, Los Angeles, Calif., April, 1963.
128. A. H. Heimbuch and W. J. Schwarz, *Atompraxis*, *10*, No. 2, 70 (1964); through *Chem. Abstr.*, *60*, 16204 (1964).
129. B. Stevens and E. Hutton, *Nature*, *186*, 1045 (1960).
130. J. B. Birks and L. G. Christophorou, *Nature*, *197*, 1064 (1963).

131. J. B. Birks and L. G. Christophorou, *Proc. Roy. Soc. (London)*, *A277*, 571 (1964).
132. T. V. Ivanova, G. A. Mokeeva, and B. Ya. Sveshnikov, *Opt. Spectry., (USSR) (English Transl.)*, *12*, 325 (1962).
133. E. Döller and T. Förster, *Z. Physik. Chem. (Frankfurt)*, *31*, 274 (1962).
134. S. S. Lehrer and G. D. Fasman, *Biopolymers*, *2*, 199 (1964).
135. I. B. Berlman, *J. Chem. Phys.*, *34*, 1083 (1961).
136. J. B. Birks and J. B. Aladekomo, *Spectrochim. Acta*, *20*, 15 (1964).
137. B. Stevens and T. Dickinson, *J. Chem. Soc.*, *1963*, 5492.
138. P. Pringsheim, *Fluorescence and Phosphorescence*, Interscience, New York, 1949, p. 285.
139. J. B. Birks, D. J. Dyson, and I. H. Munro, *Proc. Roy. Soc. (London)*, *A275*, 575 (1963).
140. J. B. Birks, D. J. Dyson, and T. A. King, *Proc. Roy. Soc. (London)*, *A277*, 270 (1964).
141. C. A. Coulson, L. E. Orgel, W. Taylor, and J. Weiss, *J. Chem. Soc.*, *1955*, 2961.
142. R. Livingston and D. W. Tanner, *Trans. Faraday Soc.*, *54*, 675 (1958).
143. J. B. Birks and J. B. Aladekomo, *Photochem. Photobiol.*, *2*, 415 (1963).
144. J. B. Birks, J. H. Appleyard, and R. Pope, *Photochem. Photobiol.*, *2*, 493 (1963).
145. T. Förster, *Pure Appl. Chem.*, *7*, 73 (1963).
146. B. Stevens and T. Dickinson, *Spectrochim. Acta*, *19*, 1865 (1963).
147. R. M. Hochstrasser, *J. Chem. Phys.*, *36*, 1099 (1962).
148. M. Furst and H. Kallmann, *Phys. Rev.*, *109*, 646 (1958).
149. G. N. Lewis, D. Lipkin, and T. T. Magel, *J. Am. Chem. Soc.*, *63*, 3005 (1941).
150. T. Azumi and S. P. McGlynn, *J. Chem. Phys.*, *39*, 1186 (1963).
151. C. A. Parker and C. G. Hatchard, *Trans. Faraday Soc.*, *57*, 1894 (1961).
152. C. A. Parker and C. G. Hatchard, *J. Phys. Chem.*, *66*, 2506 (1962).
153. C. A. Parker, *Proc. Roy. Soc. (London)*, *A276*, 125 (1963).
154. R. Williams, *J. Chem. Phys.*, *28*, 577 (1958).
155. C. A. Parker and C. G. Hatchard, *Trans. Faraday Soc.*, *59*, 284 (1963).
156. C. A. Parker and C. G. Hatchard, *Proc. Roy. Soc. (London)*, *A269*, 574 (1962).
157. T. Azumi and S. P. McGlynn, *J. Chem. Phys.*, *38*, 2773 (1963).
158. T. Azumi and S. P. McGlynn, *J. Chem. Phys.*, *39*, 3533 (1963).
159. G. N. Lewis and D. Lipkin, *J. Am. Chem. Soc.*, *64*, 2801 (1942).
160. G. N. Lewis and J. Bigeleisen, *J. Am. Chem. Soc.*, *65*, 520, 2419, 2424 (1943).
161. H. Linschitz, M. G. Berry, and D. Schweitzer, *J. Am. Chem. Soc.*, *76*, 5833 (1954).
162. P. Debye and J. O. Edwards, *J. Chem. Phys.*, *20*, 236 (1952).
163. A. C. Albrecht and M. E. Green, *J. Chem. Phys.*, *31*, 261 (1959).
164. E. C. Lim and G. W. Swenson, *J. Chem. Phys.*, *36*, 118 (1962).
165. E. C. Lim and W. Wen, *J. Chem. Phys.*, *39*, 847 (1963).
166. J. Kern, F. Dörr, and G. Scheibe, *Z. Elektrochem.*, *66*, 462 (1962).
167. H. Sponer, Y. Kanda, and L. A. Blackwell, *J. Chem. Phys.*, *29*, 721 (1958).

168. N. W. Blake and D. S. McClure, *J. Chem. Phys.*, *29*, 722 (1958).
169. H. Sternlicht, G. C. Nieman, and G. W. Robinson, *J. Chem. Phys.*, *38*, 1326 (1963).
170. K. Weber, *Z. Physik. Chem. (Leipzig)*, *B15*, 18 (1931).
171. T. Förster, *Z. Elektrochem.*, *54*, 42 (1950).
172. K. Breitschwerdt, T. Förster, and A. Weller, *Naturwissenschaften*, *43*, 443 (1956).
173. A. Weller, in G. Porter, Ed., *Progress in Reaction Kinetics*, Pergamon Press, London, 1961, Vol. 1, p. 189.
174. A. Weller, *Z. Elektrochem.*, *56*, 662 (1952).
175. D. M. Hercules and L. B. Rogers, *Spectrochim. Acta*, *15*, 393 (1959).
176. A. Weller and W. Urban, *Angew. Chem.*, *66*, 336 (1954).
177. A. Weller, *Z. Physik. Chem. (Frankfurt)*, *17*, 224 (1958).
178. L. D. Derkacheeva, *Opt. Spectry.*, *9*, 110 (1960).
179. A. Weller, *Z. Physik. Chem. (Frankfurt)*, *3*, 238 (1955).
180. W. Bartok, P. J. Lucchesi, and N. S. Snider, *J. Am. Chem. Soc.*, *84*, 1842 (1962).
181. E. L. Wehry and L. B. Rogers, to be published.
182. H. Kokubun, *Z. Elektrochem.*, *62*, 599 (1958).
183. T. Förster, in F. Daniels, Ed., *Photochemistry in the Liquid and Solid States*, Wiley, New York, 1960, p. 10.
184. G. Jackson and G. Porter, *Proc. Roy. Soc. (London)*, *A260*, 13 (1961).
185. N. Mataga, Y. Kaifu, and M. Koizumi, *Bull. Chem. Soc. Japan*, *29*, 373 (1956).
186. A. Weller, *Z. Elektrochem.*, *61*, 956 (1957).
187. C. Sandorfy, *Can. J. Chem.*, *31*, 439 (1953).
188. C. A. Coulson and J. Jacobs, *J. Chem. Soc.*, *1949*, 1984.
189. D. W. Ellis and L. B. Rogers, *Spectrochim. Acta*, *18*, 265 (1962).
190. D. W. Ellis and L. B. Rogers, *Spectrochim. Acta*, *20*, 1709 (1964).
191. J. C. Haylock, S. F. Mason, and B. E. Smith, *J. Chem. Soc.*, *1963*, 4897.
192. A. Weller, *Z. Elektrochem.*, *60*, 1144 (1956).
193. Y. V. Naboikin, B. A. Zadorozhny, and E. N. Pavlova, *Opt. Spectry.*, *8*, 347 (1960).
194. J. N. Murrell, *The Theory of the Electronic Spectra of Organic Molecules*, London, Methuen, 1963.
195. J. S. Brinen, D. D. Rosebrook, and R. C. Hirt, *J. Phys. Chem.*, *67*, 2651 (1963).
196. W. Bartok, unpublished, from ref. 198.
197. H. H. Jaffé, Preprints of the Symposium on Linear Free Energy Correlations, Durham, North Carolina, 1964, p. 173; *J. Org. Chem.*, *30*, 964 (1965).
198. H. H. Jaffé, D. L. Beveridge, and H. L. Jones, *J. Am. Chem. Soc.*, *86*, 2932 (1964).
199. H. H. Jaffé, H. L. Jones, and M. Isaks, *J. Am. Chem. Soc.*, *86*, 2934 (1964).
200. I. M. Kolthoff and V. A. Stenger, *Volumetric Analysis*, Interscience, New York, 1957, Vol. 2, p. 52.
201. B. L. Van Duuren, *Chem. Rev.*, *63*, 325 (1963).
202. N. S. Bayliss and E. G. McRae, *J. Phys. Chem.*, *58*, 1002, 1006 (1954).

203. E. G. McRae, *J. Phys. Chem.*, *61*, 562 (1957).
204. E. Lippert and F. Möll, *Z. Elektrochem.*, *58*, 714 (1954).
205. E. Lippert, *J. Phys. Radium*, *15*, 627 (1954).
206. E. Lippert, *Z. Physik. Chem. (Frankfurt)*, *6*, 125 (1956).
207. B. L. Van Duuren, *J. Org. Chem.*, *26*, 2954 (1961).
208. S. R. Veljković, *Trans. Faraday Soc.*, *53*, 1181 (1957).
209. G. Löber, *Z. Chem.*, *3*, 437 (1963).
210. A. Kawski, *Naturwissenschaften*, *51*, 82 (1964).
211. E. Lippert, *Z. Elektrochem.*, *61*, 962 (1957).
212. N. Mataga, Y. Kaifu, and M. Koizumi, *Bull. Chem. Soc. Japan*, *29*, 465 (1956).
213. J. Czekalla, *Z. Elektrochem.*, *64*, 1221 (1960).
214. J. Czekalla, W. Liptay, and K. O. Meyer, *Ber. Bunsenges. Physik. Chem.*, *67*, 465 (1963).
215. L. A. Zhmyreva and A. S. Kochemirovskii, *Russ. J. Phys. Chem. (English Transl.)*, *35*, 571 (1961).
216. N. Mataga and S. Tsuno, *Bull. Chem. Soc. Japan*, *30*, 711 (1957).
217. N. Mataga and Y. Kaifu, *Mol. Phys.*, *7*, 137 (1964).
218. N. Mataga, *Bull. Chem. Soc. Japan*, *31*, 487 (1958).
219. T. Miwa and M. Koizumi, *Bull. Chem. Soc. Japan*, *36*, 1619 (1963).
220. H. Kokubun and M. Kobayashi, *Z. Physik. Chem. (Frankfurt)*, *41*, 245 (1964).
221. L. A. Klimova, *Opt. Spectry.*, *15*, 185 (1963).
222. H. Shull, *J. Chem. Phys.*, *17*, 295 (1949).
223. E. J. Bowen and J. Sahu, *J. Phys. Chem.*, *63*, 4 (1959).
224. D. M. Hercules and L. B. Rogers, *J. Phys. Chem.*, *64*, 397 (1960).
225. E. Lippert, W. Lüder, and F. Möll, *Spectrochim. Acta*, *15*, 858 (1959).
226. M. L. Bhaumik and R. Hardwick, *J. Chem. Phys.*, *39*, 1595 (1963).
227. E. G. Brock, P. Csavinszky, F. Hormats, H. C. Nedderman, D. Stirpe, and F. Unterleitner, *J. Chem. Phys.*, *35*, 759 (1961).
228. D. J. Morantz, B. G. White, and A. J. C. Wright, *J. Chem. Phys.*, *37*, 2041 (1962).
229. M. W. Windsor, 144th Meeting, American Chemical Society, Los Angeles, Calif., April, 1963.
230. O. J. Marsh, H. Winston, C. K. Suzuki, and C. L. Telk, *J. Chem. Phys.*, *39*, 267 (1963).
231. A. Lempicki and H. Samelson, *Appl. Phys. Letters*, *2*, 159 (1963).
232. J. B. Birks and L. G. Christophorou, *Spectrochim. Acta*, *19*, 401 (1963).

chapter 4

Fluorescence of Metal Chelate Compounds

WILLIAM E. OHNESORGE*

*Department of Chemistry,
University of Rhode Island, Kingston, Rhode Island, and
Department of Chemistry and Laboratory for Nuclear Science,
Massachusetts Institute of Technology, Cambridge, Massachusetts*

I. Introduction

The formation of a metal chelate compound is usually a prerequisite to the fluorometric determination of metallic and other inorganic ions because such species, including most simple metal ion complexes (with monodentate ligands), are nonfluorescent. Fluorescence intensity measurements are generally made on dilute solutions of the metal chelate compound, operating under optimum instrumental and chemical conditions (1–5). The ability to quench the fluorescence of a fluorophore may be used as the basis for a quantitative analytical procedure for some species which are incapable of forming fluorescent chelate compounds, e.g., fluoride ion has been determined by measuring its quenching effect on the fluorescence of the aluminum–morin complex (6). Solid state luminescence has also been used to analytical advantage (4), e.g., Peattie and Rogers coprecipitated Sm^{+3} with calcium sulfate, partially reduced the Sm to the divalent state, and were able to determine *ca.* 1 nanogram of Sm (7).

II. Theory

The important processes affecting the luminescence of metal chelates are basically no different from those which influence other systems; these have been defined and discussed in detail elsewhere (8–10) (See Chapter 1).

* Present address: Department of Chemistry, Lehigh University, Bethlehem, Pennsylvania.

The excitation step is almost always the absorption of a photon by the chelate to produce π,π^* excited state of the ligand. Internal conversion to the lowest vibrational level of the first excited electronic state very quickly follows (*ca.* 10^{-12} s) (8–10).

One or more excited-state processes may now occur which dissipate part or all of the excitation energy and accordingly reduce the intensity of the emitted fluorescence.

A. INTERNAL CONVERSION

If internal conversion occurs to a large extent, most molecules return to the ground state without emission and the chelate will be nonfluorescent (11).

B. INTERSYSTEM CROSSING

The extent of intersystem crossing is often the major factor which determines the intensity of fluorescence (and phosphorescence) emitted by a metal chelate compound. At room temperature an excited species which has undergone intersystem crossing returns to the ground state from the triplet state by collisional deactivation.

If the excited species contains a paramagnetic atom (the metal ion in many chelates), it usually will not fluoresce because the rate of intersystem crossing is greatly increased by paramagnetic species. The presence of a foreign paramagnetic species in the solution of a fluorophore may produce the same effect (see Chapter 1).

The extent of intersystem crossing also depends on the atomic number of atoms in the fluorophore. Heavier atoms increase spin–orbit coupling which leads to an increase in the rate of intersystem crossing. This phenomenon (the internal Z-effect) is important for systems containing diamagnetic species. The chelates of heavier (diamagnetic) metal ions are usually less intensely fluorescent, but show a more intense phosphorescence, than the analogous chelates with lighter metals (11,12). The presence of foreign (diamagnetic) species containing heavy atoms, e.g., the solvent, can also effect increased intersystem crossing (13–15), as discussed in Chapter 1.

C. COLLISIONAL DEACTIVATION

Increasing solute–solvent interaction, e.g., by introducing polar substituent groups into the ligand structure or by using a more polar solvent, will normally result in a reduction of the fluorescence intensity. Conversely, if the fluorophore can be "insulated" from the solvent, solute–solvent interaction is reduced and the fluorescence intensity will increase. Addition of trioctylphosphine oxide (TOPO) and other similar compounds to solutions of europium chelates of β-diketones produces significant increase in the intensity of luminescence emitted by the chelate (16). TOPO is a synergic agent which presumably replaces water molecules coordinated to the europium ion, reducing solute–solvent interaction and collisional deactivation. A solvent of greater molecular weight shows less collisional deactivation of an excited fluorophore because of the reduced frequency of collisions between solute and solvent, e.g., substitution of D_2O for H_2O has been shown to result in an increase in fluorescence intensity (17).

D. Energy Transfer

This term is used here to refer to an intramolecular energy transfer from the ligand to the metallic ion. This process is important for certain rare earth chelates, for at least some transition ion chelates, and probably also for those containing an easily reduced metallic ion (18–21).

E. Excited-State Dissociation

Certain metal chelate compounds undergo photolysis when irradiated (18). If photodecomposition occurs rapidly, the chelate will be nonfluorescent, or at best, weakly fluorescent.

Unless all excitation energy has been dissipated by one or more of the above processes, the return of the metal chelate compound to the ground state (after $ca.$ 10^{-8} s) will be accompanied by emission of fluorescence radiation. Most fluorescent metal chelate compounds emit upon making the reverse transition that was made upon excitation, i.e., $\pi^* \rightarrow \pi$. Because of the nature of the combining states, the emission spectrum of a typical fluorescent metal chelate will consist of a rather broad band (often with little or no resolution of vibrational structure) having a half band-width greater than $ca.$ 2000 cm^{-1} ($ca.$ 60 mμ) at room temperature (Fig. 4-1).

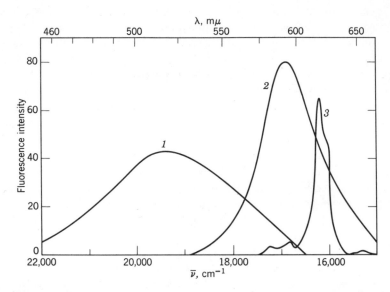

Fig. 4-1. Fluorescence spectra excited by 365 mμ radiation: *1*, tris(8-quino-linolato)–aluminum(III) in $CHCl_3$; *2*, tris(2,2'-bipyridyl)–ruthenium(II) in absolute ethanol; *3*, tris(1,3-diphenyl-1,3-propanediono)–europium (III) in absolute ethanol.

Under certain conditions, the metal chelate may emit luminescence denoted as $m^* \rightarrow m$. Subsequent to energy transfer, if some excitation energy has passed to a resonance level of the metallic ion, a radiative transition may occur from the resonance level(s) to the ground state. Because this pathway involves a radiative combination of atomic orbitals, luminescence would be characterized by a relatively narrow bandwith. Some rare earth, Cr(III), and Cu(II) chelates have been reported to show line-like emission spectra attributed to this kind of transition (18–20,22,23).

Metal chelate fluorescence has been reported in which emission accompanies the charge transfer step: $\pi^* \rightarrow m$. The band in the emission spectrum in this case would be somewhat narrower than the usual $\pi^* \rightarrow \pi$ band because one of the combining orbitals is localized on the metallic ion, but the band would be broader than the narrow $m^* \rightarrow m$ band because one of the combining states is centered on the ligand (20,24). The effect of the nature of the transition types on the width of the fluorescence emission band is shown in Figure 4-1.

III. Characteristics of Typical $\pi^* \rightarrow \pi$ Fluorescent Metal Chelate Compounds

Not all metal chelate compounds will fluoresce. The metallic ion and the ligand must possess certain structural features to form a fluorescent metal chelate.

Numerous species have been used as the ligand in preparing fluorescent metal chelate compounds (1,5); some of the more thoroughly studied ligands are shown in Figure 4-2. The important role of the $\pi \rightarrow \pi^*$ transition in the sequence of events leading to emission by most fluorescent metal chelates has been emphasized; it is hardly surprising that a ligand which forms fluorescent chelates usually has π electrons. However, ligand aromatic character while necessary, is not sufficient; e.g., benzoylacetone (structure III, Figure 4-2 with $R_1 = CH_3$, $R_2 = \phi$) and dibenzoylmethane ($R_1 = R_2 = \phi$) form fluorescent chelates, but acetylacetone ($R_1 = R_2 = CH_3$) does not.

Minor modification of the ligand structure, e.g., introduction of auxochromic groups, often produces only minor shifts in wavelengths of maximum absorption and minor changes in the intensity of the absorption by their chelates. Similarly, the emission spectrum shifts only slightly with such changes, as illustrated in Table 4-1 (25,27,28). The fluorescence intensity, however, may change markedly with such ligand modifications. The effects of these structural changes on the

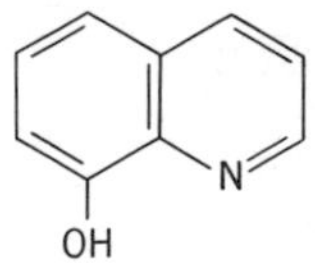

(I) 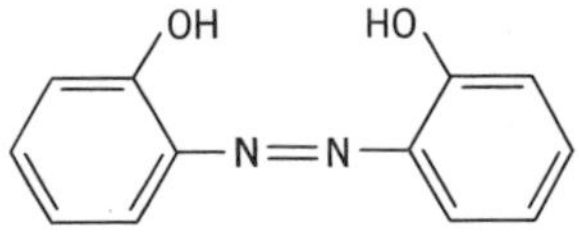   (II)

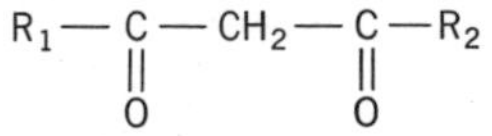

(III)

Fig. 4-2. Reagents commonly used to form fluorescent metal chelate compounds: (I), 8-quinolinol (oxine,8-hydroxyquinoline); (II), o,o'-dihydroxyazobenzene; (III), β-diketones; $R_1 = R_2 = CH_3$: 2,4-pentanedione (acetylacetone); $R_1 = CH_3$, $R_2 = \phi$: 1-phenyl-1,3-butanedione (benzoylacetone); $R_1 = R_2 = \phi$: 1,3-diphenyl-1,3-propanedione (dibenzoylmethane).

relative energies of the π and π^* orbitals are rather small, hence the minor shifts in the positions of the absorption and fluorescence spectral bands.   However, small structural changes may profoundly affect the efficiency of certain energy transfer steps, especially inter-system crossing and solute–solvent interaction, with a marked effect on fluorescence efficiency.   In certain cases the added substituent may have nonbonding (n) electrons and if these are more easily excited than the π electrons, i.e., if an n,π^* excited state is lower in energy than the lowest π,π^* excited state, a nonfluorescent species will result (10,28,29).

TABLE 4-1

Effect of Substituent Groups on Absorption and Fluorescence
Properties of Some Metal Chelate Compounds

Ligand	λ_{max} for $\pi^* \rightarrow \pi$, mμ	λ_{max} for $\pi^* \rightarrow \pi$, mμ	Relative fluorescence intensity
Zn(II)–(8-quinolinols) in CHCl$_3$ (25)			
Parent compound	380	540	32
2-Methyl derivative	386	540	50
5,7-Dichloro derivative	407	555	28
Ga(III)–o,o'-dihydroxyazobenzenes in dimethylformamide (26)			
Parent compound	492	591	1.60
4-OH derivative	487	567	5.40
4,4'-Dichloro derivative	491	578	4.30
5,5'-Dinitro derivative	501	565	0.28

The solvent may also strongly affect the fluorescence intensity observed for a metal chelate compound; changing the solvent usually causes minor changes in the wavelengths of maximum absorption or emission, and in the intensity of absorption (Table 4-2).   In general, a metal chelate compound dissolved in an inert solvent will fluoresce more intensely than it will when dissolved in a more polar solvent (25). Solute–solvent interaction appears to be the major effect, but other factors such as the external Z-effect may also be influential.

TABLE 4-2

Solvent Effects on Absorption and Fluorescence Properties
of Bis(8-quinolinolato)–Zinc(II) (25)

Solvent	λ_{max} for $\pi^* \to \pi$, mμ	λ_{max} for $\pi^* \to \pi$, mμ	Relative fluorescence intensity
Ethyl ether	378	525	96.3
THF[a]	382	535	47.5
CHCl$_3$	378	540	31.9
DMF[b]	403	560	19.2
CCl$_4$	382	520	16.4
C$_2$H$_5$OH	379	525	14.8

[a] Tetrahydrofuran.
[b] Dimethylformamide.

The influence of the metallic ion on the fluorescence characteristics of a metal chelate compound is of major importance from the analytical viewpoint. The possible use of spectrofluorometry as a technique for the simultaneous determination of metallic ions without separation is appealing.

Certain metallic ions will not form fluorescent chelates, even with ligands possessing "sufficient" aromatic character. Only those ions which are diamagnetic when coordinated and are not themselves easily reduced can normally be expected to form fluorescent metal chelate compounds. An extensive study by Stevens established that only those 8-quinolinolato chelates containing a metallic ion which is not easily reduced and which has its outer electronic subshell filled would fluoresce (30).

Among those metallic ions which do form π,π^* fluorescent metal chelate compounds, a change in the metallic ion once again has a minor effect on the intensity of $\pi \to \pi^*$ absorption (per chelated ligand) and on the positions of absorption and emission bands (the metallic ion perturbs slightly the energies of the ligand π and π^* states); such changes do have a marked effect on the intensity of fluorescence (and phosphorescence) (See Table 4-3) because the metallic ion strongly affects the efficiency of the various pathways available for dissipating the excitation energy of the chelate. Although several factors may be operative, the (internal) heavy-atom effect on the rate of intersystem crossing appears to predominate (see Chapter 1). When chelates of heavier metal ions were examined, the fluorescence intensity decreased and in some cases the intensity of phosphorescence was observed to increase (Table 4-3) (11,12,31).

TABLE 4-3

Effect of Metallic Ion on Absorption and Emission Properties
of Some Metal Chelate Compounds

Metal ion	Atomic number	λ_{max} for $\pi^* \leftarrow \pi$, $m\mu$	λ_{max} for $\pi^* \rightarrow \pi$, $m\mu$	Relative fluorescence intensity
8-Quinolinols in $CHCl_3$ (31)				
Al^{+3}	13	384	520	40
Zn^{+2}	30	377	542	32
Ga^{+3}	31	391	537	15
In^{+3}	49	393	544	14
Tl^{+3}	81	395	550	<1

Dibenzolymethanes (12)

Fluorescence intensity/phosphorescence intensity

		in C_2H_5OH	in EPA[a]
Sc^{+3}	21	5.2	6.5
Y^{+3}	39	0.98	2.3
Lu^{+3}	71	0.46	0.86

[a] Mixture of ethyl ether, n-pentane, and ethanol.

IV. Chelates Emitting by Pathways Other Than $\pi^* \rightarrow \pi$

The rare earth ions La^{+3} (f^0) and Lu^{+3} (f^{14}) form fluorescent chelates which are no different from those considered above because these ions are diamagnetic and the chelates show the usual $\pi^* \rightarrow \pi$ emission: a wide-band fluorescence spectrum (12,30,32). However, those ions near the middle of the lanthanide group: Sm^{+3}, Eu^{+3}, Gd^{+3}, Tb^{+3}, Dy^{+3} electronic configuration (f^5 through f^9), will form luminescent chelates and even some luminescent salts (4,5,19,20,33). These species have emission spectra composed of a series of narrow (line-like) bands characteristic of the metallic ion rather than of the ligand.

Moreover, the positions of the emission bands correspond to the energy of bands observed in solution absorption spectra of the hydrated metallic ions, e.g., Eu(III) species normally show (among others) a family of lines near 615 mμ. Emission and absorption are attributed to transitions between various $4f$ levels of the lanthanide ion.

Weissman and more recently Crosby and co-workers have studied intramolecular energy transfer from the ligand to the metal in rare earth ion chelates when excitation occurred by a $\pi \rightarrow \pi^*$ transition on the ligand (18,19,34–41). It has been established that intramolecular energy transfer normally occurs from the triplet (π) levels of the chelated ligand to resonance (f) levels of the lanthanide ion. Only those chelates having the lowest triplet level of the chelated ligand at higher energies than the resonance level of the rare earth ion will show line-like luminescence spectra characteristic of the metallic ion. Otherwise the typical broad-band emission spectrum characteristic of the ligand $\pi^* \rightarrow \pi$ transition is observed. Figure 4-3 shows the energies of the triplet states and resonance level of the chelated ligands and metallic ion for benzoylacetone and dibenzoylmethane chelates of trivalent dysprosium, DyB$_3$ and DyD$_3$, respectively, reported by Crosby, Whan, and Alire (18). Because the ligand triplet of DyD$_3$ lies below the Dy^{+3} resonance level, intramolecular energy transfer does not occur and the emission spectrum of DyD$_3$ shows a broad band near 500 mμ characteristic of the ligand (18,35). The DyB$_3$ chelate, however, shows line emission characteristic of Dy^{+3} because of intramolecular energy transfer from the triplet state of the ligand to the lower-energy resonance level of the lanthanide ion (18). In at least some cases, energy transfer apparently occurs from a triplet level other than the one from which molecular phosphorescence (of the ligand) originates (presumably the zeroth vibrational level of the lowest triplet state)(41,42).

An example of intramolecular energy transfer along a reverse pathway compared to the one normally followed in these systems (i.e., absorption by an $f \rightarrow f^*$ transition on the lanthanide ion and $\pi^* \rightarrow \pi$ emission by the chelated ligand) has been reported. Solutions of Gd(III)–salicylate when irradiated with 313 mμ radiation (corresponding to an $f^* \leftarrow f$ absorption of Gd^{+3}) showed increased emission of the blue–violet fluorescence characteristic of the ligand (43).

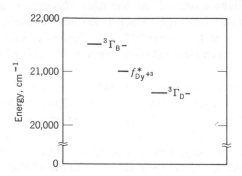

Fig. 4-3.   Energy levels in dysprosium(III) chelates with dibenzoylmethane (HD) and benzoylacetone (HB).

It has been established that intermolecular energy transfer can excite the luminescence of rare earth ions. When solutions of tris(hexafluoroacetylacetonato)–Eu(III) (wavelength of maximum absorption for $\pi \rightarrow \pi^*$ at 314 mμ; lowest triplet for the chelated ligand just below 380 mμ) containing benzophenone (wavelength of maximum absorption for $n \rightarrow \pi^*$ at 380 mμ) were irradiated at 380 mμ, the intensity of the characteristic 615 mμ luminescence of Eu(III) increased (44).

Solutions of certain Eu(III)–(β-diketone) chelates show laser action (45–47). Interest in these species as liquid lasers has generated numerous studies of their luminescence properties by several groups (35,42,48–58).

Transition metal ion chelates are normally nonfluorescent. Most of these species are paramagnetic because of unfilled outer d subshells with unpaired electrons on the metallic ion; often the metallic ion is easily reduced. However, several examples of transition metal ion chelate fluorescence in solution have been reported.

Tetracyano-platinate(II) and bis(pyridyl) platinum(II) fluoresce weakly in solution (59). The emission spectrum of the former is a rather broad band (with shoulders); its general appearance is suggestive of a $\pi^* \rightarrow \pi$ transition. The species is diamagnetic [all platinum(II) complexes are] as expected from the large ligand field splitting caused by cyanide ion for a d^8 ion in a square–coplanar configuration (60–63).

Ruthenium(II) forms fluorescent chelates with 2,2'-bipyridine, 1,10-phenanthroline and some derivatives of these ligands. This observation was used to analytical advantage by Veening and Brandt who devised a fluorometric method for the quantitative determination of ruthenium in the presence of other platinum metals (28). These ligands produce a large ligand field splitting of the ruthenium d-orbitals: with the d^6 electronic configuration of Ru^{+2} and an octahedral arrangement of the ligands, a low-spin diamagnetic complex is formed (60). Although $\pi^* \rightarrow \pi$ emission might be anticipated, it was concluded by Paris and Brandt, on the basis of low temperature luminescence studies and assignment of absorption spectral bands, that excitation and emission were due to charge transfer $d-\pi^*$ transitions where the initial state for the emission step was the ligand π triplet (20,24).

Paris has pointed out that "charge transfer" fluorescence may be expected for (diamagnetic) transition metal ion chelates when the $d-\pi^*$ transition occurs at lower energy than any $d-d$ (ligand field) transition on the metallic ion—in other words, if the metallic ion is not too difficult to oxidize, and the ligand accepts electrons readily and produces large ligand field splitting (or the d-orbitals of the metallic ion are filled). Based on these considerations, he predicted and observed $\pi^* \rightarrow d$ fluorescence from Cu(I)–pyridine complexes (24).

Luminescence from transition metal ion chelates with partially filled d-orbitals arising from a mechanism similar to that described for most rare earth ion chelates has been reported (21,64–66). In these systems intramolecular energy transfer from the ligand excites d levels of the transition metal ion; $d^* \rightarrow d$ transitions follow accompanied by emission of a narrow-band luminescence.

Because the outer electron shell is partially occupied, the energies of the f-levels of a chelated rare earth ion are only slightly affected by the presence of the ligand. Similarly, the energy of the π states of a ligand do not vary greatly among chelates with various rare earth ions (18). Therefore, the position of molecular (ligand) phosphorescence and (metal) "line" spectral bands can be predicted with fairly good accuracy in these systems.

The situation is much more complicated for transition metal ion chelates for several reasons. The ligand field splitting of the (outer) d-orbitals of the metallic ion depends on the nature of the ligand (origin of the spectrochemical series) (61,62). Moreover, d orbitals are capable of considerable interaction with the ligand (π bonding) which also affects not only the ligand field splitting (energy spacing between d orbitals), but also the energies of the ligand π orbitals (62,67). Therefore, the location of spectral bands (molecular phosphorescence of the ligand and $d^* \rightarrow d$ "lines" of the metallic ion) cannot easily be predicted with good accuracy. In a series of Cr(III) chelates, Forster reported the $d^* \rightarrow d$ bands ($^2E \rightarrow {}^4A_2$) at 665 mμ for the ethylenediamine chelate (no π bonding) and at 830 mμ for the strongly π-bonding dibenzoylmethane chelate (21). Interaction between d-orbitals of the chelated transition metal ion and π orbitals of the ligand also introduces some molecular character into the d orbitals. As a result, spectral band widths for $d^* \rightarrow d$ transitions will usually be greater than those observed with $f^* \rightarrow f$ transitions in rare earth chelate systems.

Halide complexes of Tl(I), Sn(II), and Pb(II) fluoresce in solution (68). Results of recent studies of thallous halide complexes suggest that a charge transfer electronic transition from the halide ion to the metallic ion occurs on absorption and the reverse charge transfer transition is responsible for the fluorescence (69).

V. Applications

Although very useful in certain cases, e.g., the accurate determination of trace amounts of some elements, spectrofluorometry lacks the wide range of analytical application to inorganic systems enjoyed by certain other techniques and by spectrofluorometry for the analysis of organic species. One reason for this is the close proximity of the broad emission bands from chelates of a given ligand with various metallic ions. This high degree of emission overlap precludes, in most cases, the accurate simultaneous determination without prior separation of the metallic ions which form fluorescent chelates. However, it is possible to utilize analytically the more pronounced differences in the fluorescence efficiency of chelates of different metallic ions with a given ligand. Collat and Rogers adapted the approximately threefold difference in the "excitability" of aluminum and gallium 8-quinolinol chelates to develop a procedure for their simultaneous fluorometric determination in a mixture (70).

The other major limitation to more widespread use of fluorometry in inorganic analysis stems from the failure of most transition metal ions to form fluorescent metal chelates.   This behavior, however, may be viewed as an advantage in terms of avoiding interference by the chelates of transition metal ions in the fluorometric determination of other metals.

Full development of an analytical technique includes the exploitation of the method for solving chemical problems other than the accurate determination of amounts of various species.   In this area, too, the luminescence of metal chelate compounds has not been fully utilized.

White and Freeman (26) used spectrofluorometric data obtained in kinetic and continuous variation studies to establish the stoichiometry of several o,o'-dihydroxyazobenzene chelates and to determine their stability constants.   White and Argauer (71) described a method based on differences in absorption and excitation spectra for evaluating formation constants of a metal chelate compound in systems containing a single fluorescent complex.   Fletcher and Milkey (72) studied the fluorescence of the thorium–morin system and presented a general equation relating fluorescence intensity to the concentrations of the metallic ion, ligand, and complex, assuming that each may fluoresce.   Recently the structure, stability, and reactivity of some chelates of the 8-quinolinol family in absolute ethanol have been investigated using spectrofluorometry to considerable advantage as a supplement to spectrophotometry and potentiometry (73–76).

In the latter studies, fluorescence intensity, wavelength of maximum emission, absorbance at selected wavelengths, and pH have been measured on solutions containing the metallic ion, ligand, and base or acid.   Conventional experimental design has been used, e.g., mole ratio studies, continuous variations, and Calvin-Wilson titrations (77,78).   In general, the fluorescence emitted by the lower 8-quinolinol chelates was more intense and appeared at shorter wavelength than the emission from higher complexes, Table 4-4.   Lower complexes generally exist in polynuclear forms in absolute ethanol.   In the Zn^{++}–(2-methyl-8-quinolinol) system, the 1:1 complex was shown to exist in two acid-forms:

$$[Zn(ROH)_2L]^+ \quad \text{and} \quad [Zn(ROH)(RO)L]$$

TABLE 4-4

Fluorescence Characteristics of Some Metal Chelates of 8-Quinolinol (HQ)
and 2-Methyl-8-Quinolinol (HL) in Absolute Ethanol Solution

Species	λ_{max} for fluorescence, $m\mu$	Relative fluorescence intensity
AlQ, neutral form	508	32
AlQ$_3$	512	20
InL	520	24
InL$_3$	530	5
ZnL, neutral form	500	23
ZnL, acid form	530	9
ZnL$_2$	530	7

where $R = C_2H_5$ and $L = $ 2-methyl-8-quinolinolate ion. These
species have almost identical absorption characteristics as expected
because the (solvated) metallic ion has little effect on the energies of
the π states of the ligand. However, the fluorescence emitted by
these two forms of the 1:1 chelate is markedly different in intensity.
This, too, is not surprising because the efficiencies of the various
energy transfer steps from the excited π state of the chelate are very
dependent on the metallic ion and on its environment.

A recent study of aluminum–(8-quinolinol) chelates in absolute
ethanol (SH) has established the existence of 1:1 and 2:1 complexes,
each existing in two acid-forms, the latter also in polynuclear (I) and
mononuclear (II) forms.

(I)   (II)

The mononuclear acid-form of the 2:1 complex is intensely fluorescent, thermodynamically stable, and labile to the addition of a third
ligand when neutralized; its polynuclear counterpart is less intensely
fluorescent, inert to depolymerization, and will not add a third ligand
when neutralized (79).

Further use of spectrofluorometry in the study of the structure, stability, and reactivity of certain chelates promises to provide considerable valuable information not readily accessible by the more commonly used techniques.   One advantage to using spectrofluorometry for this purpose is its utility in nonaqueous solvents where many techniques, e.g., potentiometry, do not yield reliable quantitative data (80).   Another advantage is the sensitivity of the fluorescence characteristics of a species to certain structural and environmental changes in or near the fluorophore; other techniques, e.g., spectrophotometry, are often insensitive to such modifications, as illustrated in the Zn–(2-methyl-8-quinolinol) system.

This work was supported in part by the Department of Chemistry, University of Rhode Island, and by the U. S. Atomic Energy Commission under Contract AT(30–1)–905.

References

1. C. E. White, "Fluorometry," in J. H. Yoe and H. J. Koch, Jr., Eds., *Trace Analysis*, Wiley, New York, 1957, Chap. 7.
2. A. Weissler and C. E. White, "Fluorescence Analysis," in L. Meites, Ed., *Handbook of Analytical Chemistry*, McGraw-Hill, New York, 1963, pp. 6–176 ff.
3. C. A. Parker, and W. T. Rees, *Analyst*, *87*, 83 (1962).
4. C. E. White and A. Weissler, *Anal. Chem.*, *36*, 116R (1964); *34*, 81R (1962).
5. C. E. White, *Anal. Chem.*, *32*, 47R (1960); *30*, 729 (1958); *28*, 621 (1956); *26*, 129 (1954); *24*, 85 (1952); *22*, 69 (1950); *21*, 104 (1949).
6. H. H. Willard and C. A. Horton, *Anal. Chem.*, *24*, 862 (1952).
7. C. G. Peattie and L. B. Rogers, *Spectrochim. Acta*, *9*, 307 (1957).
8. D. M. Hercules, "Theory of Luminescence Processes," in D. M. Hercules, Ed., *Fluorescence and Phosphorescence Analysis*, Interscience, New York, 1966, Chap. 1.
9. M. Kasha, *Radiation Res. Suppl.*, *2*, 243 (1960).
10. M. Kasha, *Discussions Faraday Soc.*, *9*, 14 (1950).
11. J. B. Allison and R. S. Becker, *J. Chem. Phys.*, *32*, 1410 (1960).
12. P. Yuster and S. I. Weissman, *J. Chem. Phys.*, *17*, 1182 (1949).
13. S. P. McGlynn, J. Daigre, and F. J. Smith, *J. Chem. Phys.*, *39*, 675 (1963).
14. S. P. McGlynn, M. J. Reynolds, G. W. Daigre, and N. D. Christodouleas, *J. Phys. Chem.*, *66*, 2499 (1962).
15. M. Kasha, *J. Chem. Phys.*, *20*, 71 (1952).
16. F. Halverson, J. S. Brinen, and J. R. Leto, *J. Chem. Phys.*, *41*, 157 (1964).
17. J. L. Kropp and M. W. Windsor, *J. Chem. Phys.*, *39*, 2769 (1963).
18. G. A. Crosby, R. E. Whan, and R. M. Alire, *J. Chem. Phys.*, *34*, 743 (1961).
19. S. I. Weissman, *J. Chem. Phys.*, *10*, 214 (1942).
20. J. P. Paris and W. W. Brandt, *J. Am. Chem. Soc.*, *81*, 5001 (1959).

21. K. De Armond and L. S. Forster, *Spectrochim. Acta, 19,* 1403 (1963).
22. A. V. Karyakin and Y. I. Kalenichencho, *Dokl. Akad. Nauk SSSR, 66,* 191 (1949); through *Chem. Abstr., 43,* 6085h (1949).
23. M. Kasha and S. P. McGlynn, *Ann. Rev. Phys. Chem., 7,* 415 (1956).
24. J. P. Paris, *Studies on Molecular Electronic Transitions,* Ph.D. Thesis, Purdue University 1960, University Microfilms Inc., Ann Arbor, Mich., Mic. 60-4199, pp. 76–120.
25. O. Popovych and L. B. Rogers, *Spectrochim. Acta, 16,* 49 (1960).
26. D. C. Freeman, Jr. and C. E. White, *J. Am. Chem. Soc., 78,* 2678 (1956).
27. R. J. Argauer and C. E. White, *Anal. Chem., 36,* 2141 (1964).
28. H. Veening and W. W. Brandt, *Anal. Chem., 32,* 1426 (1960).
29. O. Popovych and L. B. Rogers, *Spectrochim. Acta, 15,* 584 (1959).
30. H. M. Stevens, *Anal. Chim. Acta, 20,* 389 (1959).
31. W. E. Ohnesorge and L. B. Rogers, *Spectrochim. Acta, 14,* 27 (1959).
32. V. A. Fassel and R. H. Heidel, *Anal. Chem., 26,* 1134 (1954).
33. P. Pringsheim, *Fluorescence and Phosphorescence,* Interscience, New York, 1949, pp. 458–480.
34. G. A. Crosby and R. E. Whan, *J. Phys. Chem., 66,* 2493 (1962).
35. G. A. Crosby and R. E. Whan, *J. Mol. Spectry., 8,* 315 (1962).
36. G. A. Crosby and R. E. Whan, *J. Chem. Phys., 36,* 863 (1962).
37. J. J. Freeman and G. A. Crosby, *J. Phys. Chem., 67,* 2717 (1963).
38. G. A. Crosby and R. E. Whan, *J. Chem. Phys., 32,* 614 (1960).
39. G. A. Crosby and R. E. Whan, *Naturwiss., 47,* 276 (1960).
40. G. A. Crosby and M. Kasha, *Spectrochim. Acta, 10,* 377 (1958).
41. R. E. Whan, *Dissertation,* University of New Mexico, 1961.
42. H. Samelson, A. Lempicki, and C. Brecher, *J. Chem. Phys., 40,* 2553 (1964).
43. R. Tomaschek, *Reichsper. Physik., 1,* 139 (1944); through P. Pringsheim, *Fluorescence and Phosphorescence,* Interscience, New York, 1949, p. 288.
44. M. A. El-Sayed and M. L. Bhaumik, *J. Chem. Phys., 39,* 2391 (1963).
45. A. Lempicki and H. Samelson, *Phys. Rev. Letters, 4,* 133 (1963).
46. M. L. Bhaumik, P. C. Fletcher, L. J. Nugent, S. M. Lee, S. Higa, C. L. Telk, and M. Weinberg, *J. Phys. Chem., 68,* 1490 (1964).
47. E. J. Schimitschek, *Appl. Phys. Letters, 3,* 117 (1963).
48. E. J. Schimitschek and R. B. Nehrich, Jr., *J. Appl. Phys., 35,* 2786 (1964).
49. H. Samelson and A. Lempicki, *J. Chem. Phys., 39,* 110 (1963).
50. H. Samelson, A. Lempicki, V. A. Brophy, and C. Brecher, *J. Chem. Phys., 40,* 2547 (1964).
51. A. Lempicki, H. Samelson, and C. Brecher, *J. Chem. Phys., 41,* 1214 (1964).
52. L. J. Nugent, M. L. Bhaumik, S. George, and S. M. Lee, *J. Chem. Phys., 41,* 1305 (1964).
53. M. L. Bhaumik, H. Lyons, and P. C. Fletcher, *J. Chem. Phys., 38,* 568 (1963).
54. M. L. Bhaumik, *J. Chem. Phys., 40,* 3711 (1964).
55 M. L. Bhaumik and C. L. Telk, *J. Opt. Soc. Am., 54,* 1211 (1964).
56. R. A. Gudmundsen, O. J. Marsh, and E. Matovich, *J. Chem. Phys., 39,* 272 (1963).
57. H. Winston, O. Marsh, C. K. Suzuki, and C. L. Telk, *J. Chem. Phys., 39,* 267 (1963).

58. F. Halverson, J. S. Brinen, and J. R. Leto, *J. Chem. Phys.*, *40*, 2790 (1964).
59. P. Pringsheim, *Fluorescence and Phosphorescence*, Interscience, New York, 1949, p. 502.
60. F. A. Cotton and G. Wilkinson, *Advanced Inorganic Chemistry*, Interscience, New York, 1962, Chaps. 24, 25, 26, 29, 30.
61. L. E. Orgel, *An Introduction to Transition-Metal Chemistry*, Methuen, London, 1960.
62. C. K. Jorgensen, *Absorption Spectra and Chemical Bonding in Complexes*, Addison-Wesley, Reading, Mass., 1962.
63. J. Lewis and R. G. Wilkins, Eds., *Modern Coordination Chemistry*, Interscience, New York, 1960, Chaps. 1, 2, 4.
64. K. De Armond and L. S. Forster, *Spectrochim. Acta*, *19*, 1393 (1963).
65. K. De Armond, and L. S. Forster, *Spectrochim. Acta*, *19*, 1687 (1963).
66. K. K. Chatterjee and L. S. Forster, *Spectrochim. Acta*, *20*, 1603 (1964).
67. D. P. Craig, A. Maccoll, R. S. Nyholm, L. E. Orgel, and L. E. Sutton, *J. Chem. Soc.*, *1954*, 332.
68. P. Pringsheim, *Fluorescence and Phosphorescence*, Interscience New York, 1949, pp. 498–501.
69. R. E. Curtice, and A. B. Scott, *Inorg. Chem.*, *3*, 1383 (1964).
70. J. W. Collat and L. B. Rogers, *Anal. Chem.*, *27*, 961 (1955).
71. R. J. Argauer and C. E. White, *Spectrochim. Acta*, *20*, 1323 (1964).
72. R. G. Milkey and M. H. Fletcher, *J. Am. Chem. Soc.*, *79*, 5425 (1957).
73. W. E. Ohnesorge and A. Capotosto, Jr., *J. Inorg. Nucl. Chem.*, *24*, 829 (1962).
74. W. E. Ohnesorge and A. L. Burlingame, *Anal. Chem.*, *34*, 1086 (1962).
75. W. E. Ohnesorge, *Anal. Chem.*, *35*, 1137 (1963).
76. D. A. Carter and W. E. Ohnesorge, *Anal. Chem.*, *36*, 327 (1964).
77. F. J. C. Rossotti and H. Rossotti, *The Determination of Stability Constants*, McGraw-Hill, New York, 1961.
78. S. Fronaeus, "Determination of Formation Constants of Complexes," in H. B. Jonassen and A. Weissberger, Eds., *Technique of Inorganic Chemistry*, Vol. 1, Interscience, New York, 1963, Chap. 1.
79. W. E. Ohnesorge, unpublished results.
80. A. I. Popov, "Techniques with Non-Aqueous Solvents," in H. B. Jonassen and A. Weissberger, Eds., *Technique of Inorganic Chemistry*, Vol. 1, Interscience, New York, 1963, Chap. 2.

chapter 5

Analytical Uses of Phosphorescence

J. D. WINEFORDNER

Department of Chemistry, University of Florida,
Gainesville, Florida

I. Introduction

This chapter is concerned primarily with the use of phosphorescence as a means of quantitative analysis for organic molecules. The method is commonly called phosphorimetry. Because commercial equipment was lacking until recently and because phosphorimetry appears at first glance to be fairly complicated, few applications have been reported until the past few years. In addition, a very small number of phosphorescence emission and excitation spectra and lifetimes have been recorded in the literature. An additional difficulty is that many of the phosphorescence spectra recorded in the literature were obtained with samples in solvents which crack or form snows when cooled to the temperature of liquid nitrogen (77°K). The use of low temperature is specified by the lifetimes of the relevant excited states. Therefore, many analysts take the road of least resistance by applying a method for which fundamental data are already available. Certainly the method of phosphorimetry will not be used to any great extent until sufficient literature is available to indicate that the method can be relied upon to give accurate, precise, and rapid results on trace concentrations of species in the presence of possible contaminants.

This chapter will be divided into two sections. In the first section, phosphorimetry will be compared with fluorimetry and absorptiometry as methods of quantitatively analyzing trace amounts of organic molecules. In the second section, phosphorescence research performed in three areas of application will be summarized. These include the analysis of trace concentrations of drugs and other organic molecules in biological fluids, the analysis of organic compounds of petrochemical interest, and the detection and estimation of organic compounds on paper and thin-layer chromatograms.

II. Comparison with Other Methods

A. MECHANISMS

In order to compare phosphorimetry with fluorimetry, it is necessary to recall briefly the mechanisms of phosphorescence and fluorescence.   Fluorescence occurs when a molecule undergoes a radiative transition from an excited singlet state to the ground state.   This process normally has a high transition probability and a short lifetime, i.e., about 10^{-8} s.   Phosphorescence occurs when a molecule undergoes a radiative transition from a triplet state to the ground state. In this process, the molecule reaches the triplet level by means of a nonradiative crossover from an excited singlet state, as discussed in Chapter 1.   The lifetime of phosphorescence is much longer than fluorescence, i.e., about 10^{-4} to 20 s.   In order to have a reasonable probability of observing a triplet–singlet transition, it is necessary to minimize collisional deactivation of molecules in the triplet state. Therefore, phosphorescence studies are generally performed by placing the sample in a rigid medium, which usually is an organic solvent such as EPA (ether:isopentane:ethanol in volume ratio of 5:5:2) or ethanol at a low temperature (77°K).   It is possible to measure phosphorescence emission in the absence of fluorescence emission and incident light scattering by means of a rotating shutter phosphoroscope which allows periodic excitation of the sample and periodic out-of-phase measurement of the luminescence.   On the other hand, fluorescence measurements are generally made at room temperature, which avoids interference from phosphorescence.   For a more thorough discussion of the general theory of phosphorescence and of the experimental requirements of phosphorimetry, see Chapters 1 and 2.

B. SENSITIVITY

Luminescence techniques in many cases will be considerably more sensitive than absorptiometric methods.   The limit of detection in any spectrometric technique is determined by the capability of the detection system to distinguish between the photodetector signal due to the sample and the photodetector noise signal due to the phototube shot effect, source flicker, electrometer noise, etc.   In absorptiometry, the detector noise is generally greater than in luminescence techniques due to the greater intensity reaching the detector. In addition, the detector must distinguish a small difference between two large signals. In fluorimetry and phosphorimetry, the detector must only be capable of detecting a signal over a generally small background signal and background noise. Therefore the sensitivity of luminescence methods is often 10–1000 times greater than the sensitivity of absorptiometric methods. Of course, if the luminescence quantum efficiency is extremely small, e.g., 0.001 or less, or if the instrument's source intensity in the region of absorption is not great, then the sensitivities obtained by absorption methods may exceed the sensitivities of luminescence techniques. However, even if the quantum efficiency is small, it may still be possible to obtain greater sensitivities by luminescence methods than by absorptiometry by using an intense, stable source of excitation.

C. Selectivity

Perhaps of even greater significance than sensitivity is the selectivity of analysis. Certainly it is well-known that many more types of molecules absorb than re-emit radiation. This factor means there will usually be fewer interferences when using any luminescence technique. However, in luminescence methods the analyst also has an additional parameter to enhance selectivity. He can choose to a degree the wavelength region over which the emission will be viewed and also the wavelength band for excitation. In absorptiometry, the analyst is limited to choosing only the wavelength region over which absorption occurs. If a dilute solution of a complex mixture is to be analyzed and if the components of interest luminesce with appreciable intensities, then a luminescence technique is often to be preferred. If a simple system is to be analyzed and if sensitivity is not the primary consideration, then the choice of an absorptiometric method may be advisable, because of the somewhat simpler experimental procedures involved in sample preparation and in instrument operation.

D. Accuracy, Precision, and Speed

The accuracy, precision, and speed of an absorptiometric, fluorimetric, or phosphorimetric analysis depend to a large extent on the number and kind of separation steps involved and the purity of chemical reagents used in the experimental procedure. These will generally be nearly the same for the three methods. Phosphorimetry should, however, be somewhat more selective than fluorimetry. In both methods, the analyst can choose to a certain extent the wavelength region best suited for excitation and the wavelength region over which emission is a maximum. In phosphorimetry, the analyst can also choose by relatively simple experimental techniques, the time phosphorescence emission will be measured after cutoff of excitation. This method permits one to differentiate between two molecules of different phosphorescence lifetimes and is called phosphoroscopic resolution. A variation of this technique, which will be described later in this Chapter, is the direct measurement of the logarithm of the output signal of the phototube. Since most organic molecules have a first order phosphorescence decay, a log intensity vs. time plot on a recorder allows differentiation between similar molecules having different phosphorescent lifetimes. Although similar techniques can be used in fluorimetry, the cost of the elaborate electronic equipment required is out of reach for most analytical chemists. Because most phosphorimetric measurements are performed on the native molecule whereas many fluorimetric measurements are made on a reaction product between the species of interest and an external reagent, phosphorimetry often is the more convenient of the two methods.

The sensitivity of analysis in many cases will be appreciably greater in phosphorimetry than in fluorimetry. Because in phosphorimetry one does not observe emission during excitation, it is possible to excite molecules with unfiltered radiation from the excitation source or at least with a wide wavelength band of radiation from an excitation–monochromator source combination. In fluorimetry, narrow slits are generally used to minimize scattering of exciting radiation by optical surfaces and by dust particles. The use of a rotating shutter (phosphoroscope) in phosphorimetry eliminates nearly all of the scattering problems so prevalent in fluorimetry. In addition many molecules which have small fluorescence quantum efficiencies often have large phosphorescence quantum efficiencies which often approach unity for samples at the temperature of liquid nitrogen. It should, therefore, be emphasized that phosphorimetry and fluorimetry many times are not competitive analytical methods but rather are complementary methods of analysis. For example, salicylic acid can be analyzed at low concentrations by fluorimetry but is very insensitive by phosphorimetry. On the other hand aspirin can be analyzed at low concentrations by phosphorimetry and is very insensitive by fluorimetry. The reversal of sensitivities is a well established phenomenon due to a reversal in magnitudes of the quantum efficiencies, as discussed in Chapter 1.

E. TEMPERATURE

Most fluorimetric measurements are made at room temperature because of the simplicity of instrumentation and the freedom from phosphorescence. However, the fluorescence intensity of some molecules is quite sensitive to changes in solution temperature. Because ambient temperature can vary, and because the source of excitation will often heat up the solution being analyzed (especially if the analysis requires considerable time), it is necessary to thermostat all solutions and sample cells prior to and during the measurements and to take all readings in a short period of time. In phosphorimetry, all measurements are taken with the sample thermostated at a low temperature, usually 77°K.

F. CONCENTRATION

The range of concentrations over which the analytical curve is linear is somewhat larger in phosphorimetry than in fluorimetry. McGlynn, Neely, and Neely (13) have also indicated this to be valid. A typical analytical curve for metycaine hydrochloride (24) is shown in Figure 5-1. The low concentration section of this curve is linear over a concentration range of about 10^3. The phosphorescence intensity in quanta/s over the linear range is given approximately (19) by the expression

$$I_p = 2.32g\phi_p a_m b C_M I^0$$

where ϕ_p is the quantum efficiency of phosphorescence (the number of quanta emitted by the phosphorescence process to the number of quanta absorbed in a unit time), a_m is the molar absorptivity coefficient of the absorbing species, b is the path length of the absorber, C_M is the molar concentration of the absorber, I^0 is the intensity of the exciting radiation in quanta/s, and g is a geometry factor. The lowest concentration detectable, therefore, will be decreased, the larger the parameters ϕ_p, I^0, a_m, and b.

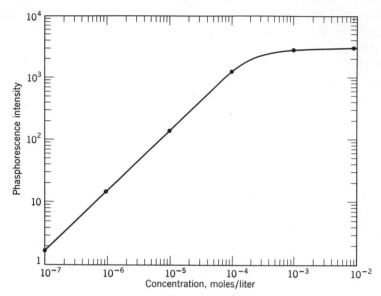

Fig. 5-1.   Typical analytical curve for phosphorescence
(Metycaine·HCl at 77°K).

G. Impurities

Perhaps the greatest limitation to obtaining even greater sensitivities in phosphorimetry is the presence of phosphorescent impurities in solvents and reagent grade chemicals and the pickup of phosphorescent impurities by adsorption on the sample cells and glassware used for analysis.   Solvents of high purity can be obtained commercially (Hartman-Leddon Co., Philadelphia, Pennsylvania) or can be prepared by using column distillation with a large reflux ratio (24).   Phosphorimetry is particularly limited by the lack of solvents which form clear, rigid glasses at 77°K.   Winefordner and St. John (23) made a thorough study of suitable solvents for low temperature spectral measurements.

H. Sample Tubes

Certainly the use of liquid nitrogen and small sample tubes, which are somewhat tedious to clean, fill, and empty, and the use of solvents (usually nonpolar) which must form clear, rigid glasses at 77°K are disadvantages in phosphorimetry when compared with most other methods. However, the great sensitivity, selectivity, and speed of analysis will, in many cases, completely outweigh these relatively minor limitations. The availability of a versatile, commercial spectrofluorimeter with phosphoroscope attachment, marketed by the American Instrument Co., Inc., Silver Spring, Maryland, has eliminated the necessity of constructing one's own instrument.

III. Applications of Phosphorimetry

The possibility of qualitatively identifying organic molecules by their phosphorescence spectra was first suggested by Lewis and Kasha (12) in 1944. In 1956, Freed and Salmre (5) used phosphorimetry for the analysis of trace concentrations of materials in biological fluids. In 1957, Keirs, Britt, and Wentworth (9) published an evaluation of phosphorimetry as a means of quantitative analysis. They demonstrated the potential value of this method by analyzing synthetic mixtures of two or three components by suitable choice of excitation wavelength, of wavelength over which emission is observed, of observation time after cutoff of the exciting radiation, or by any combination of the above. They analyzed several complex mixtures in a short time. The same analyses using other methods would require time consuming physical separation of components before an accurate analysis could be performed. On the basis of this excellent work, Aminco developed their instrument for phosphorimetric studies.

In 1959, Holzbecher (8) reviewed the principles of phosphorimetry, compared phosphorimetry with fluorimetry, and indicated the possibility of applying phosphorimetry to the quantitative analysis of components. In 1962, Parker and Hatchard (16) described the construction of a spectrophosphorimeter from a spectrofluorimeter. Using this instrument (15,16), fluorescence to phosphorescence ratios as low as 10^{-5} could be measured. Several organic molecules were also studied, and a sensitivity of the order of 0.03 $\mu g/ml$ for anthraquinone was reported. Because of the inconvenience of making phosphorescence measurements with their instrument, they recommend the use of spectrofluorimetry at room temperature unless the sensitivity was insufficient. Winefordner and Latz (21) described the construction of a spectrophosphorimeter. In their instrument, unfiltered radiation from a 150 W mercury arc was used for excitation, and a rotating can phosphoroscope was used for observation of the phosphorescence.

A. TRACE CONCENTRATIONS OF ORGANIC MOLECULES OF INTEREST TO BIOCHEMISTRY

Just as in fluorimetry (19), the greatest number of applications in phosphorimetry have been found in the areas of biology and medicine. Winefordner and Latz (21) investigated the possibility of applying phosphorimetry to the trace analysis of drugs in blood and urine. Latz (10) showed that the small background phosphorescence of the EPA solution of the residue resulting from evaporating the chloroform extract of acidified blood serum or plasma was primarily a result of tryptophan, and that the other constituents normally present in blood exhibited little phosphorescence. Therefore, phosphorimetry is of little use for the analysis of any of the constituents normally present in blood due either to their low solubility in chloroform or to their weak phosphorescence or to both. However, phosphorimetry may have some general use as a rapid means of characterizing normal blood serum or plasma. The low phosphorescence background of blood is a fortunate circumstance because this allows accurate measurement of trace concentrations of a variety of drugs.

Latz (10) studied the phosphorescence emission spectra of a number of sulfa drugs and found intense, nearly identical spectra for all of them. He obtained somewhat poorer sensitivities for several alkaloids, namely, atropine, homatropine, and codeine, but great sensitivities for several analgesics, e.g., aspirin, phenacetin, and caffeine. Winefordner and Latz (21) developed a method for the rapid, accurate analysis of aspirin in blood serum and plasma. Fortunately salicylic acid, the only metabolic product of aspirin which will phosphoresce, is nearly 500 times less sensitive than aspirin. In this method, the blood sample was acidified and extracted with chloroform, the chloroform extract was rapidly evaporated using a stream of dry nitrogen gas, the resulting residue was dissolved in EPA, and the aspirin concentration was measured phosphorimetrically. Aspirin concentrations of 2–100 mg/100 ml of blood serum were analyzed in 10 min with relative errors of less than ±10%. The limiting detectable concentration was about 0.2 mg of aspirin/100 ml of blood serum.

Latz (10) also studied the phosphorescence of the EPA solution resulting from the residue of a chloroform extraction of urine. He found that the phosphorescence intensity was extremely dependent on pH of the urine during extraction. As the pH of the urine was increased, the resulting phosphorescence background decreased from a large value down to a value of the same magnitude as that resulting from extraction of acidified blood serum. The analysis of hippuric acid by a technique similar to the aspirin analysis was unsuccessful because of the large variable background resulting from acidified urine.

Winefordner and Tin (24) give the phosphorescence excitation and emission spectral peaks, the phosphorescence lifetimes, the analytical curves and the limits of detection of 23 organic compounds of pharmacological importance. All phosphorimetric measurements were performed in rigid ethanolic solutions at 77°K and were made using the Aminco instrument. High-purity ethanol was used in these studies and was prepared by means of a distillation column having a reflux ratio of 20:1. Ethanol was used because it was a much better solvent for most drugs than EPA and because it usually formed a clear, rigid glass at 77°K (23). Limiting detectable concentrations of about 0.01 μg of drug/ml of ethanol were obtained for most of the drugs studied.

Winefordner and Tin (25) also analyzed for low concentrations of procaine, cocaine, phenobarbital, and chlorpromazine in blood serum and cocaine and atropine in urine. Each drug was extracted from the biological fluid at a high pH using chloroform or ether, the solvent used for extraction was evaporated using a rotary evaporator and the resulting residue was dissolved in EPA and measured phosphorimetrically. Again the Aminco instrument was used. The time for each analysis was only 30 min and recoveries of 100 $\pm$ 6% and relative standard deviations of 2–5% were obtained for most drugs. The sensitivities obtained were as low as or considerably lower than those obtained using other methods.

Freed and co-workers (5,6) were the first to use phosphorimetry as a means of chemical analysis of biological materials. For their studies, a Bequerel type phosphoroscope was used. Freed and Salmre (5) in 1956 studied the phosphorescence spectra of indole, tryptophan, serotonin, and reserpine, and obtained sensitivities better than those obtained by fluorimetry. Freed and Vise (6) in 1963 described the construction of a spectrophosphorimeter which was used to determine phosphorescence excitation and emission spectra of N-acetyl-L-tyrosine ethyl ester, which gave the tyrosine emission, and the enzyme α-chymotrypsin, which gave the tryptophan emission. The solvent system $H_2O:MeOH:EtOH$ in the volume ratio of $5:11:4$ was used for all studies.   To obtain reproducible results at 113°K, chips of fused silica were added to the sample tubes.   Benzyl alcohol was used as the internal standard for all measurements.   The chief limitation of all their measurements was the purity of the solvent, which resulted in a limit of reproducibility of ±0.1 $\mu g/ml$ for N-acetyl-L-tyrosine ethyl ester.

B. ORGANIC COMPOUNDS ON PAPER AND ON THIN-LAYER CHROMATOGRAMS

Winefordner and Moye (22) recently analyzed a number of tobacco samples for the three major alkaloids, nicotine, nornicotine, and anabasine.   In this method, the sample was ground and extracted with chloroform and a portion of the chloroform extract was separated using thin layer chromatography.   Each of the alkaloids was completely removed from the alumina thin-layer by scraping the spot into a container and dissolving in a solvent containing ethanol and sulfuric acid.   A small volume of the resulting ethanol solution was then measured phosphorimetrically using the Aminco instrument. The phosphorescence background due to the alumina thin-layer was small and constant, and was due to impurities in the chromatographic solvent.   Excellent recoveries of small amounts of tobacco alkaloids were obtained, e.g., 90–100% recovery on μg quantities.   Relative standard deviations for each alkaloid were less than 6%, and the time for a complete analysis of the three alkaloids in a commercial tobacco sample was less than 90 min, which is considerably less than by other methods previously used.

In all of the studies performed by Winefordner and co-workers (except those of Latz who used a standard aspirin solution), a standard solution of toluene was used prior to all measurements for calibration of the photometer circuit to assure the same sensitivity from day to day.   Also, all emission and excitation curves listed in their papers are uncorrected for instrumental factors.   Most analysts will find the uncorrected curves of more use than the corrected ones.   However, if one is interested in correcting spectra for instrumental characteristics (1,3,15,20), Chapter 2 should be consulted.

Recently, several other studies have been initiated or completed at the University of Florida. Moye has developed an accurate, sensitive method for the analysis of trace amounts of p-nitrophenol, the metabolic product of parathion, in urine. In this method, a urine sample, after boiling, is extracted with ether and the extract is applied to a thin layer of silica gel. The chromatogram is developed, the spot dissolved in ethanol, and the ethanol solution phosphorimetrically analyzed. The entire determination requires only 20 min, has relative errors of less than $\pm 5\%$, and concentrations of p-nitrophenol in ethanol as low as 0.0001 μg/ml can be detected. McCarthy has developed a rapid, simple, and sensitive method for the analysis of trace concentrations of biphenyl in fresh orange juice or orange juice concentrate. In this method, the orange juice is extracted with ether, the extract is applied to an alumina thin-layer and developed and the spot corresponding to biphenyl is removed and analyzed by phosphorimetry. Results with relative errors of less than $\pm 10\%$ are obtained in only 30 min. Concentrations of biphenyl in ethanol as low as 0.001 μg/ml can be determined. St. John is using the method of phosphoroscopic resolution to analyze simultaneously mixtures of tryptophan and tyrosine in the presence of phenylalanine in small amounts of various hydrolyzed proteins. The method being used is based on theory developed in radiochemical analysis. Because most organic phosphors decay exponentially after cutoff of the exciting radiation, a plot of the logarithm of the phosphorescence intensity signal vs. time after shutoff should result in an approximately linear region corresponding to each of the spectral components. This, of course, assumes that the organic species differ by approximately a factor of 10 in their decay times, and that the concentrations of these species are about equal.

A plot of the logarithm of the total phosphorescence intensity vs. time is shown in Figure 5-2 for a two-component system containing species F (the faster-decaying component) and S (the slower-decaying component). At sufficiently long times after cutoff of the exciting radiation, the contribution of component F to the total phosphorescence intensity will be negligibly small, and the measured value will be determined only by S. Extrapolation of the second linear portion of the curve in Figure 5-2 to zero time gives the component of the initial phosphorescence intensity due to S, and is a measure of its concentration. The difference between the initial total phosphorescence intensity and the extrapolated value determined above

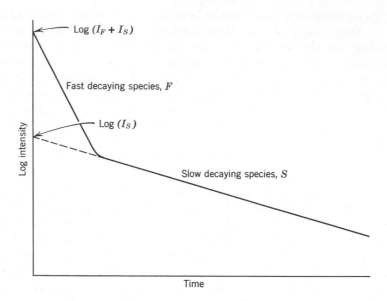

Fig. 5-2. Phosphorescence decay curve for a binary mixture.

is proportional to the concentration of F. This process can be repeated for several components so long as the T's differ sufficiently. An Aminco instrument can be used by amplifying the recorder output and feeding the amplified signal into a Moseley logarithmic converter and then into an x-y recorder. This technique should be quite valuable in terms of saving time for many other complex mixture analyses where a time consuming physical separation is normally required.

C. Analysis of Organic Compounds of Interest in Petrochemistry

Several articles have been written concerning the analysis of organic molecules of interest in petroleum chemistry. McGlynn, Neely, and Neely (13) in 1963, using the Aminco instrument, measured the low temperature fluorescence and phosphorescence emission and excitation spectra, analytical curves and limits of detection, and phosphorescence lifetimes of naphthalene, phenanthrene, and 1,2,4,5-tetramethylbenzene. They obtained good results for the individual molecules but fairly poor results for a mixture of the three. The limit of detection was about 1 μg of each/ml of EPA. They found that phosphorimetry was of comparable sensitivity to fluorimetry and could be used at higher concentrations due to less self-absorption. Drushel and Sommers (2) in 1964 determined phosphorimetrically and fluorimetrically several of the common polymer inhibitors in films. They used the Aminco spectrofluorimeter with phosphoroscope attachment and a special film holder which they constructed. They developed luminescence procedures for the direct analysis of some polymer inhibitors. Factors such as film thickness, concentration quenching, background absorption, and others which influence the linearity of the analytical working curves and the precision of measurements were studied. Muel and Lacroix (14) in 1960 analyzed 3,4-benzopyrene by phosphorimetry and obtained a limit of detection of 10^{-4} μg/cc. They had relative errors of the order of $\pm 10\%$. Lewis (11) in 1964 described the use of phosphorescence decay times and spectra to distinguish between crude oils from different geochemical environments.

IV. Limits of Detection

In Table 5-1, the available phosphorimetric limits of detection for a number of organic compounds analyzed using spectrophosphorimeters are given.

The detection of chromatographic spots has always been somewhat tedious. A method apparently developed by Szent-Gyorgyi (18) is based on observation of the low temperature fluorescence and phosphorescence when the chromatographic spot is placed under liquid nitrogen and excited with UV radiation. Several studies of this type have been published in recent years (4,7), but the most complete work along this line was performed by Sawicki and Johnson (17) in 1964, who tabulated the approximate visual phosphorimetric and fluorimetric detection limits and colors of about 200 organic compounds of interest in air-pollution studies. Many of the compounds studied were carcinogens, and so this study is also of great importance in the areas of biology and medicine. They describe several means of qualitatively differentiating between molecules but gave no accurate quantitative techniques. The techniques developed by Moye could probably be applied in this case in order to be able to analyze accurately small amounts of organic compounds of interest in air pollution studies.

Phosphorimetry is a rapid, sensitive, specific, and accurate method which should certainly find a place in the realm of analytical methods. There is certainly a growing need in modern chemistry for trace analysis and the tools to accomplish them. It is hoped that new applications of phosphorimetry will be made as a result of this discussion.

TABLE 5-1

Phosphorimetric Limits of Detection[a]

Compound	Experimental		Limits of detection in ethanol or EPA, mg/ml	References
	Setup	Source		
Phenobarbital	Aminco	Xenon	0.1	24
Mebaral	"	"	0.01	24
Rutonal	"	"	0.02	24
Atropine	"	"	0.1	24
Benzocaine	"	"	0.007	24
Procaine	"	"	0.01	24
p-Aminobenzoic acid	"	"	0.004	24
Butacaine	"	"	0.05	24
Cyclaine	"	"	0.006	24
Metycaine	"	"	0.006	24
Benzoic acid	"	"	0.005	24
Cocaine	"	"	0.01	24
Quinidine	"	"	0.05	24
Quinine	"	"	0.04	24
Lidocaine	"	"	1.2	24
Caffeine	"	"	0.2	24
Ephedrine	"	"	0.2	24
Phenylephrine	"	"	0.01	24
Tronothane	"	"	0.02	24
Cinchophen	"	"	0.02	24
Physostigmine	"	"	0.03	24
Chlortetracycline	"	"	0.05	24
Chlorpromazine	"	"	0.03	25
Aspirin	Laboratory constructed	Mercury	0.1	10, 21
Phenacetin	"	"	0.2	10
Caffeine	"	"	1.0	10
Hippuric acid	"	"	0.1	10
Salicylic acid	"	"	50	10

(*Continued*)

TABLE 5-1 (*continued*)

Phosphorimetric Limits of Detection[a]

Compound	Experimental		Limits of detection in ethanol or EPA, mg/ml	References
	Setup	Source		
Biphenyl	Aminco	"	0.001	b
p-Nitrophenol	"	Hg–Xenon	0.0001	b
Parathion	"	"	0.1	b
Nicotine	"	Xenon	1.0	22
Nornicotine	"	"	1.0	22
Anabasine	"	"	1.0	22
Tryptophan	"	Hg–Xenon	0.002	b
Tyrosine	"	"	0.01	b
Phenylalanine	"	"	0.4	b
Naphthalene	"	Xenon	0.7	13
Phenanthrene	"	"	1.0	13
1,2,4,5-Tetramethyl benzene	"	"	1.8	13
3,4-Benzopyrene	Laboratory constructed	Mercury	0.0001	14
N-acetyl-L-tyrosine ethyl ester	"	"	0.1	6
5,7-Dimethyl-1,2 benzacridine	Aminco	Hg–Xenon	0.2	b
1,2,5,6-Dibenz-anthracene	"	"	0.03	b
1,2 Benzanthracene	"	"	0.2	b
2 Aminofluorene	"	"	0.01	b

[a] Only limits of detection obtained using a spectrometric system are included in the above table.   Sawicki and Johnson (17) give visual phosphorimetric limits of detection for about 200 organic compounds.

[b] Unpublished data obtained at the Department of Chemistry, University of Florida, Gainesville, Florida.

References

1. R. J. Argauer and C. E. White, *Anal. Chem.*, *36*, 3681 (1964).
2. H. V. Drushel and A. L. Sommers, *Anal. Chem.*, *36*, 836 (1964).
3. H. V. Drushel, A. L. Sommers, and R. C. Cox, *Anal. Chem.*, *35*, 2166 (1963).
4. J. Eisenbrand, *Parhm. Acta Helv.*, *39*, 232 (1964).
5. S. Freed and W. Salmre, *Science*, *128*, 1341 (1956).
6. S. Freed and M. H. Vise, *Anal. Biochem.*, *5*, 338 (1963).
7. M. P. Gordon and D. South, *J. Chromatog.*, *10*, 513 (1963).
8. Z. Holzbecher, *Chem. Listy*, *53*, 713 (1959).

9. R. J. Keirs, R. D. Britt, Jr., and W. E. Wentworth, *Anal. Chem.*, *29*, 202 (1957).
10. H. W. Latz, Ph.D. Thesis, University of Florida, June 1963.
11. R. Lewis, Talk No. 26 at 15th Mid-America Conference on Spectroscopy, Chicago, Illinois, June 1964.
12. G. N. Lewis and M. Kasha, *J. Am. Chem. Soc.*, *66*, 2100 (1944).
13. S. P. McGlynn, B. T. Neely, and W. C. Neely, *Anal. Chem. Acta*, *28*, 472 (1963).
14. B. Muel and G. Lacroix, *Bull. Soc. Chim. France, 11/12*, 2139 (1960).
15. C. A. Parker, *Anal. Chem.*, *34*, 502 (1962).
16. C. A. Parker and C. G. Hatchard, *Analyst*, *87*, 664 (1962).
17. E. Sawicki and H. Johnson, *Microchem. J.*, *8*, 85 (1964).
18. A. Szent-Gyorgyi, *Science*, *126*, 757 (1957).
19. S. Udenfriend, *Fluorescence Assay in Biology and Medicine*, Academic Press, 1962.
20. C. E. White, M. Ho, and E. O. Weimer, *Anal. Chem.*, *32*, 438 (1960).
21. J. D. Winefordner and H. W. Latz, *Anal. Chem.*, *35*, 1517 (1963).
22. J. D. Winefordner and H. A. Moye, *Anal. Chim. Acta*, *32*, 278 (1965).
23. J. D. Winefordner and P. A. St. John, *Anal. Chem.*, *35*, 2211 (1963).
24. J. D. Winefordner and M. Tin, *Anal. Chim. Acta*, *31*, 239 (1964).
25. J. D. Winefordner and M. Tin, *Anal. Chim. Acta*, *32*, 64 (1965).

chapter 6

Chemiluminescence and Other Luminescence Processes

J. P. Paris

Radiation Physics Laboratory, Engineering Department,
E. I. du Pont de Nemours and Company, Wilmington, Delaware

I. Introduction

The field of chemiluminescence is rapidly gaining respect as a science, rather than as a laboratory curiosity. Understanding chemiluminescent phenomena requires a complete knowledge of reaction mechanisms, coupled with an analysis of the spectroscopic properties of the molecules involved in the reaction. The magnitude of the problem is well illustrated by the classic chemiluminescent reaction (Fig. 6-1) employed by fireflies for mating purposes.

II. Reaction Mechanisms

In general, the objective of all scientists studying chemiluminescence, bioluminescence, thermoluminescence, and electroluminescence is to isolate the one key step in the reaction mechanism which produces the excited state responsible for the observed emission. Four representative reactions, shown below in eqs. (6-1) to (6-4), fulfill the energy requirements to produce products in their excited states. The purpose of this paper is to review a number of luminescent reactions with particular emphasis on the excitation mechanism.

Excitation Produced by Chemical Reaction

$$R\cdot + R'\cdot \rightarrow R-R + h\nu \text{ (single bond formation)} \qquad (6\text{-}1)$$

$$\cdot R\cdot + \cdot R\cdot' \rightarrow R=R + h\nu \text{ (double bond formation)} \qquad (6\text{-}2)$$

$$RO_2 \xrightarrow{\Delta} \cdot R\cdot + O_2 \rightarrow R + h\nu \qquad (6\text{-}3)$$

$$R^+ + e^- \rightarrow R + h\nu \text{ (electron capture)} \qquad (6\text{-}4)$$

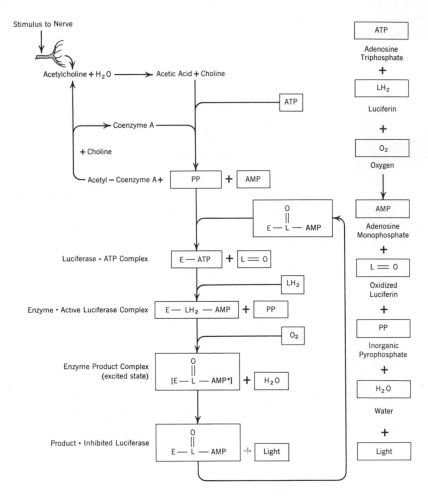

Fig. 6-1. Firefly flash is probably triggered by a nerve impulse delivered to the luminous gland.   A sequence of chemical reactions then produces light.   The substances consumed in the reaction, as shown in the summary at right, are adenosine triphosphate (ATP), luciferin (LH_2), and oxygen (O_2).   The products are oxidized luciferin (L=O), two phosphate compounds, water, and light.   The reaction is catalyzed by the enzyme luciferase, represented by E (1).

A. RADICAL–RADICAL REACTIONS

1. $NO + O \rightarrow NO_2 + h\nu$

Over a pressure range of 3–20 μ, Reeves et al. (2) have shown that the light emitting reaction of nitric oxide with oxygen atoms is second order. The major source of emission appears to be a simple reaction of the two components to produce excited NO_2.

2. $H + NO \rightarrow HNO + h\nu$

Clement and Ramsay (3) made a detailed spectroscopic investigation of the luminescent reaction of hydrogen and deuterium atoms with nitric oxide. From the sharp breaking-off in the K-rotational structure due to predissociation in the excited state, they set upper limits for the dissociation energies of HNO and DNO at 48.6 and 49.1 kcal/mole, respectively.

3. $2O_2 \xrightarrow{\text{electric discharge}} 2O_2(^1\Delta_g) \rightleftarrows O_4^* \rightarrow O_4 + h\nu$

The gas phase study on oxygen in an electric discharge by Arnold et al. (4) is particularly important because of its relationship to studies on oxygen producing reactions in solution. Emission peaks at 6340 and 7040 A. were assigned to emission from the O_4^* molecule, leaving O_4 in either the ground vibrational state or a one-quantum vibrationally excited state. A thorough examination of the reaction of chlorine with alkaline hydrogen peroxide, $Cl_2 + HO_2^- + OH^- \rightarrow 2Cl^- + H_2O + O_2$, by Browne and Ogryzlo (5) revealed the existence of several bands which were assigned to excited states of O_2 and O_4. Their assignments are given following the emission wavelengths:

$$12{,}700 \text{ A.}(O_2,\ ^1\Delta_g \ \leftrightarrow\ ^3\Sigma_g^- \ 0{,}0)$$
$$10{,}700 \text{ A.}(O_2,\ ^1\Delta_g \ \leftrightarrow\ ^3\Sigma_g^- \ 1{,}0)$$
$$8{,}645 \text{ A.}(O_2,\ ^1\Sigma_g^+ \ \leftrightarrow\ ^3\Sigma_g^- \ 0{,}1)$$
$$7{,}619 \text{ A.}(O_2,\ ^1\Sigma_g^+ \ \leftrightarrow\ ^3\Sigma_g^- \ 0{,}0)$$

and the 6334 and 7032 A. peaks assigned to O_4^* transitions as described above for gas phase O_4. It is notable that, since Mallet (6) discovered the red chemiluminescent emission from the reaction of hydrogen peroxide and sodium hypochlorite in 1927, the general reaction has been rediscovered twice and now appears to be almost understood.   Kahn and Kasha (7) suggest, alternatively, that the 6334 and 7032 A. bands may be due to solvated O_2^* states rather than O_4^*.

$$4.\ 2RO_2\cdot\ \rightarrow R_2 + O_4^* \rightarrow h\nu$$

Stauff et al. (8) have suggested a general reaction of peroxy radicals to generate excited O_4 molecules.   Alternatively, it should be possible to arrive at the O_4^* configuration by the following route:

$$2RO_2\cdot\ \rightarrow ROOR + O_2^*$$

$$2O_2^* \rightarrow O_4^*$$

Bowen and Lloyd (9) have also suggested that excited oxygen molecules are generated during the decomposition of organic peroxides.

5. Organic Oxidations → hν

Numerous examples of organic reactions have been reported in the literature to be weakly chemiluminescent.   In most all of these cases the yield of light is about 1 quanta for 10^6 molecules oxidized.   There are, however, exceptions in nature where certain bioluminescent reactions approach a quantum yield of one, based on the number of molecules oxidized.   A detailed commentary on most of these systems is not warranted as yet, because, in general, the excitation mechanisms are still open to question.

B. CARBENE REACTIONS

1.

Trozzolo, Murray, and Wasserman (10) noted the emission of triplet benzophenone during the warmup of a frozen solution of diphenylmethylene in the presence of oxygen.   Reactions of this type are of particular interest because of the very high energies localized at a single carbon atom.   Formation of a double bond with this carbon atom provides sufficient energy for electronic excitation to the first, second, and even higher excited states of the product.

$$2.\ 2CH_2 \rightarrow H_2C{=}CH_2 + h\nu$$

Photolysis of diazomethane at low temperature in an inert matrix is a convenient method of preparing methylene.   When Goldfarb and Pimentel (11) allowed methylene in solid argon to warm up, an orange–red luminescence was observed which correlated with the amount of ethylene produced.   Contrary to the diphenylmethylene system, no luminescence was observed when oxygen was introduced into the system.

Although dimerization of two methylene fragments is a plausible reaction mechanism for the excitation, the reaction of a methylene with an unphotolyzed diazomethane molecule to produce excited ethylene has not been ruled out (11).   The low energy transition from ethylene at 6030 A. is postulated to occur between two excited states of ethylene in a perpendicular configuration.   The quantum yield is estimated at 10^{-4}, based on ethylene production.

C. PEROXIDE DISSOCIATION

In 1926, Moureu, Dufraisse, and Butler (12) discovered that the photoperoxide of rubrene (5,6,11,12-tetraphenylnaphthacene) liberates its bound oxygen and produces light when heated.   This class of compounds (polynuclear aromatic hydrocarbon peroxides) has been referred to as photoperoxides because they are readily prepared by irradiation in a solvent, such as benzene, in the presence of oxygen. Since most chemiluminescent reactions involving oxygen generally cause marked structural changes, it is striking to see a nondestructive reversible reaction of this type.   Unfortunately, quantum yields are not yet available for this system.

Etienne and Bichet (13) found that photoperoxides of substituted anthracenes, e.g., 1,4-diethoxy-9,10-diphenylanthracene, behaved similarly to rubrene.   Under irradiation, in solution with oxygen, a bridged peroxide is formed, which when heated emits light characteristic of the fluorescence of the parent hydrocarbon.

D. ELECTRON TRANSFER REACTIONS

Electron transfer processes leading to luminescence include some areas of chemiluminescence, as well as most phenomena observed in thermoluminescence and electroluminescence processes.   The first requirement is that the electron approach the acceptor at an energy level equal to or greater than the first excited state of the system. Secondly, the excited system must be free from a strong quenching environment.

$$1. \ CdS \xrightarrow[\text{bombardment}]{\text{electron 20 keV}} CdS + \text{(positive hole)} + \text{(electron}$$
$$\text{in conduction band)} \rightarrow h\nu$$

Bombardment of a cadmium sulfide crystal with 20 keV electrons produces a high density of free carriers in the crystal.   Balkanski and Gans (14) observed that, at a given temperature, the shortest wavelength emission observed corresponds to the absorption edge of the spectrum.   Specifically, at room temperature there is a green emission at 5200 A., and at 77°K a blue band at 4900 A., which coincides with the shift in edge absorption between these temperatures.   They interpret this emission as a radiative recombination of a thermalized electron in the conduction band with a positive hole in the valence band.

$$2. \ GaAs \ (p\text{-}n \text{ junction}) \xrightarrow[\text{conduction}]{\text{electron}} h\nu$$

Probably the most perfect example of electron–hole recombination phenomena is found at the junction of certain p-n semiconductors. The discontinuity in energy states experienced by an electron passing over the junction is analogous to that for water making the rapid and violent trip over Niagara Falls. The energy of this transition is released as radiation in the case of the electron.

Nathan et al. (15) prepared GaAs p-n junctions by diffusing Zn into GaAs doped with Te. They observed an emission line at 1.47 eV with currents of 1 to 10^4 A/cm² which was interpreted as a transition between the conduction band and a Zn acceptor level. Remarkable quantum efficiencies (based on electrons injected) of close to 1 were obtained for currents greater than 10 A/cm².

3. $R + h\nu \rightleftarrows R^+ + e^-$ (solvated)

For organic molecules, the process of photoionization followed by recombination luminescence was first investigated by Lewis and co-workers (16,17). In general, an electron rich species, such as an aromatic amine, can be dissolved in a solvent making a transparent low temperature glass, e.g., EPA (ether, isopentane, alcohol mixture, 5:5:2 ratio), then photoionized with ultraviolet radiation at 77°K. As the temperature is allowed to rise, a burst of light is observed due to the recombination of the solvated electron with the positive ion.

Linschitz, Berry, and Schweitzer (18) identified the near infrared absorption of the solvated electrons produced by ultraviolet irradiation of potassium triphenylmethide, lithium diphenylmethide, and N-lithium carbazole in a 77°K glassy solvent of EPTM (ether, isopentane, triethylamine, methylamine, 2:3:3:2). This solvated electron spectrum disappeared on warming, as well as that of the ionized aromatic molecule. In their studies (18) on the recombination luminescence, only spectra corresponding to the normal phosphorescence of the molecule were observed. Similar experiments by Lim and Swenson (19) on acriflavine and Dolan and Albrecht (20) on N,N,N',N'-tetramethylparaphenylenediamine have shown that both fluorescence and phosphorescence can be observed for the electron recombination process.

In order to gain further insight into the energetics of the electron recombination mechanism, it is important to know the ratio of the fluorescence and phosphorescence yields. Assuming a statistical average in populating the available states, one would expect to form three times as many triplet states as singlets. The observable emission would then depend on the rate constants for intersystem crossing and radiationless conversion to the ground state.

Brocklehurst, Porter, and Yates (21) prepared photoionized solutions of naphthalene by γ-irradiation of a $10^{-2}M$ naphthalene solution in MP (methylcyclohexane–isopentane) at 77°K. The enhancement of phosphorescence to fluorescence yield by recombination processes amounts to a factor of 5 compared to the ratio observed for normal ultraviolet excitation of phosphorescence and fluorescence emission. This enhancement agrees very well with the calculated factor of 5.8 (21) assuming the recombination process favors direct triplet excitation over singlet excitation in a ratio of 3:1.

$$4.\ Ar^+ + Ar^- \rightarrow Ar + Ar^* \rightarrow h\nu$$

Since recombination luminescence occurs so efficiently in solid solutions at 77°K, it might also be expected to occur in solution at room temperature if the proper cation and anion are available for reaction. An ideal matching of energy levels occurs for the cation and anion of the same aromatic hydrocarbon (Ar). However, the experimental problem of having a solvent which can support both the anion and cation has seriously retarded a complete analysis of this reaction.

Hercules (22) has reported preliminary studies on chemiluminescence resulting from electrolysis of aromatic hydrocarbons, such as rubrene, in dimethylformamide. In these studies, using alternating current, emission was observed principally at the cathode, and appeared to require transport of the oxidized species to the cathode. Although the mechanism has not been positively assigned to a $+,-$ radical reaction, it is definitely a redox reaction of some type giving rise to the normal hydrocarbon fluorescence.

Studies by Chandross and Sonntag (23) have demonstrated a general chemiluminescent reaction of aromatic hydrocarbon radical anions with oxidizing agents. These include the reaction of the 9,10-diphenylanthracene mono-anion with benzoylperoxide, oxalyl chloride, mercuric chloride, and aluminum chloride. All of these reactions produce luminescence characteristic of the fluorescence spectrum of 9,10-diphenylanthracene. The suggested mechanism for this excitation process is that an electron in a bonding orbital of the 9,10-diphenylanthracene anion is transferred to the oxidizing agent leaving behind the excited state aromatic molecule.   Further studies are needed to establish definitively whether direct excitation is always observed or if an energy transfer step is required for excitation.

References

1. W. D. McElroy and H. H. Seliger, *Sci. Am.*, *207*, 82 (1962).
2. R. R. Reeves, P. Harteck, and W. H. Chace, *J. Chem. Phys.*, *41*, 764 (1964).
3. M. J. Y. Clement and D. A. Ramsay, *Can. J. Phys.*, *39*, 205 (1961).
4. S. J. Arnold, E. A. Ogryzlo, and H. Witzke, *J. Chem. Phys.*, *40*, 1769 (1964).
5. R. J. Browne and E. A. Ogryzlo, *Proc. Chem. Soc.*, *1964*, 117.
6. L. Mallet, *Compt. Rend.*, *185*, 352 (1927).
7. A. V. Khan and M. Kasha, *Nature*, *204*, 241 (1964).
8. J. Stauff, H. Schmidkung, and G. Hartmann, *Nature*, *198*, 281 (1963).
9. E. J. Bowen and R. A. Lloyd, *Proc. Roy. Soc. London*, *275A*, 465 (1963).
10. A. M. Trozzolo, R. W. Murray, and E. Wasserman, *J. Am. Chem. Soc.*, *84*, 4990 (1962).
11. T. D. Goldfarb and G. C. Pimentel, *J. Chem. Phys.*, *33*, 105 (1960).
12. C. Moureu, C. Dufraisse, and C. L. Butler, *Compt. Rend.*, *183*, 101 (1926).
13. A. Etienne and G. Bichet, *Compt. Rend.*, *228*, 1134 (1949).
14. M. Balkanski and F. Gans, in H. P. Kallman and G. M Spruch, Eds., *Luminescence of Organic and Inorganic Materials*, Wiley, New York, 1962, p. 318.
15. M. I. Nathan, W. P. Dumke, G. Burns, F. H. Dill, Jr., and G. Lasher, *Appl. Phys. Letters*, *1*, 62 (1962).
16. G. N. Lewis and D. Lipkin, *J. Am. Chem. Soc.*, *64*, 2801 (1942).
17. G. N. Lewis and J. Bigeleisen, *J. Am. Chem. Soc.*, *65*, 520, 1144, 2419, 2424 (1943).
18. H. Linschitz, M. G. Berry, and D. Schweitzer, *J. Am. Chem. Soc.*, *76*, 5833 (1954).
19. E. C. Lim and G. W. Swenson, *J. Chem. Phys.*, *36*, 118 (1962).
20. E. Dolan and A. C. Albrecht, *J. Chem. Phys.*, *37*, 1149 (1962).
21. B. Brocklehurst, G. Porter, and J. M. Yates, *J. Phys. Chem.*, *68*, 203 (1964).
22. D. M. Hercules, *Science*, *145*, 808 (1964).
23. E. A. Chandross and F. I. Sonntag, *J. Am. Chem. Soc.*, *86*, 3179 (1964).

chapter 7

Fluorescence in Biomedical Research

B. L. Van Duuren

Institute of Environmental Medicine,
New York University Medical Center, New York, New York

I. Introduction

Fluorescence spectroscopy has, in recent years, become widely used in biomedical research. In this area, it has been used largely as an analytical tool for the assay of a host of materials of biological origin (1), in the examination of carcinogenic materials in our environment (2), in metabolic studies of aromatic hydrocarbon carcinogens (3), and for determining other fluorescent materials.

Since most of these analytical techniques and results have been adequately reviewed (1), this report will be concerned with the application of fluorescence spectroscopy to a few specific problems in biomedical research carried out in our laboratory. In this work, fluorescence spectroscopy plays a direct role in the examination and interpretation of fundamental phenomena of biological significance concerning the mode of action of chemical carcinogens and mutagens in solution.

The work described in this report was carried out with the use of a Farrand recording spectrofluorometer; all measurements were made at room temperature and fluorescence spectra are uncorrected.

II. The Binding of Dyes to Nucleic Acids

The first aspect to be discussed concerns the binding of acridine (structure 7-1) and acridine orange (2,8-dimethylaminoacridine, structure 7-2; AO) to various nucleic acids and to inorganic polyphosphates. In the discussion of this problem, reference will be made to *both absorption and fluorescence spectra* since they complement each other in the interpretation of the results.

195

7-1: Acridine, R= H
7-2: Acridine orange,
R = N(CH3)2

AO is widely used for the staining of biological tissues for fluorescence microscopic examination and is used in a screening procedure for cancerous tissue (4). The phenomenon responsible for its metachromatic effect is the aggregation of acridine orange which is accompanied by visible and fluorescence spectroscopic changes (5). Because of the known mutagenicity of the dye, the nature of its interaction with nucleic acids is of significance, and, although numerous studies have been carried out in this area (6), the exact nature of the binding is still not satisfactorily explained.

The present report concerns some findings on the fluorescence spectroscopic changes accompanying the binding of acridine orange and of the parent base acridine (structure 7-1) to polyanions, including nucleic acids and inorganic polyphosphates.

All binding studies were carried out at pH 6.7 in cacodylic acid–cacodylate buffer, or at pH 5 in acetate buffer; measurements were made at low ionic strength since this factor effects the nature of binding to nucleic acids.

Acridine orange shows, in dilute solution (below $10^{-5}M$), two bands in the visible absorption spectrum, one at 492 mμ and another as a shoulder at 464 mμ (Fig. 7-1). At high concentration (10^{-2} to $10^{-3}M$) a single band appears at 452 mμ. In the fluorescence emission, there is a shift to longer wavelength from 522 mμ at $10^{-5}M$ to 560 mμ at $10^{-3}M$. Quenching of fluorescence occurs above $10^{-5}M$ as the maximum of fluorescence shifts to longer wavelength.

When AO is bound to polyanions, it undergoes changes in spectra which are in some respects similar to that produced by aggregation and it has been proposed (7,8) that when bound to polymers the dye molecules undergo interaction with each other similar to aggregation. As increasing amounts of DNA are added to a dilute solution of AO, of which the final concentration is kept constant ($10^{-5}M$ or below), there is a decrease in the intensity of the 492 mμ band and an increase in the intensity of the 464 mμ band. When the ratio of AO molecules

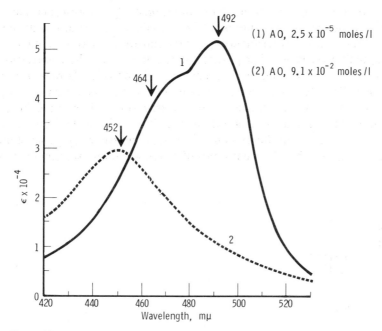

Fig. 7-1. Absorption spectra of acridine orange: curve 1, $2 \times 10^{-5}M$; curve 2, $9.1 \times 10^{-2}M$.

to binding sites (as adenosine monophosphate units) reaches one to one, the 464 mμ band reaches a maximum. After this 1:1 point, further addition of DNA results in a second reversal of the band maxima. If one plots the optical density of the 492 mμ band vs. increasing amounts of DNA, a titration curve is obtained, as shown in Figure 7-2. This curve was obtained using salmon sperm deoxyribonucleic acid (DNA) at pH 6.7.

This behavior has been interpreted to be due to stacking of AO cations on the DNA polymer at the phosphate anionic centers, i.e., there is stacking in cardpack fashion (7,8) and interaction between adjacent AO molecules, so that the absorption spectrum appears similar to that of the AO aggregate. In the presence of excess DNA there are a large number of available binding sites, so that the probability of stacking becomes small and hence the absorption spectrum appears unchanged from that of a dilute solution of AO in the absence

of nucleic acid.   That the true situation is not quite as simple as this
has become apparent from an examination of the fluorescence spectra.
When increasing amounts of DNA are added to a dilute solution of
AO in which the concentration is kept constant, there is a quenching
of the fluorescence.   The position of maximum quenching corresponds
to the 1:1 equivalence point as shown in Figure 7-3.   However, there,
is no shift in the fluorescence emission maximum to longer wavelength
which one would associate with aggregation.   The quenching of
fluorescence remains constant until a 2:1 ratio of DNA to AO is
reached before the fluorescence intensity increases again as shown.
This suggests that different kinds of AO interactions are involved, one

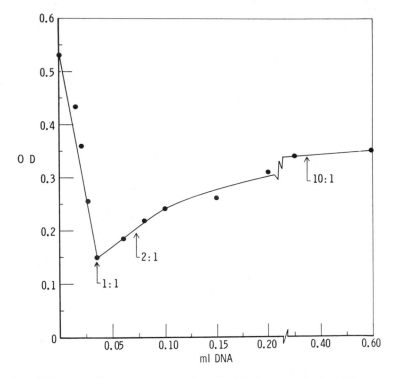

Fig. 7-2.   Titration curve: change in OD of 492 mμ band of acridine orange
upon addition of DNA at pH 6.7 in cacodylate buffer.   The desired amount of
DNA is added to 1 ml of $10^{-4}M$ AO (0.1 μM) and made up to 10 ml in buffer.
1.0 ml DNA = 2.85 μM as adenosine monophosphate units.

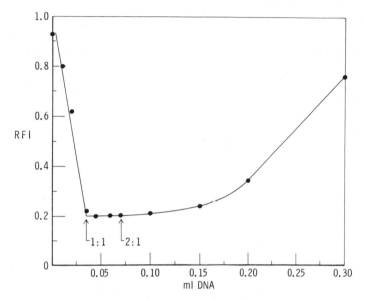

Fig. 7-3. Titration curve: quenching of fluorescence emission of acridine orange (530 mμ) upon addition of DNA. Same procedure and concentrations as given for Figure 7-2.

of which is apparent in both the fluorescence and absorption to the 1:1 ratio, and another which effects only the fluorescence.

In order to determine the significance, if any, of the dimethylamino functions of AO, the absorption and fluorescence changes accompanying the binding of the parent base, acridine, to DNA were also examined. Acridine does not aggregate but undergoes the expected concentration quenching of fluorescence. The binding of acridine to DNA paralleled very closely that of AO, and again there are no shifts in fluorescence emission upon binding. As in the case of AO, the quenching remained constant until a ratio 2:1 for polymer sites to acridine was reached, and beyond this point the fluorescence intensity increased again with further addition of DNA.

The spectra of mixtures of AO and mononucleotides were also examined in order to determine whether the binding *per se* was responsible for the observed spectral shifts. Deoxyadenylic acid and deoxycytidylic acid were chosen as representative purine and pyrimi-

dine nucleotides respectively.   AO $(10^{-5}M)$ was mixed with equi-
molar proportions of mononucleotides and up to a ratio of one AO to
1000 mononucleotide molecules.   No spectral changes were observed.
These results imply that only when there is interaction between AO
molecules bound to polymer do the fluorescence and absorption
changes occur.   However, the interactions are different from that of
free AO in the absence of polyanions.

In contrast to native DNA, which is a double-stranded helix,
polyadenylic acid is in the form of a single-stranded coil at pH 6.7,
and it is homogeneous with respect to the heterocyclic basic moiety
of adenine, so that it was of interest to examine the binding of AO to
this nucleic acid.   The binding experiments were carried out in the
same manner as that described for DNA.   The absorption spectra
showed the reversal of band intensities at the 1:1 equivalence point,
but did not revert back to the monomer spectrum upon further
addition of polymer as was the case with DNA.   Only when the
polymer–dye ratio reached 20:1 did the spectrum revert and the
492 mμ peak again appear as a maximum.   The fluorescence quenching curve parallels closely the changes in the absorption spectrum,
i.e., the 1:1 point is marked by the position of maximum quenching
after which it remains unchanged upon further addition of polyadenylic acid up to the 20:1 ratio, at which point the fluorescence
intensity increases again with further addition of polymer.   The
clearcut differences in binding patterns for DNA and polyadenylic
acid can be explained, at least in part, by the fact that polyadenylic
acid has a flexible coil structure at pH 6.7 whereas native DNA has
a rigid double-helical structure.

In an attempt to gain a clearer insight into the nature of the binding
described, spectral changes accompanying binding of AO to inorganic
phosphates were next examined.   The phosphates used are shown in
structures 7-3 to 7-6.   The first three of these, structures 7-3, 7-4, and
7-5, did not cause any spectral changes when mixed with AO in
various proportions and up to high ratios of phosphate to cation.
From this, one could conclude, assuming that in these small molecules
electrostatic binding occurs as it does in the polymers, that more than
3 or 4 adjacent AO molecules are required before the spectral changes
occur, i.e., the spectral changes are a characteristic of aggreagates
of AO molecules, bound to polymer.

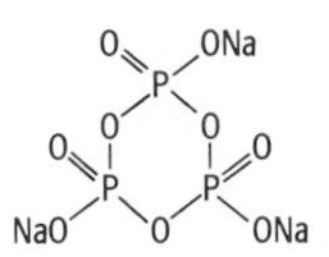

Sodium trimetaphosphate
7-3

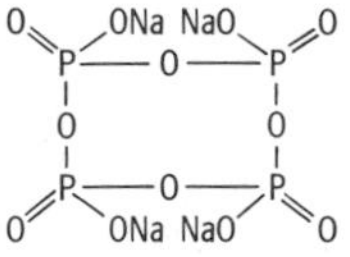

Sodium tetrametaphosphate
7-4

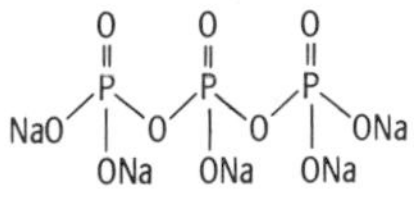

Sodium tripolyphosphate
7-5

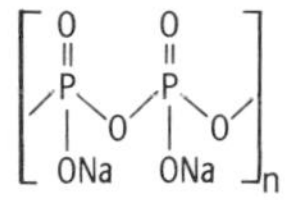

Glassy sodium polyphosphate
Sodium hexametaphosphate
7-6

The two inorganic polyphosphates examined both contain repeating phosphate units as shown in structure 7-6. These materials brought about fluorescence and absorption changes which were very similar to that found for the nucleic acids. Sodium hexametaphosphate, for example, showed the fluorescence quenching curve given in Figure 7-4. This polyphosphate is a mixture of polymers of various sizes and has an average chain length of twelve units as determined by end group titration. Because of the short chain length relative to the nucleic acids, binding at end groups will play a role in determining the ratios at which spectral changes occur. Nevertheless, the binding pattern is very much the same in its general features as that observed with the nucleic acids.

The quenching of fluorescence reaches a maximum at the point corresponding to 6:1 (anionic phosphate:AO) and remains constant at this level, which is one-fourth of the fluorescence intensity of free AO at the same concentration. At the 100:1 point, fluorescence intensity increases again but does not reach the maximum of fluorescence intensity until the ratio of anionic phosphate binding sites to dye has reached 3000 to 1. The changes in the absorption spectra parallel closely these fluorescence changes, as shown in Figure 7-5.

In an earlier study on the metachromatic effect of toluidine blue–sodium hexametaphosphate, Wiame (9) noted that the absorption changes occur at an 8:1 ratio of polymer to dye rather than at the equivalence point, which is similar to our findings with AO and sodium hexametaphosphate.

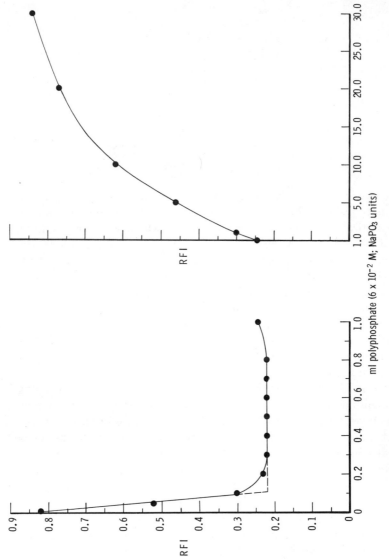

Fig. 7-4.   Titration curve: quenching of fluorescence emission of acridine orange upon addition of sodium hexametaphosphate at pH 6.7 in cacodylate buffer.   Same procedure as given for Figure 7-2.

In flexible structures such as the inorganic polyphosphates, one can visualize a random coil such that there is interaction between AO molecules which are remote from one another in terms of their positions on the polymer, but close to one another in space; this situation may arise because of the tendency of AO to aggregate. This will account for the fact that even in very high polymer-to-dye ratios there is still interaction between AO molecules.

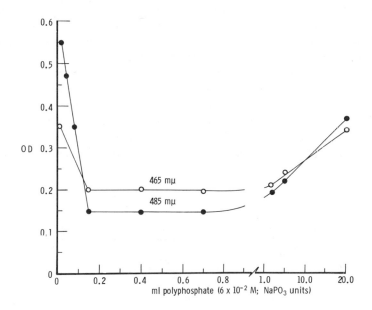

Fig. 7-5.   Titration curve: change in OD of acridine orange upon addition of sodium hexametaphosphate.   Same procedure as given for Figure 7-2.

Oster (10) originally suggested that the dye molecules become sandwiched between purine and pyrimidine bases and this attractive "intercalation theory" has recently received renewed support (11). However, as described here, similar binding patterns are obtained with inorganic polyphosphate where purine and pyrimidine bases are not involved.   Also, if intercalation of AO does occur in nucleic acids, one would expect spectral shifts resulting from interaction between AO and adjacent purine and pyrimidine bases. Such interactions are expected to result in shifts on the basis of the results described in the second half of this discussion.

The external electrostatic binding, as described by Bradley and Wolf (7) explains most of the spectroscopic observations without involving the intercalation theory. However, still to be explained on the Bradley and Wolf model of stacking is the lack of fluorescence spectral shifts associated with aggregation. Furthermore, AO alone undergoes fluorescence quenching at $10^{-3}M$ to only 1% of that of a $10^{-5}M$ solution; whereas, when bound, the quenching is never more than to 20% of the fluorescence without nucleic acid.

It is likely that in the dye aggregate in solution, the positive charges are opposed, as shown in Figure 7-6; whereas, when bound at the phosphate anionic sites, they are parallel. This will undoubtedly affect the nature of the interaction between adjacent AO molecules, resulting in quenching of fluorescence without shifts in fluorescence maxima. The fluorescence quenching and optical density patterns,

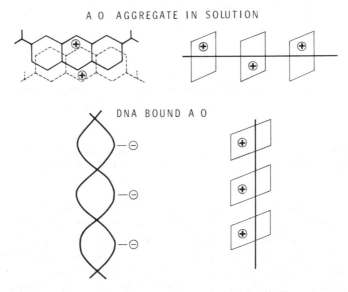

Fig. 7-6.   Orientation of acridine orange aggregate in solution and when bound to DNA.

in both AO bound to nucleic acids and AO bound to inorganic polyphosphates, indicate clearly that at least two types of AO–AO interactions are involved; in one type, both the ground and excited states are affected; in the second, only the excited state is affected.

III. The Fluorescence of Tetramethyluric Acid Complexes of Aromatic Hydrocarbons, Heterocyclics, and Related Compounds

Many attempts have been made to explain the forces of interaction responsible for the solubilization of aromatic hydrocarbons in aqueous medium by purines and nucleic acids (12–15).   An understanding of this phenomenon is of importance in learning about the mechanism of cancer induction by aromatic hydrocarbons, since it is possible that the initial interaction is a complex formation between the hydrocarbon and a vital cell constituent, such as the nucleic acids.   Several workers have examined the absorption spectroscopy of solutions containing these materials (12,14).   Minor shifts to long wavelength were observed in ultraviolet absorption maxima in the presence of 1,3,7,9-tetramethyluric acid (TMU) structure 7-7, or caffeine. Shifting of infrared absorption bands has also been reported, and it was suggested that the observed solubilization is due to complex formation.   X-ray studies of the crystal structure of the pyrene–tetramethyluric acid complex, in which the ratio of hydrocarbon to purine is 1:1, indicated an alternate stacking of pyrene and tetramethyluric acid molecules in the crystal (13).   Coronene and benzo(a)pyrene, on the other hand, form complexes in which the ratio of hydrocarbon to purine is one to two, but in their crystal structures the hydrocarbons are also sandwiched between the purines (13).

In dilute solution, these three hydrocarbon complexes do not show any shifts in fluorescence maxima.   Even in concentrated solutions, in the presence of an excess of TMU, benzo(a)pyrene and coronene show no shifts in their maxima; however, pyrene at high concentration

7-7

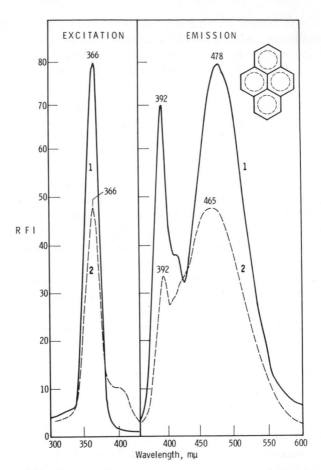

Fig. 7-7. Fluorescence spectra of pyrene and pyrene–TMU in solution: curve 1, pyrene, $0.89 \times 10^{-2}M$ in dioxane; curve 2, pyrene, $0.89 \times 10^{-2}M$ in presence of TMU, $4.0 \times 10^{-2}M$; excitation spectra with emission at 478 mμ for curve 1 and at 465 mμ for curve 2; emission spectra with excitation at 366 mμ for both curve 1 and curve 2; 5 mμ slits, no filters.

($10^{-2}M$ in dioxane) as shown in Figure 7-7 exhibits a shift of the excited dimer emission band to shorter wavelength in the presence of an excess of TMU ($4 \times 10^{-2}M$).   The excited dimer emission band of pyrene was shifted from 478 to 465 mμ.   Notably the monomer emission maximum remained unchanged at 392 mμ.   These findings suggested that the complex formation is a short-range effect and it was therefore desirable to examine these materials also in the crystalline state.

In an earlier report from this laboratory (16), a procedure for the measurement of the fluorescence spectra of aromatic hydrocarbons and their π-complexes in potassium bromide pellets was described. Some of the features of this method will be recalled before the spectra of the crystalline purine complexes are described.

In this method, potassium bromide pellets of the materials are prepared in the same manner as that used for infrared spectroscopy. The Farrand Optical Company constructed a special solid sample holder for use with the pellets.   In this salt medium, one can measure the fluorescence of solid solutions of the hydrocarbons or of the crystalline hydrocarbons dispersed in the salt, depending upon the concentration.

The effect of concentration on the fluorescence emission spectra of dibenz(a,h)anthracene is shown in Figure 7-8.   Curve 1 shows the fluorescence emission spectrum of dibenz(a,h)anthracene at high concentration; curve 2 shows the same spectrum at a lower concentration; and curve 3 shows the emission spectrum of the hydrocarbon in dilute solution in cyclohexane.   It is noted that dibenz(a,h)anthracene maxima at 397 and 420 mμ are the most pronounced peaks in the more dilute pellet, and that this spectrum corresponds to that of the dilute solution in cyclohexane, i.e., a solid solution in potassium bromide is obtained at low concentration.   The same holds also for benzo(a)pyrene and for several other hydrocarbons.

However, some hydrocarbons give the same spectra regardless of concentration, e.g., fluoranthene.   In addition, this and several other hydrocarbons show the same spectra in the solid state and in solution (Fig. 7-9).

The fluorescence excitation and emission spectra of dibenz(a,h)anthracene in a potassium bromide pellet (Fig. 7-10) are compared with the spectra measured on dibenz(a,h)anthracene as a powder (Fig. 7-11).   The powder spectrum was kindly run by Dr. D. T. Palumbo of Sylvania Electric Products, Inc., Towanda, Pa.; these spectra show excellent agreement between spectra run on powders and in potassium bromide pellets.

Potassium bromide was the medium of choice because the pellets can be used interchangeably for UV, IR, and fluorescence work, and this salt is virtually fluorescence-free.   However, other media can also be used.   Starch, for example, is another medium that has been found useful in our work.

The complexes of aromatic hydrocarbons, heterocyclics, and amines with 1,3,7,9-tetramethyluric acid were examined, since these form well-defined crystalline complexes of known composition (15,17). Caffeine also forms crystalline complexes, but with fewer compounds

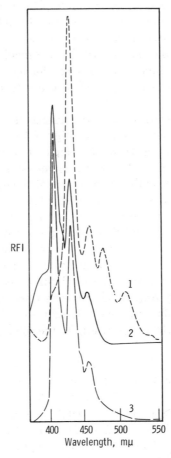

Fig. 7-8.   Fluorescence emission spectra of dibenz(a,h)anthracene: curve 1, 0.2 mmole/g KBr.   Primary filter #7-54.   Secondary filter #3-75.   Excitation at 300 mμ; curve 2, same as 1 but at 0.0002 mmole/g KBr; curve 3, DBA in cyclohexane solution, 0.004 mmole/l.

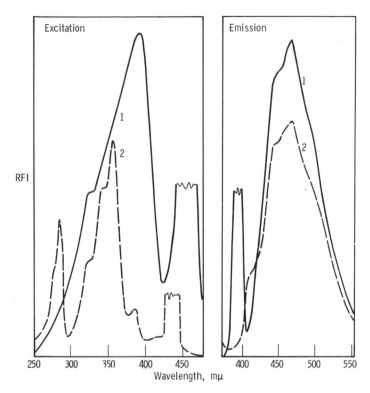

Fig. 7-9. Fluorescence spectra of fluoranthene: curve 1, 0.01 mmole/g KBr. Primary filter #1-64. Secondary filter #3-75. Excitation with emission at 460 mμ. Emission with excitation at 385 mμ. Curve 2, 0.07 mmole/l. in cyclohexane. Excitation with emission at 440 mμ. Emission with excitation at 360 mμ. No filters.

of interest. The TMU complexes examined are listed in Table 7-1. Analytical data were obtained on all these complexes; the ratio of hydrocarbon to purine varies in the different complexes as shown. The purine, TMU, used in this work did not show any measureable fluorescence.

The results obtained in the examination of the pyrene–TMU complex are summarized in Table 7-2. The excited-state dimer band of pyrene which occurs at 463 mμ in the pellet is shifted to 430 mμ in the complex.

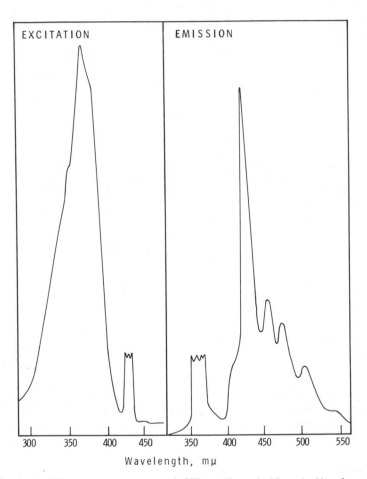

Fig. 7-10. Fluorescence spectra of KBr pellet of dibenz(a,h)anthracene, measured with Farrand spectrofluorimeter, 0.1 mmole/g KBr. Primary filter #7-54; secondary filter #0-52. Excitation with emission at 430 mμ; emission with excitation at 375 mμ.

The results obtained with benzo(a)pyrene and its TMU complex are summarized in Table 7-3. At high concentrations, the benzo(a)-pyrene pellet spectrum shows a peak at 485 mμ, with a shoulder at 505 mμ. At lower concentrations, a series of peaks is obtained with the same maxima as that of a dilute solution of benzo(*a*)pyrene in cyclohexane.   In the potassium bromide pellet of the TMU complex, the emission maximum is shifted to 447 mμ with a shoulder at 475 mμ. The shoulder at 475 mμ is ascribed to uncomplexed hydrocarbon. Unlike pyrene, benzo(*a*)pyrene does not show a clear excited dimer band at high concentrations in solution.   The broad 480–500 mμ shoulder which is ascribed to the excited-state dimer does, however, become more pronounced at higher concentrations.   If there is a shift in this peak in the presence of TMU in solution, it would not be visible because of the weakness and broadness of this dimer emission peak.

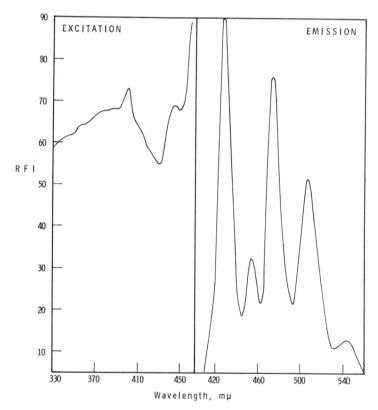

Fig. 7-11.   Fluorescence spectra of powdered dibenz(*a*,*h*)anthracene measured with a Perkin-Elmer Model 195 constant energy spectrofluorimeter.   Excitation spectrum with emission at 476 mμ; emission spectrum with excitation at 340 mμ.

TABLE 7-1

1,3,7,9-Tetramethyluric Acid Complexes

Compound	Molecular formula of complex	mp, °C
Pyrene	$C_{16}H_{10} \cdot C_9H_{12}N_4O_3$	207
Benzo(a)pyrene	$C_{20}H_{12} \cdot (C_9H_{12}N_4O_3)_2$	191
Coronene	$C_{24}H_{12} \cdot (C_9H_{12}N_4O_3)_2$	256–280
β-Naphthylamine	$C_{10}H_9N \cdot C_9H_{12}N_4O_3$	147–148
Dibenz(a,j)acridine	$C_{21}H_{13}N \cdot (C_9H_{12}N_4O_3)_3$	214
α-Naphthol	$C_{10}H_8O \cdot C_9H_{12}N_4O_3$	167–168
Benzidine	$C_{12}H_{12}N_2 \cdot (C_9H_{12}N_4O_3)_2$	207–208

The potassium bromide pellet spectra of coronene and its TMU complex are summarized in Figure 7-12. In this diagram, curves 1 and 2 represent the fluorescence emission spectra of coronene at two concentration levels. Four shorter wavelength maxima that appear in curve 2 are identical in their positions with that of the dilute solution of coronene; that is, behavior similar to that exhibited by benzo(a)pyrene and dibenz(a,h)anthracene. In the complex of coronene–TMU, the emission maximum appears at 490 mμ with

TABLE 7-2

Fluorescence of Pyrene and Its TMU Complex

	Medium and concentration	Excitation maxima, mμ[b]	Emission maxima, mμ[c]
Pyrene	Cyclohexane, $10^{-2}M$	*366*	*478*
	$10^{-5}M$	305, 320, *335*	372(sh)*385*, 392
	KBr,[a] 2.4×10^{-7} moles/g	325(sh)*366*	*463*, 485(sh)
	Microcrystalline deposit on glass[a]	*365*	*465*
Pyrene–TMU	KBr[a] 1.1×10^{-5} moles/g	*373*	*430*
	KBr[a,d] 1.0×10^{-6} moles/g	*370*	*455*

[a] Primary filter #1-64; secondary filter #3-75.
[b] At italic emission maxima shown in next column.
[c] At italic excitation maxima shown in previous column.
[d] Prepared by dry grinding of solids.

TABLE 7-3

Fluorescence of Benzo(a)pyrene and Its TMU Complex[a]

		Excitation at, mμ	Emission maxima, mμ
Benzo(a)pyrene	$10^{-4}M$ in cyclohexane	385	*405*, 417(sh), 428, 457, 485(sh)
	2.0×10^{-6} moles/g KBr	380	*485*, 505(sh)
	2.0×10^{-7} moles/g KBr	380	*405*, 417(sh), 428, 457, 485(sh)
Benzo(a)pyrene–TMU complex	2.0×10^{-5} moles/g KBr	*367*, 380	*447*, 475(sh)

[a] Pellet spectra measured with primary filter #7-51 and secondary filter #0-51.

shoulders at longer wavelengths. This spectrum is essentially unchanged at lower concentrations, as shown in curve 4, except that a shoulder now appears at 475 mμ which is undoubtedly due to uncomplexed hydrocarbon. There is, therefore, a shift in the emission maxima from 505 mμ for the hydrocarbon to 490 mμ for the complex, and there is a great enhancement in fluorescence intensity (Fig. 7-12) in going from coronene to its complex. Such an increase in fluorescence intensity was not noticed in the case of the other two hydrocarbon complexes.

Both benzidine and dibenz(a,j)acridine showed shifts to shorter wavelength in the fluorescence emission maxima of the complexes compared to the parent compounds, i.e., the same as noticed for the aromatic hydrocarbons. These data are summarized in Table 7-4.

β-Naphthylamine and α-naphthol were unusual in that the fluorescence emission maxima are not affected by TMU complex formation; however, the β-naphthylamine complex showed a tenfold increase in fluorescence intensity over that of the free amine.

These results suggest that the complexes referred to in this study are not π-complexes but are probably polarization bonding complexes. The nature of the complexes are described in a recent paper from this Laboratory.

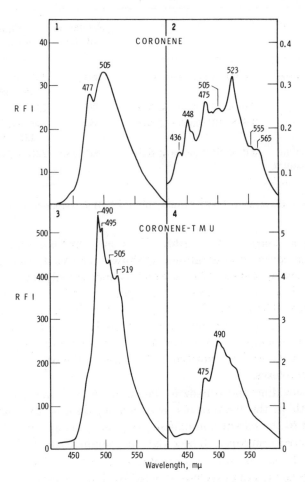

Fig. 7-12. Fluorescence emission spectra of coronene and its TMU complex. Curve 1: coronene in KBr, 8.0×10^{-5} mole/g, sensitivity 1.0.   Curve 2: coronene in KBr, 1.3×10^{-8} mole/g, sensitivity 0.01.   Curve 3: coronene–TMU in KBr, 6.5×10^{-6} mole/g (coronene concentration 2.6×10^{-6} mole/g), sensitivity 10.0. Curve 4: coronene–TMU in KBr, 6.5×10^{-9} mole/g (coronene concentration 2.6×10^{-9} mole/g), sensitivity 0.1.   Curves 1 and 3 ran at 375 mμ excitation; curves 2 and 4 ran at 350 mμ excitation; 5 mμ slits; primary filter #7-51 and secondary filter #3-75 were used for all four curves.

TABLE 7-4

Fluorescence of Benzidine and Dibenz(a,j)acridine and Their
TMU Complexes[a]

	Filters		Excitation, mμ	Emission, mμ
	Primary	Secondary		
Benzidine	7-39 or 7-59	0-52 or 0-53	350[b]	385
Benzidine–TMU	same		350[b]	370
Dibenz(a,j)acridine	1-64	3-75	400	500 shoulders at 428, 448, 465, 525
Dibenz(a,j)acridine–TMU	same		417	450, 475 (doublet)

[a] All in pellets, 1 mg of material in 200 mg potassium bromide.
[b] Because of closeness of excitation and emission maxima, emission spectra were run using 330 mμ for excitation.

This study was supported by Grant C-5946 from the National Cancer Institute, National Institutes of Health, U. S. Public Health Service and by Grant L-46 from the American Cancer Society, New York, N. Y. Coworkers associated with this work were: C. Bardi, M. Krumerman, and C. Nyheim. Figures 7-8 and 7-9 are reproduced from *Anal. Chem.*, *35*, 2198 (1963), and Figures 7-7 and 7-12 from *J. Phys. Chem.*, *68*, 2544 (1964), copyright by the American Chemical Society, by permission of the copyright owner.

References

1. S. Udenfriend, *Fluorescence Assay in Biology and Medicine*, Academic Press, New York, 1962.
2. B. L. Van Duuren, *J. Natl. Cancer Inst. Monograph No. 9*, 135 (1962).
3. B. L. Van Duuren, *Acta Unio Intern. Contra Cancrum*, *19*, 524 (1963).
4. L. Von Bertalanffy, M. Masin, and F. Masin, *Cancer*, *11*, 873 (1958).
5. V. Zanker, M. Held, and H. Rammensee, *Z. Naturforsch.*, *14*, 789 (1959).
6. B. L. Van Duuren, *Chem. Rev.*, *63*, 325 (1963).
7. D. F. Bradley and M. K. Wolf, *Proc. Natl. Acad. Sci. U. S.*, *45*, 944 (1959).
8. A. L. Stone and D. F. Bradley, *J. Am. Chem. Soc.*, *83*, 3627 (1962).
9. J. M. Wiame, *J. Am. Chem. Soc.*, *69*, 3146 (1947).
10. G. Oster, *Trans. Faraday Soc.*, *67*, 660 (1951).
11. L. S. Lerman, *J. Mol. Biol.*, *3*, 18 (1961).
12. J. Booth, E. Boyland and S. F. D. Orr, *J. Chem. Soc.*, *1954*, 598.
13. F. DeSantis, E. Giglio, A. M. Liquori, and A. Ripamonti, *Nature*, *191*, 900 (1961).

14. A. M. Liquori, B. DeLerma, F. Ascoli, C. Botré, and M. Trasciatti, *J. Mol. Biol.*, *5*, 521 (1962).
15. H. Weil-Malherbe, *Biochem. J.*, *40*, 351 (1946).
16. B. L. Van Duuren and C. Bardi, *Anal. Chem.*, *35*, 2198 (1963).
17. W. J. P. Neish, *Rec. Trav. Chim.*, *67*, 361 (1948).
18. B. L. Van Duuren, *J. Phys. Chem.*, *68*, 2544 (1964).

chapter 8

Polarization of the Fluorescence of Solutions

Gregorio Weber

Division of Biochemistry, University of Illinois, Urbana, Illinois

We analyze here the origin of the polarization of the fluorescence emitted by molecules in solution, and the main causes of its variation. In other words, we shall attempt to describe the properties of fluorescent molecules, the existence of which may be inferred from a study of the polarization of their fluorescence. The treatment will be one in which only the more general quantitative aspects will be dealt with.

I. The Fluorescence Transition

It is well known that the fluorescence emission of organic molecules in solution corresponds to the allowed electronic transition S_1–S_0, where S_1 is the first singlet excited state and S_0 the singlet ground state of the molecule. The lifetime of the excited state for an allowed transition of this type (1,2) may be expected to be in the range of nanoseconds (1 ns $= 10^{-9}$ s). Most of the lifetimes experimentally determined (3–5) fall in the region of 1–20 ns. It is within this time interval that the causes which modify the fluorescence emission must act if they are to be at all effective. Thus we need only consider molecular processes having an intrinsic rate of 10^8/s or greater as effective in our case.

II. Origin of the Polarization of the Fluorescence

To introduce the notion of fluorescence polarization, it is useful to consider the actual manner in which the experimental measurements of the polarization are made (Fig. 8-1). A fluorescent solution placed at the center of coordinates, O, is illuminated by a beam of polarized light whose electric vector is in the OZ direction. The fluorescent light emitted along OY is observed, and the intensity of two linearly

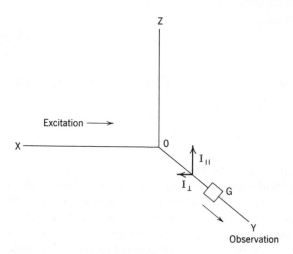

Fig. 8-1.   Determination of fluorescence polarization.   The solution observed is placed at O.   The exciting light reaches it from X and is polarized with electric vector along OZ.   The fluorescence emitted towards Y is observed, and the intensities $I_{\parallel}$ and $I_{\perp}$ are measured by orienting G in two suitable positions.

polarized components at 90° is measured.   One of the components, $I_{\parallel}$, vibrates parallel to OZ and the other, $I_{\perp}$, vibrates along OX.   The intensity of each component is determined by orienting a suitable selecting device (Nicol prism or polarizing film) G so as to transmit first one component, then the other.   The polarization, p, is given by

$$p = (I_{\parallel} - I_{\perp})/(I_{\parallel} + I_{\perp}) \qquad (8\text{-}1)$$

It is clear that the value of p occurs between 1 (when $I_{\perp} = 0$) and -1 (when $I_{\parallel} = 0$).   Natural light, in which $I_{\perp} = I_{\parallel}$, corresponds to $p = 0$.

III. Molecular Geometry and Polarized Light Absorption

Observations of the absorption of polarized light by crystals of organic molecules (6) have shown that, for suitable orientations of the crystals, the absorption of plane polarized light shows maxima and minima as the plane of polarization is rotated through 90°.   Maximum absorption takes place when the plane of polarization of the exciting light coincides with the direction of the transition moment in absorption (7), and, in the simpler cases at least, one may expect a different well-defined direction, linked rigidly to the molecular geometry, for each absorption band present in the visible and ultraviolet absorption spectrum. As an example of this very simple type, we may take the molecule of phenol; solutions of phenol in a variety of solvents present two absorption bands with maxima at approximately 230 and 275 mμ, respectively. The fluorescence emission consists of a single band with maximum at 298 mμ, which is the mirror image of the absorption band with maximum at 275 mμ. The absorption spectrum and the energy levels involved—insofar as they are required for our purpose—are shown schematically in Figure 8-2. The absorption band with the 275 mμ maximum is a transition between the singlet ground state, S_0, and the first excited singlet, S_1. The absorption band with maximum at 230 mμ corresponds to a transition between the ground state and the second singlet excited state, S_2. The transitions are then, respectively, S_0–S_1 and S_0–S_2. The fluorescence band corresponds to the S_1–S_0 transition and is therefore the reciprocal to the transition of least frequency in the absorption spectrum. The fluorescence is excited with equal yield (8) by

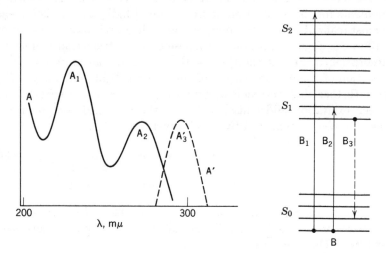

Fig. 8-2. Schematics of absorption spectrum. (A), fluorescence spectrum, A', and electronic energy levels, B, in phenol: area A_1 and line B_1, absorption corresponding to S_0–S_2 transition; area A_2 and line B_2, absorption corresponding to S_0–S_1 transition; area A_3' and line B_3, emission corresponding to S_1–S_0 transition; S_0 = ground singlet; S_1 = first excited singlet; S_2 = second excited singlet.

absorption in the S_0–S_1 and S_0–S_2 transitions. In the latter case, the excess energy is converted into heat by the vibrational decay from S_2 to S_1 (9) following absorption. This decay is known from indirect evidence to be accomplished in a time of 10^{-11} s or less, which is short in comparison with the total lifetime of the excited state. From the description of its absorption spectrum, we expect the phenol molecule to show two principal directions of the transition moment in absorption corresponding to the two observed absorption bands. We also expect the direction of the transition moment in emission to be parallel, or nearly so, to the direction of the transition moment in absorption for the absorption band of longest wavelength, since these two transitions are reciprocals. In crystals in which the molecules are oriented parallel to each other, the emission of virtually completely polarized fluorescence may be expected and has been, in fact, observed (10). In these cases, the relation of the molecular geometry to the direction of the transition moment in emission may be directly determined.

IV. Polarization in Solution and Molecular Orientation

Consider a single molecule A (Fig. 8-3) in which the transition moments for the absorption and emission of light are parallel, a case almost realized in practice in many cases when excitation falls entirely within the S_0–S_1 transition. Suppose that the transition moment in absorption makes, at the time of the excitation, an angle θ with the direction of the electric vector of the exciting light (OZ axis). Suppose further that the molecule does not change its orientation between excitation and emission. Then the polarized components of the emission, determined by an observer along Y, are:

$$I_{\parallel} \ (\theta,\varphi) \ = \ \cos^2 \theta \qquad (8\text{-}2)$$

$$I_{\perp} \ (\theta,\varphi) \ = \ \sin^2 \theta \sin^2 \varphi \qquad (8\text{-}3)$$

where φ is the azimuth angle of OA about OZ. If we consider all molecules with equal θ, φ will take at random all values between 0 and 2π. Therefore $\overline{\sin^2 \varphi} = \frac{1}{2}$ and

$$I_{\parallel} \ (\theta) \ = \ \cos^2 \theta \qquad (8\text{-}4)$$

$$I_{\perp} \ (\theta) \ = \ (1/2) \sin^2 \theta \qquad (8\text{-}5)$$

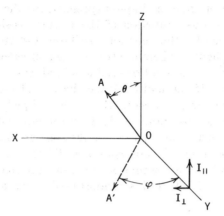

Fig. 8-3. Relation of oscillator orientation to polarization. Directions of excitation and observation as in Figure 8-1. A, direction of the transition moment in emission (S_1–S_0 transition); θ, angle of A with the electric vector of the exciting wave; A', projection of A on the XY plane; φ, azimuthal angle of A.

If the emission from a collection of molecules with variable angle θ is now observed, and since the intensities of the different groups are additive, we must have:

$$I_{\parallel} = \sum_{\theta=0}^{\theta=\pi/2} I_{\parallel}(\theta) = \sum_{\theta=0}^{\theta=\pi/2} f(\theta)\cos^2\theta = \overline{\cos^2\theta} \qquad (8\text{-}6)$$

$$I_{\perp} = \sum_{\theta=0}^{\theta=\pi/2} I_{\perp}(\theta) = \sum_{\theta=0}^{\theta=\pi/2} f(\theta)(1/2)\sin^2\theta = \overline{\sin^2\theta}/2 \qquad (8\text{-}7)$$

where $f(\theta)$ is the fraction of molecules making an angle θ with OZ. From the definition of p [eq. (8-1)]:

$$p = \frac{(3/2)\,\overline{\cos^2\theta} - (1/2)}{(1/2) + (\overline{\cos^2\theta}/2)} \qquad (8\text{-}8)$$

$$(1/p) - (1/3) = \frac{(2/3)}{(3/2)\,\overline{\cos^2\theta} - (1/2)} \qquad (8\text{-}9)$$

The last equation gives a simple expression for the polarization observed in solution as a function of the average cosine square of the angle determined by the emission oscillator and the electric vector of the exciting light. Therefore the problem of calculating the fluorescence polarization of solutions reduces in all cases to that of calculation of $\overline{\cos^2\theta}$. If the molecules can be considered motionless between excitation and emission, then θ is uniquely determined by the probability of absorption of light by the molecules as a function of θ. It is known that this probability is proportional to $\cos^2\theta$. Moreover, in solution, the absorption oscillators are distributed with random orientations at the time of the absorption, so that the number making an angle θ with OZ is proportional to $\sin\theta$ (Fig. 8-3), thus

$$\overline{\cos^2\theta} = \frac{\int_0^{\pi/2} \cos^2\theta \cos^2\theta \sin\theta \, d\theta}{\int_0^{\pi/2} \cos^2\theta \sin\theta \, d\theta} = 3/5; p = 1/2 \quad (8\text{-}10)$$

When the oscillators of absorption and emission are not parallel, but determine an angle λ, $\cos^2\theta$ is always smaller than in the previous case, and the dependence of p upon λ is given by eq. (8-11).

$$(1/p_0) - (1/3) = (5/3) [2/(3 \cos^2\lambda - 1)] \quad (8\text{-}11)$$

The last equation reduces to the previous one for $\lambda = 0$. If $\lambda = 90°$, $\cos^2\lambda = 0$, and

$$p_0 = -(1/3)$$

Therefore the value of the polarization of fluorescence occurs between the limits of $\frac{1}{2}$ and $-\frac{1}{3}$. The first value is approached in many cases on excitation of the pure S_0–S_1 transition. Values of p as large as 0.45 have been reported (12,13). Negative polarization values approaching the theoretical maximum of 0.33 have also been observed (12).

The appearance of negative polarizations may be qualitatively understood by reference to Figure 8-4. The orientation of the absorption oscillators actually excited is always preferential in the OZ direction, as already discussed. If the transition in emission is parallel to that in absorption, the parallel component of the polarization will be greater than the perpendicular. The opposite will happen if the excitation is within an absorption band the transition moment of which is normal to the direction of transition moment in emission (Fig. 8-4c). It is clear that the polarization, p_0, observed in a medium in which no appreciable loss of orientation takes place between excitation and emission, depends only upon the angle λ determined by the oscillators of absorption and emission. The loss of polarization from the maximum value of $\frac{1}{2}$ may be considered in this case as due to intrinsic causes in opposition to the extrinsic causes that produce further loss of orientation by acting during the lifetime of the excited state, either through migration of the excitation or through Brownian rotations.

The value of the polarization in the presence of these extrinsic causes of depolarization is given by the following equation:

$$(1/p) - (1/3) = (5/3) [2/(3 \cos^2 \lambda - 1)] [2/(3 \overline{\cos^2 \omega} - 1)]$$
$$= [(1/p_0) - (1/3)] [2/(3 \overline{\cos^2 \omega} - 1)] \qquad (8\text{-}12)$$

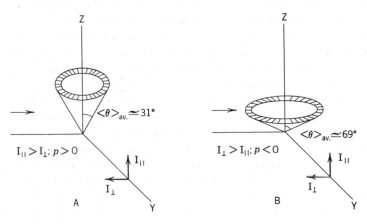

Fig. 8-4. Origin of positive and negative polarizations: A, oscillators of absorption and emission parallel (e.g., S_0–S_1 and S_1–S_0); the shaded zone corresponds to the average angle of the excited molecule with OZ, approximately 31°. $I_{\parallel} > I_{\perp}$ (by eqs. 8-4 and 8-5) and $p > 0$. B, oscillators of absorption and emission normal to each other; the shaded zone corresponds to $\theta \simeq 68°$, so that $I_{\perp} > I_{\parallel}$; $p < 0$.

where $\overline{\cos^2 \omega}$ is the average cosine square determined by the position of the emission oscillators at the times of absorption and emission, respectively. If there is no loss of orientation, $\overline{\cos^2 \omega} = 1$ and the last equation reduces to eq. (8-11).

Eqs. (8-9), (8-11), and (8-12) permit us to write:

$$2/(3 \overline{\cos^2 \theta} - 1) = (5/3) [2/(3 \cos^2 \lambda - 1)] [2/(3 \overline{\cos^2 \omega} - 1)]$$

or descriptively,

Total depolarization factor $= (5/3) \times$ (Intrinsic depolarization factor) $\times$ (Extrinsic depolarization factor)

This multiplication law of the depolarizing effects has its origin in the properties of the quantities $(3/2) \cos^2 \alpha - (1/2)$ first pointed out by Soleillet (14,15).

V. The Fluorescence Polarization Spectrum

From the preceding discussion it is clear that the value of p_0, the polarization in the absence of extrinsic causes of depolarization, depends solely upon the angle λ determined by the directions of the transition moments in the absorption and emission concerned. In practice, if a sufficiently dilute solution is observed in a medium of high viscosity, all such extrinsic causes may be considered absent, and the plot of the observed polarization against wavelength constitutes the fluorescence polarization–excitation spectrum, or simply the fluorescence polarization spectrum of the substance in question. Such a plot obtained for a solution of phenol in propylene glycol at $-70°C$ is shown in Figure 8-5. A region of high positive polarization and a region of negative polarization are seen in the spectrum corresponding to the two absorption bands that we have labled S_0–S_1 and S_0–S_2, respectively. It appears that the transition moments of these two absorptions must be at a large angle to each other. If it is assumed that both transition moments are contained in the same plane (all π–π^* transitions), it may be calculated that the angle λ is close to 90°.

The simple picture of the fluorescence polarization spectrum (consisting only of regions of constant polarization corresponding to the absorption maxima, and regions of rapidly varying polarization corresponding to the absorption minima) is not uniformly found (16,18).

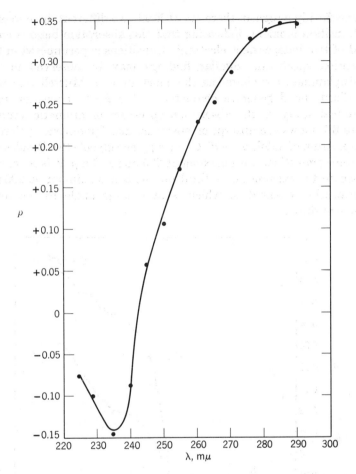

Fig. 8-5.   Fluorescence polarization spectrum of phenol at $-70°C$ in propylene glycol.   Ordinate=polarization, p; abscissa, exciting wavelength in mμ. Redrawn from Weber (18).

In case of degenerate electronic transitions, it is possible for the polarization spectrum to show complexities that are not easily expected from an examination of the absorption spectrum alone. Figure 8-6 shows the polarization spectrum of aniline in propylene glycol at $-70°C$. It is seen that, corresponding to the band with absorption maximum at 283 mμ, to which a single S_0–S_1 transition could

be superficially assigned, there are at least two different directions of
the transition moment, indicating that this absorption band is composed of two independent electronic transitions superimposed in the
absorption spectrum. Similar findings may be observed in the
naphthylamines, corroborating the conclusions of Murrell (17) who
recognized the degenerate character of the S_0–S_1 transition in a
theoretical study of the absorption spectrum of aromatic amines.
Figure 8-7 shows the absorption spectrum and fluorescence polarization spectrum of indole at −70°C in propylene glycol (18). Besides the
electronic transitions with maxima at 235 and 280 mμ, it is necessary
to assume the existence of a third one with a maximum at 290mμ,
the transition moment of which is at a large angle to the main
S_0–S_1 transition.

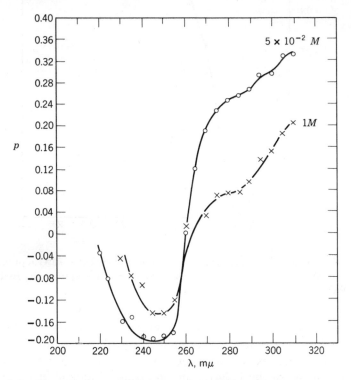

Fig. 8-6. Fluorescence polarization spectrum of aniline at −70°C in propylene glycol. Abscissa and ordinate as in Figure 8-5. Unpublished data of the
author.

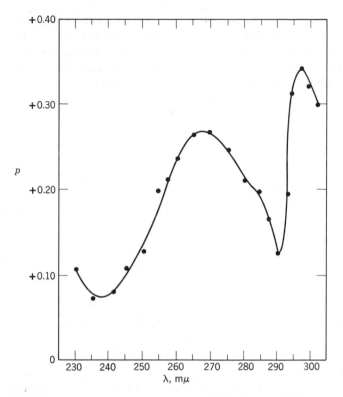

Fig. 8-7. Fluorescence polarization spectrum of indole at $-70°C$ in propylene glycol. Abscissa and ordinate as in Figure 8-5. Redrawn from Weber (18).

The examples quoted are sufficient to show that the fluorescence polarization spectrum is of importance in the determination of the number and character of the electronic transitions that make up the absorption spectrum of organic molecules in the visible and ultra-violet regions.

VI. Depolarization Owing to Extrinsic Causes

Extrinsic causes, which act during the lifetime of the excited state of the fluorescent molecule, are the migration of the excited state from the originally excited molecule to a neighboring molecule, and the Brownian molecular rotation of the excited molecule. Both processes may be clearly separated; for concentrated solutions in viscous solvents, Brownian rotations are negligible and energy migration is the sole extrinsic cause of depolarization; for dilute solutions in solvents of low viscosity, energy migration is negligible and Brownian rotations are the only cause of extrinsic depolarization. The following scheme summarizes the circumstances that lead to changes in the polarization of the fluorescence of solutions of a pure compound.

Condition	Observed polarization	Molecular properties responsible
1. Dilute solution in very viscous solvents (poise)	Maximum possible $|p_0|$ observed for a given exciting wavelength	Electronic structure of the molecule
2. Concentrated solutions in very viscous solvents	$0 < |p| \leq |p_0|$ Decrease in polarization due to energy migration	Electromagnetic coupling of neighboring molecules
3. Dilute solutions in solvents of low viscosity (centipoise)	$0 < |p| \leq |p_0|$ Decrease in polarization due to Brownian rotations	Size and shape of the kinetic unit carrying the emission oscillator

To give a unified description of processes 2 and 3, we require only a relation, calculable on purely geometric premises, of the polarization that would be observed when the emission oscillators are subject to a series of small changes in orientation each of average amplitude, characterized by $\overline{\sin^2 \theta}$, occurring in mean number $\bar{n}$ during the lifetime of the excited state. The process may be conceived in either case as rotational diffusion of the direction of the emission oscillators occurring during the lifetime of the excited state. In energy migration, the rotational diffusion process is brought about by the transfer of the excited state from the molecule originally excited to a neighboring one favorably oriented, though perhaps not perfectly parallel to the donor molecule (Fig. 8-8).

According to Weber (19), the dependence sought of the observed polarization p upon $\bar{n}$ and $\overline{\sin^2 \theta}$ is given by

$$(1/p) - (1/3) = (1/p_0) - (1/3)[1 + (3/2) \overline{\sin^2 \theta \, \bar{n}}] \qquad (8\text{-}13)$$

The last relation is a purely geometrical one. Any mechanism of
depolarization is possible provided the changes in orientation of the
oscillator of emission occur in random directions with respect to the
system of coordinates of the observer (Fig. 8-2).   It may be stressed
at this point that this assumption already results in some loss in
generality, at least in the case of depolarization by molecular rotations; in the case of an elongated molecule carrying an emission

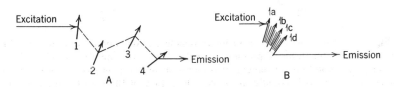

Fig. 8-8.   Similarity of depolarization by energy migration and by Brownian
rotation.   In A, the molecules placed in a viscous solvent cannot appreciably
change orientation.   The depolarization is brought about by the transfer of the
excited state so that the orientation of the emitting molecule bears little relation
to the one originally excited.   In B, the depolarization is brought about by
progressive changes in orientation of the excited molecule.

oscillator in the equatorial plane, the probability of a change in
orientation of the long axis is, at any time, much smaller than that of
the short axis (Fig. 8-9).   As a result, the condition of random
orientation of the small deflections is not fulfilled.   In these cases, a
more complex theory is required (15,20,21).   Equation (8-13) is
therefore limited to a description of the depolarization in "globular
molecules," that is, in those in which the linear dimensions are similar.
With this proviso, a simple expression relating p to the rotational
diffusion constant of the molecule may be obtained; according to
Einstein (22), the mean square value of the angle θ, determined by a
molecular direction at the beginning and end of a small time interval,
δt, is given by the expression

$$\overline{\theta^2} = (2RT/3\eta v)\ \delta t \qquad\qquad (8\text{-}14)$$

where V is the molar volume of the molecule supposed spherical, R
the gas constant, T the absolute temperature, and η the viscosity of

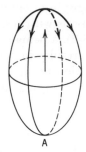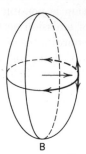

A   B

Fig. 8-9. Dependence of rotational depolarization upon direction of the emission oscillator in an ellipsoidal molecule. In A, the direction of S_1–S_0 is in the axis of revolution. Changes in orientation of the axis along any of the 4 indicated directions is equally probable. Equation (8-13) may be applied. In B, the emission oscillator is in the equator (normal to axis of revolution). Changes in orientation along the equator are more probable than changes in orientation that carry the end of the oscillator along a great circle. Equation (8-13) is not applicable.

the solvent in poises. Instead of the volume, V, an equivalent expression may be written as a function of the rotational relaxation time or the rotational diffusion coefficient of the molecule*.

$$\overline{\theta^2} = 2\delta t/\rho = 4\Re \ \delta t \tag{8-15}$$

Since the elementary rotations are small, $\sin^2 \theta = \theta^2$. Also, if $\bar{n}$ is the mean number of elementary rotations expected in time τ, the lifetime of the excited state is $\bar{n} = \tau/\delta t$. By direct substitutions of the values of $\sin^2 \theta$ and $\bar{n}$ into eq. (8-13) we find:

$$\frac{1}{p} - \frac{1}{3} = \left(\frac{1}{p_0} - \frac{1}{3}\right)\left(1 + \frac{3\tau}{\rho}\right) = \left(\frac{1}{p_0} - \frac{1}{3}\right)\left(1 + 6\Re\tau\right) \tag{8-16}$$

$$\frac{1}{p} - \frac{1}{3} = \left(\frac{1}{p_0} - \frac{1}{3}\right)\left(1 + \frac{RT}{\eta V}\tau\right) \tag{8-17}$$

* The rotational relaxation time, ρ, is defined as the time, t, required for the value of $\cos \theta$ to change from 1 (value at $t = 0$) to e^{-1}. For a sphere, $\rho = 3\eta V/RT$. The rotational diffusion coefficient $\Re = RT/Nf_r$, where N is Avogadro's number and f_r the average frictional coefficient. For a sphere, $\Re = 1/2\rho$ (20).

Equation (8-17), derived by Perrin in 1926 (12), describes the depolarization due to the Brownian motion of a spherical molecule. It is customary to plot $(1/p) - (1/3)$ against T/η, in which case eq. (8-16) predicts that a straight line should be obtained with intercept $(1/p_0) - (1/3)$ and slope $[(1/p_0) - (1/3)] RT/V$ (12). If the molecular volume in solution is known, τ may be determined. On the other hand, if τ is known, the molecular volume, or at least an effective volume in solution, may be calculated. When the molecules are compact, fused-ring structures, as in the case of many organic aromatic molecules, the assumption of a quasi-spherical shape is probably justified (12). Figure 8-10 shows the polarization of the fluorescence of flavin (6,7-dimethyl isoalloxazin) derivatives in water solution at 20°C. All these derivatives have very similar absorption spectra and all except flavin–adenine dinucleotide have the same quantum yield, so that the lifetime of the excited state may be considered equivalent (within error) in all of them. From observations of the quantum yield of riboflavin (0.27) and the oscillator strength of the absorption band corresponding to the S_0–S_1 transition, τ may be estimated to be approximately 5 ns. Since p is small in all cases (0.01–0.03) $(1/p) - (1/3)$ may be replaced by $1/p$, giving

$$p \simeq \left(\frac{1}{p_0} - \frac{1}{3}\right)^{-1} \frac{V}{10^4 + V} \simeq \frac{10^{-4}}{\left(\dfrac{1}{p_0} - \dfrac{1}{3}\right)} V \qquad (8\text{-}18)$$

In the right hand side, V, which is in all cases less than 10^3, has been considered negligible in comparison with 10^4. In Figure 8-10 we have plotted the molecular weights of the compounds against the observed polarizations. A close correlation between molecular size and polarization is observed. The increase in molecular volume due to replacement of the NH in the 3 position by N–CH$_3$ is easily detected as an increase in polarization in 3 N–methyl lumiflavin and 3 N–methyl riboflavin tetra-O-acetyl over the corresponding non-methylated compounds. The slope of the line in the plot of p vs. molecular weight is approximately 3×10^{-5}. Since p_0, obtained from the observations of several flavins in glycerol, is 0.43, the predicted value of the slope of p against *molecular volume* should be 5×10^{-6}, which is in reasonable agreement with the value found experimentally.

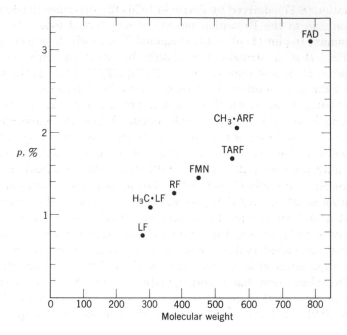

Fig. 8-10.   A plot of the fluorescence polarization, p, vs. molecular weight for a series of derivatives of 6,7-dimethyl isoalloxazine: LF = lumiflavin; $H_3C \cdot LF$ = 3-N-methyllumiflavin; RF = riboflavin; FMN = flavin mononucleotide; TARF = tetra-O-acetyl riboflavin; $CH_3 \cdot ARF$ = N-methyl tetra-O-acetyl riboflavin; FAD = flavin adenine dinucleotide.

The polarization of fluorescence has been extensively applied to the study of proteins in solution (15,23).   The molecular volumes of proteins calculated from the slope of the plots of polarization against T/η are within a factor of 2 of the expected molecular volumes in solution.   The difference is to be attributed to the departure of the protein molecules from the spherical shape.   Therefore, although the method cannot be used to determine directly the molecular volume of proteins in solution, it is possible to estimate it within certain limits, and in cases in which this is known from other data, the fluorescence polarization method can contribute some information concerning the molecular shape.   The great advantage of the fluorescence polarization method over other methods of measurement of the rotational diffusion properties of proteins is to be found in the ease and accuracy of the determinations, the variety of ionic environments possible, and the large concentration range and temperature range over which the molecules may be examined.   One of the most interesting advantages of the method is to be found in its relative insensitivity to purely hydrodynamic concentration effects such as are commonly encountered in studies of sedimentation and translational diffusion of macromolecules (20,23).   This insensitivity has probably more than one origin; the distribution of charges on the surface of the protein molecules is sufficiently symmetric to make long range interactions unimportant in restricting rotational motion, although these same interactions may not be negligible in linear diffusion, which involves actual changes in the average distance among molecules.   Another cause of insensitivity to concentration effects is found in comparing the fluorescence polarization method to other methods of study of rotational diffusion, such as electric birefringence and dielectric dispersion. In these latter methods, the presence of the electric field produces a small preferential orientation of the molecular population, and it is the disappearance of this by diffusion that produces the observed effects.   In fluorescence polarization, the difference in orientation applies only to the excited molecules, not to the molecular population as a whole, which remains randomly oriented at all times, the excited molecules exchanging orientations with the unexcited ones.   The process of diffusion may be said to be maintained by the entropy of mixing of the 2 types of molecules, rather than by the existence of a true gradient in the orientations of the whole molecular population.

An example of the usefulness of this independence of fluorescence polarization upon concentration is found in the study of aggregating systems.   Figure 8-11 shows the effect of dilution upon the fluorescence polarization of a protein digest in which the original protein (bovine serum albumin) had been labeled with dimethylaminonaphthalene sulfochloride (24).   The concentration region at which reversible aggregation takes place, and the region at which this is negligible, are clearly seen.

VII. Fluorescence Polarization and Energy Transfer

Equation (8-13) was originally derived to describe the loss in polarization due to migration of the excited state.   To this purpose, it is only necessary to introduce suitable assumptions as regards the

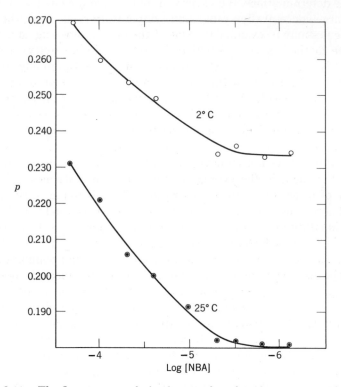

Fig. 8-11. The fluorescence polarization, p, plotted against concentration for a peptic digest of bovine albumin conjugated with dimethylaminonaphthalene sulfochloride: ordinate = p; abscissa, log [NBA] = logarithm of the molar concentration of original albumin [from Weber and Young (24)].

angular and radial dependence of the probability of transfer of the excited state. The radial dependence is given by the well-known relation (25,26):

$$\nu(r) = \lambda \, (R/r)^6 \tag{8-19}$$

where $\nu(r)$ is the transition probability of transfer for a pair of point dipole oscillators oriented parallel at distance r, and $\lambda = 1/\tau$ is the transition probability of emission. Clearly the constant R is a characteristic distance at which $\nu = \lambda$, that is, the distance at which transfer of the excited state and emission without transfer are equally likely.   The angular probability of transfer is proportional to the mutual interaction energy of two dipoles, D_1 and D_2, as a function of their orientation.   The angular variables φ and ω that determine the angle θ between the dipole directions are shown in Figure 8-12. From this

$$\cos \theta = \cos \omega_1 \cos \omega_2 + \sin \omega_1 \sin \omega_2 \cos \varphi \qquad (8\text{-}20)$$

and the angular probability of transfer is

$$\nu(\theta) = (\sin \omega_1 \sin \omega_2 \cos \varphi - 2 \cos \omega_1 \cos \omega_2)^2 \qquad (8\text{-}21)$$

Using the expression

$$\overline{\sin^2 \theta} = 1 - \overline{\cos^2 \theta} = 1 - \frac{\int_{\theta=0}^{\theta=\pi/2} \nu(\theta) \cos^2 \theta \, d\theta}{\int_{\theta=0}^{\theta=\pi/2} \nu(\theta) \, d\theta} \qquad (8\text{-}22)$$

introducing in it the values of $\cos^2 \theta$ and $\nu(\theta)$ from eqs. (8-20) and (8-21) and performing the integrations, we have

$$\overline{\nu(\theta)} = 2/3; \; \overline{\sin^2 \theta} = 0.64; \; (3/2) \sin^2 \theta \simeq 1$$

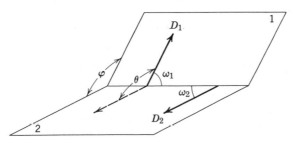

Fig. 8-12   Angular variables in dipole–dipole interactions.   The planes 1 and 2 are determined respectively by each dipole direction and the line joining both point dipoles. ω_1 and ω_2 are the angles of each dipole direction with the line joining them. θ is the angle between the dipoles, φ the angle between the planes. ω_1 and ω_2 are angles in space; φ is in a plane.   Therefore the average values, used in calculating the integral of eq. (8–22) are: $\overline{\sin^2 \omega_1} = \overline{\sin^2 \omega_2} = 2/3; \; \overline{\cos^2 \omega_1} = \overline{\cos^2 \omega_2} = 1/3; \; \overline{\cos^2 \varphi} = 1/2; \; \overline{\sin^4 \omega_1} = \overline{\sin^4 \omega_2} = 8/15; \; \overline{\cos^4 \omega_1} = \overline{\cos^4 \omega_2} = 3/15; \; \overline{\cos^2 \omega_1 \sin^2 \omega_1} = \overline{\cos^2 \omega_2 \sin^2 \omega_2} = 2/15; \; \overline{\cos^4 \varphi} = 3/8.$

Moreover, if the average probability of energy transfer is $\bar{\nu}/(\bar{\nu} + \lambda)$ and the probability of any one transfer is on average independent of the others, we must have

$$\bar{n} = \frac{\sum_{n=0}^{n=\infty} n \left(\frac{\bar{\nu}}{\bar{\nu} + \lambda}\right)^n}{\sum_{n=0}^{n=\infty} \left(\frac{\bar{\nu}}{\bar{\nu} + \lambda}\right)^n} = \bar{\nu}/\lambda \qquad (8\text{-}23)$$

To obtain the average value of $\bar{\nu}$ we can set

$$\bar{\nu}/\lambda = \frac{\overline{\nu(\theta)\nu(r)}}{\lambda} = (2/3)\int_{2a}^{\infty} (R^6/r^6)\, 4\pi r^2 NC 10^{-3}\, dr \qquad (8\text{-}24)$$

In the last equation, N is Avogadro's number and C is the concentration in moles/l, so that $4\pi r^2 NC \times 10^{-3}\, dr$ gives the number of molecules in the spherial shell of volume $4\pi r^2\, dr$, that is, those at distance r from the excited molecule. Performing the integration with a lower limit, $2a$, the distance of closest approach of any molecule to the excited molecule (a = molecular radius),

$$\bar{\nu}/\lambda = 1.684 \times 10^{21}[R^6/(2a)^3]\, C \qquad (8\text{-}25)$$

or using $(2a)^3 = 10^{-21}$

$$(1/p) - (1/3) \simeq [(1/p_0) - (1/3)][1 + 1.68(R/2a)^6 C] \qquad (8\text{-}26)$$

In a plot of $1/p$ vs. C, a straight line should be obtained from the slope of which the value of $(R/2a)$ and therefore R may be calculated. The linear dependence of $1/p$ upon C has been well verified (27,18). The values of the slope obtained for small molecules in viscous solvents are in the range of 10^2–10^4, $(R/2a)$ equals 2–4, and therefore R is in the range of 15–40 A. Figure 8-13 shows the polarization as a function of concentration in phenol dissolved in propylene glycol. A layer of 30-μ thickness was used to avoid depolarization by radiative transfer (18).

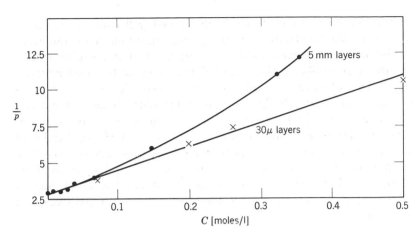

Fig. 8-13. A plot of $1/p$ vs. C for phenol in propylene glycol at $-70°C$ [redrawn from Weber (18)]. The slope equals 17, so that $R \simeq 16$ A. The linear law is followed in the thin layers in which radiative transfer is negligible. The depolarization in thick layers is spuriously high because of the radiative transfer in the more concentrated solutions.

VIII. Polarization of the Fluorescence in an Electric Field

If an electric field of strength E is applied parallel to the direction OZ (Fig. 8-1), the polarization of the fluorescence, p_e, is found to be slightly greater than p, the value in the absence of the field. Czekalla (28,29) observed such an increase in polarization for a series of fluorescent compounds dissolved in nonpolar solvents to which fields of the order of 100 kV/cm were applied. The increase in polarization is due to the existence of a permanent dipole moment, μ^*, in the molecules in the lowest singlet excited state. μ^* may be calculated under the assumption that by the time of the emission the dipoles have reached the equilibrium distribution in the field (30). In this way, Czekalla found (for several stilbene derivatives) values of μ^* in the region of 15–20 D. Since the dimension of these molecules are of the order of 10 A., it follows that the minimum amount of charge separated in the excited state is of the order of 50% of the electron charge. In these cases, the lowest excited state appears to possess a great deal more charge separation than the ground state and the S_0–S_1 transition may be properly called an intramolecular charge-transfer transition. A theory taking into account the diffusion of the dipoles in the electric field may be developed (30), and if μ is known, μ^* may be calculated without making the assumption that equilibrium in the field has been established. Such calculations give results qualitatively similar to those of Czekalla. One of the most interesting of these observations (due to Czekalla and Meyer) (32) refers to a complex of hexamethylbenzene and tetrachlorophthalic anhydride, the fluorescence of which is the mirror image of the charge-transfer band characteristic of the complex. Czekalla and Meyer found that $\mu = 3.5$ D, $\mu^* = 14$ D. The latter value corresponds to the complete transfer of an electron between two parallel neighboring aromatic rings, and thus gives a direct proof of the validity of Mulliken's ideas (33) of the ionic nature of the excited state in these molecular complexes.

IX. Other Uses of Fluorescence Polarization

Apart from those practical applications already mentioned, fluorescence polarization has proved a useful tool in the study of molecular processes, some in the biochemical field.

A. DETERMINATION OF LIFETIMES OF THE EXCITED STATE

By a plot of $(1/p) - (1/3)$ against T/η using media of different viscosity (e.g., glycerol–water mixtures), τ may be determined with accuracy dependent upon that of the value of V, assumed or determined (12). In cases of the quenching of fluorescence by a process competitive with the emission, the changes in lifetimes and yield are proportional (12), while if a dark complex is formed between quencher and fluorescent molecule, the change in lifetime is less than proportional to yield, and in some cases undetectable (34,35). A distinction among collisional quenching, quenching by ground state complex, and mixed quenching processes is thus possible by observations on the change in polarization upon quenching.

B. ENERGY MIGRATION IN BIOLOGICAL SYSTEMS

The low polarization of the fluorescence of chlorophyll in chloroplasts, first observed by Arnold and Meek (36), is one of the more powerful arguments in favor of energy migration in the chloroplast, and is postulated by all modern views of photosynthesis (37).

In proteins, energy transfer among the tyrosine residues is probably the cause of the decrease in p_0 (λ) observed in proteins containing tyrosine (38), as compared with the values for phenol or tyrosine.

C. Binding Equilibria

If a small molecule, the polarization of fluorescence of which is small, becomes attached to a larger one (e.g., a protein molecule), p must increase due to the larger effective volume of the complex. If the values of p characteristic of the free molecule and complex are determined, the fraction of complexes and free molecules present under given conditions may be calculated, and the equilibrium constant of the binding process determined. This method was used by Laurence (39) to study the binding of dyes to serum albumin and by Velick (40) to study enzyme–coenzyme interactions, and is doubtessly capable of wider application.

References

1. Th. Förster, *Fluoreszens Organisches. Verbindungen*, Vandenhoeck and Ruprecht, Gottingen, 1951, Chapter VII.
2. S. J. Strickler and R. A. Berg, *J. Chem. Phys.*, *37*, 814 (1962).
3. A. Schmillen, *Z. Physik*, *135*, 294 (1953).
4. W. R. Ware and B. A. Baldwin, *J. Chem. Phys.*, *40*, 1703 (1964).
5. J. B. Birks and D. J. Dyson, *Proc. Roy. Soc. (London)*, *A275*, 135 (1963).
6. K. S. Krishnan and P. K. Seshan, *Proc. Ind. Acad. Sci.*, *A8*, 487 (1938).
7. D. P. Craig and P. C. Hobbins, *J. Chem. Soc.*, *1955*, 539.
8. G. Weber and F. W. J. Teale, *Trans. Faraday Soc.*, *54*, 640 (1958).
9. B. S. Neporent, *Zh. Fiz. Khim.*, *21*, 1111 (1947).
10. I. V. Obreimov, A. F. Prichotko, and K. G. Shabaldas, *J. Exp. Theor. Phys. USSR*, *6*, 1062 (1936).
11. A. Jablonski, *Z. Physik.*, *96*, 236 (1935).
12. F. Perrin, *Ann. Phys. (Paris)*, *12*, 169 (1929).
13. G. Weber, *J. Opt. Soc. Am.*, *46*, 962 (1956).
14. P. Soleillet, *Ann. Phys. (Paris)*, *12*, 23 (1929).
15. G. Weber, *Advan. Protein Chem.*, *8*, 415 (1953).
16. H. Zimmerman and N. Joop, *Z. Elektrochem.*, *64*, 1215 (1960).
17. J. N. Murrell, *The Theory of the Electron Structure of Organic Molecules*, Methuen and Company, London, 1963, Chapter 10.
18. G. Weber, *Biochem. J.*, *75*, 335 (1960).
19. G. Weber, *Trans. Faraday Soc.*, *50*, 554 (1954).
20. F. Perrin, *J. Physique*, *7*, 1 (1936).
21. R. Memming, *Z. Physik. Chem. (Frankfurt)*, *28*, 168 (1961).

22. A. Einstein, *Ann. Physik.*, *19*, 371 (1906).
23. R. F. Steiner and H. Edelhoch, *Chem. Rev.*, *62*, 462 (1962).
24. G. Weber and L. B. Young, *J. Biol. Chem.*, *239*, 1415 (1964).
25. F. Perrin, *Ann. Phys. (Paris)*, *17*, 283 (1932).
26. Th. Förster, *Ann. Physik.*, *2*, 55 (1947).
27. P. Pheofilov and B. Sveshnikov, *J. Phys. USSR*, *3*, 493 (1963).
28. J. Czekalla, *Z. Elektrochem.*, *64*, 1221 (1960).
29. J. Czekalla and G. Wick, *Z. Elektrochem.*, *65*, 727 (1961).
30. P. Langevin, *J. Phys. (Paris)*, *4*, 678 (1905).
31. G. Weber, *J. Chem. Phys.*, *43*, 521 (1965).
32. J. Czekalla and K. O. Meyer, *Z. Physik Chem. (Frankfurt)*, *27*, 185 (1961).
33. R. S. Mulliken, *Rec. Trav. Chim.*, *75*, 845 (1956).
34. G. Weber, *Trans. Faraday Soc.*, *44*, 185 (1948).
35. R. Epple and Th. Förster, *Z. Elektrochem.*, *58*, 783 (1954).
36. W. Arnold and E. S. Meek, *Arch. Biochem. Biophys.*, *60*, 82 (1956).
37. M. Kamen, *Primary Processes in Photosynthesis*, Academic Press, New York, 1963.
38. G. Weber, *Biochem. J.*, *75*, 345 (1960).
39. D. J. B. Laurence, *Biochem. J.*, *51*, 168 (1952).
40. S. F. Velick, *J. Biol. Chem.*, *233*, 1455 (1958).

Author Index*

A

Abraham, R., 50 (ref. 40), 77
Adelman, A., 98 (ref. 60), 145
Aladekomo, J. B., 117 (ref. 143), 147
Alberti, G., 51 (ref. 48), 77
Albrecht, A. C., 123 (ref. 163), 147, 191, 193
Alire, R. M., 153 (ref. 18), 154 (ref. 18), 159, 161 (ref. 18), 165
Allison, J. B., 28 (ref. 33), 40, 73 (ref. 37), 77, 152 (ref. 11), 158 (ref. 11), 165
Al'perovich, L. I., 98 (ref. 61), 145
Amesz, J., 74, 78
Appleyard, J. H., 117 (ref. 144), 147
Argauer, R. J., 50, 54 (ref. 23), 55 (ref. 23), 56, 57, 59 (ref. 23), 76, 155 (ref. 27), 163, 166, 167, 178 (ref. 1), 183
Arnold, S. J., 187, 193
Arnold, W., 238, 240
Ascoli, F., 205 (ref. 14), 216
Ausloos, P., 84 (ref. 10), 143
Avivi, P., 112, 146
Azumi, T., 35 (ref. 49), 36 (ref. 55), 40, 108 (ref. 106), 120 (ref. 150), 122–124, 146, 147

B

Bäckström, H. L. J., 22 (ref. 21), 35 (ref. 46), 40
Baer, J. E., 51 (ref. 41), 53 (ref. 41), 77
Bailey, E. A., Jr., 75 (ref. 108), 78
Baldwin, B. A., 217 (ref. 4), 239
Balkanski, M., 190, 193
Bar, V., 111 (ref. 122), 146
Bardi, C. E., 50 (ref. 39), 77, 207 (ref. 16), 216
Barnes, W. J., 49 (ref. 17), 51 (ref. 17), 55 (ref. 17), 57 (ref. 17), 76

Bartok, W., 16 (ref. 16), 39, 126 (ref. 180), 127 (ref. 180), 128, 132, 148
Basile, L. J., 95 (ref. 47), 112 (ref. 125), 144, 146
Bayliss, N. S., 137, 148
Becker, R. S., 28 (ref. 33), 39, 40, 92 (ref. 36), 141, 144, 152 (ref. 11) 158 (ref. 11), 165
Beer, M., 20 (ref. 20), 39
Bellin, J. S., 97 (ref. 58), 145
Bender, D. F., 51 (ref. 49), 77
Bennett, H. E., 47 (ref. 14), 76
Bennett, R. G., 29 (ref. 35), 40, 75 (ref. 109), 78, 102 (refs. 76, 77), 145
Berg, R. A., 75 (ref. 110), 78, 217 (ref. 2), 239
Bergmann, F., 99 (ref. 64), 145
Berlman, I. B., 114 (ref. 135), 147
Berry, M. G., 123, 147, 191, 193
Beveridge, D. L., 133 (ref. 198), 134 (ref. 198), 148
Bhaumik, M. L., 102 (ref. 80), 140, 145, 149, 160 (refs. 44, 46, 52–55), 166
Bichet, G., 190, 193
Bigeleisen, J., 123 (ref. 160), 147, 191 (ref. 17), 193
Bird, L. H., 53, 77
Birks, J. B., 100 (ref. 70), 103 (ref. 86), 107 (ref. 97), 109 (ref. 110), 114–116, 117 (refs. 131, 143, 144), 145–147, 149, 217 (ref. 5), 239
Blackwell, L. A., 124 (ref. 167), 147
Blake, N. W., 124 (ref. 168), 148
Bolland, J. L., 37 (ref. 58), 40
Booth, J., 205 (ref. 12), 215
Botré, C., 205 (ref. 14), 216
Bould, H., 112 (ref. 127), 146

* *Italic* numbers refer to reference pages.

241

Bovey, F. A., 95 (ref. 51), 114 (ref. 51), *144*

Bowen, E. J., 26 (ref. 28), 34 (ref. 43), *40*, 49 (ref. 18), 52, 54, *76, 77*, 85 (ref. 16), 102, 107, 140 (refs. 99, 223), *143, 145, 146, 149*, 188, *193*

Bowman, R. L., 62 (ref. 85), 68, *78*

Boyland, E., 205 (ref. 12), *215*

Bradley, D. F., 196 (refs. 7, 8), 197 (refs. 7, 8), 204, *215*

Bradshaw, J. S., 100 (ref. 69), *145*

Brandt, W. W., 153 (ref. 20), 154 (ref. 20), 155 (ref. 28), 156 (ref. 28), 158 (ref. 20), 161, *165, 166*

Brauner, J. W., 52 (ref. 62), *77*

Brealey, G. J., 29 (ref. 34), *40*, 92 (ref. 34), *144*

Brecher, C., 159 (ref. 42), 160 (refs. 42, 50, 51), *166*

Bredereck, K., 92 (ref. 31), *144*

Breitschwerdt, K., 125 (ref. 172), *148*

Brewer, L., 75 (ref. 110), *78*

Brewer, R. G., 75 (ref. 110), *78*

Bridge, N. K., 37 (ref. 56), *40*

Brinen, J. S., 132 (ref. 195), *148*, 153 (ref. 16), 160 (ref. 58), *165, 167*

Britt, R. D., Jr., 74 (ref. 96), *78*, 175, *184*

Brock, E. G., 142 (ref. 227), *149*

Brocklehurst, B., 34 (ref. 43), *40*, 192, *193*

Brodie, B. B., 51 (refs. 41, 43), 52 (ref. 55), 53, *77*

Brooks, F. D., 109 (ref. 111), *146*

Brophy, V. A., 160 (ref. 50), *166*

Brown, F. H., 111 (ref. 119), *146*

Brown, G. C., Jr., 75 (ref. 111), *78*

Browne, R. J., 187, *193*

Burdett, R. A., 67 (ref. 91), *78*

Burlingame, A. L., 163 (ref. 74), *167*

Burns, G., 191 (ref. 15), *193*

Burton, M., 75, *79*, 109 (ref. 114), 111, *146*

Butler, C. L., 189, *193*

C

Calvin, M., 96 (ref. 54), *144*

Capotosto, A., Jr., 163 (ref. 73), *167*

Carter, D. A., 163 (ref. 76), *167*

Caughey, M. R., 50 (ref. 25), *76*

Caulfield, P. A., 68 (ref. 92), *78*

Chace, W. H., 187 (ref. 2), *193*

Chance, B., 74, *78*

Chandross, E. A., 192, *193*

Chapman, J. H., 54 (ref. 66), *77*

Chatterjee, K. K., 161 (ref. 66), *167*

Chaudhury, N. K., 103, *145*

Chenkin, T., 52 (ref. 55), *77*

Cherkasov, A. S., 99 (ref. 66), *145*

Choi, S. I., 104 (ref. 89), *145*

Chowdhury, M., *40*, 92 (ref. 38), 93 (ref. 38), *144*

Christodouleas, N. D., 108 (refs. 103, 105), *146*, 152 (ref. 14), *165*

Christophorou, L. G., 107 (ref. 97), 114, 115, 116 (ref. 232), 117 (ref. 131), *146, 147, 149*

Clement, M. J. Y., 187, *193*

Collat, J. W., 50 (ref. 19), 59 (ref. 19), *76*, 162, *167*

Cook, R. J., 107 (ref. 98), *146*

Cooper, H. R., 37 (ref. 58), *40*

Corkill, J. M., 108 (ref. 102), *146*

Cotton, F. A., 160 (ref. 60), 161 (ref. 60), *167*

Coulson, C. A., 117 (ref. 141), 130 (ref. 188), *147, 148*

Counsell, R. C., 100 (ref. 69), *145*

Cowan, D. O., 100 (ref. 69), *145*

Cox, R. C., 55 (ref. 74), 57 (ref. 74), 58 (ref. 74), *77*, 178 (ref. 3), *183*

Craig, D. P., 162 (ref. 67), *167*, 219 (ref. 7), *239*

Crosby, G. A., 153 (ref. 18), 154 (ref. 18), 159, 160 (ref. 35), 161 (ref. 18), *165, 166*

Csavinszky, P., 142 (ref. 227), *149*

Curtice, R. E., 162 (ref. 69), *167*

Curtis, W., 96 (ref. 55), 97, *144*

Czekalla, J., 137, *149*, 237, 238, *240*

D

Daigre, G. W., 108 (ref. 105), *146*, 152 (ref. 14), *165*

Daigre, J., 108 (ref. 104), *146*, 152 (ref. 13), *165*
D'Alessio, J. T., 75 (ref. 114), *79*
Dalton, C., 100 (ref. 69), *145*
Davydov, A. V., 104, *145*
De Armond, K., 153 (ref. 21), 161 (refs. 21, 64, 65), 162 (ref. 21), *166, 167*
Debye, P., 123 (ref. 162), *147*
Dekker, A., 103 (ref. 84), *145*
DeLerma, B., 205 (ref. 14), *216*
Derkacheeva, L. D., 127 (ref. 178), *148*
DeSantis, F., 205 (ref. 13), *215*
Dickinson, T., 115 (ref. 137), 117 (refs. 137, 146), *147*
Dill, F. H., Jr., 191 (ref. 15), *193*
Dill, W., 52 (ref. 55), *77*
Doede, C. M., 41, *76*
Döller, E., 114 (ref. 133), 115 (ref. 133), *147*
Dörr, D., 124 (ref. 166), *147*
Dörr, F., 93 (ref. 42), *144*
Dolan, E., 191, *193*
Drushel, H. V., 55, 57 (ref. 74), 58 (ref. 74), *77*, 94, *144*, 178 (ref. 3), 181, *183*
Dubois, J. T., 51 (ref. 46), *77*, 83, 106 (ref. 95), *143, 146*
Dudley, D., 95 (ref. 52), 98 (ref. 52), *144*
Dufraisse, C., 189, *193*
Duggan, D. E., 51 (ref. 42), *77*
Dumke, W. P., 191 (ref. 15), *193*
Duysens, L. N. M., 74, *78*
Dyck, R. H., 100, *145*
Dyson, D. J., 100 (ref. 70), 115 (refs. 139, 140), *145, 147*, 217 (ref. 5), *239*

E

Edelhoch, H., 232 (ref. 23), 233 (ref. 23), *240*
Edelman, G. M., 74 (ref. 100), *78*
Edwards, J. O., 123 (ref. 162), *147*
Einstein, A., 229, *240*
Eisenberg, L., 74 (ref. 100), *78*
Eisenbrand, J., 181 (ref. 4), *183*
El-Bayoumi, M. A., *40*
Ellis, D. W., 41, 50 (refs. 29, 34), 60

(ref. 34), *76*, 130, 131 (ref. 190), *148*
El-Sayed, M. A., 87, 89 (ref. 28), 92 (ref. 35), 93 (ref. 39), 99 (ref. 62), 102 (ref. 80), *144–146*, 160 (ref. 44), *166*
Epple, R., 238 (ref. 35), *240*
Ermolaev, V. L., 34 (refs. 44, 45), *40*, 91 (ref. 29), 102 (ref. 75), *144, 145*
Etienne, A., 190, *193*
Evans, D. F., 108 (ref. 107), *146*
Ewald, A. H., 52, *77*

F

Farr, A. L., 62 (ref. 83), *78*
Fasman, G. D., 114, *147*
Fassel, V. A., 47, *76*, 158 (ref. 32), *166*
Fletcher, M. H., 67 (ref. 90), 74 (ref. 99), *78*, 163, *167*
Fletcher, P. C., 160 (refs. 46, 53), *166*
Förster, T., 33 (refs. 41, 42), 36 (refs. 50, 51), 37 (ref. 51), 38 (ref. 62), *39, 40*, 50 (ref. 35), 54 (ref. 66), *76, 77*, 92 (ref. 31), 101, 103, 107 (ref. 96), 113, 114, 115 (ref. 133), 125, 129 (ref. 183), *144–148*, 217 (ref. 1), 234 (ref. 26), 238 (ref. 35), *239, 240*
Forster, C. F., 94 (ref. 44), 112 (ref. 44), *144*
Forster, L. S., 58 (ref. 77), 60 (ref. 77), 61 (ref. 77), *78*, 95 (ref. 52), 98 (ref. 52), *144*, 153 (ref. 21), 161 (refs. 21, 64–66), 162 (ref. 21), *166, 167*
Frankel, H., 46 (ref. 8), 57 (ref. 8), 58 (ref. 8), *76*
Freed, S., 175, 177, 183 (ref. 6), *183*
Freeman, D. C., Jr., 156 (ref. 26), 163, *166*
Freeman, J. J., 159 (ref. 37), *166*
French, C. S., 74, *78*
Frenkel, J., 104, *145*
Fronaeus, S., 163 (ref. 78), *167*
Funt, B. L., 106 (ref. 93), 111 (ref. 123), 112 (ref. 123), *145, 146*
Furst, M., 109, 110 (ref. 117), 111 (refs. 112, 119), 115 (ref. 148), 118 (ref. 148), *146, 147*

G

Gachkovskii, V. F., 94 (ref. 46), 95 (ref. 46), *144*

Gandy, H. W., 75 (ref. 118), *79*

Ganguly, S. C., 103, *145*

Gans, F., 190, *193*

Geacintov, N., 94 (ref. 43), *144*

Gee, H., 112 (ref. 127), *146*

George, S., 160 (ref. 52), *166*

Gibson, G. E., 27 (ref. 31), *40*, 58 (ref. 78), 60 (ref. 78), 61 (ref. 78), *78*

Giesecke, P., 41 (ref. 1), *76*

Giglio, E., 205 (ref. 13), *215*

Gilmore, E. H., 27 (ref. 31), *40*, 58 (ref. 78), 60 (ref. 78), 61 (ref. 78), *78*

Glick, D., 62 (ref. 82), *78*

Goldfarb, T. D., 189, *193*

Goodman, L., *40*, 86, 87 (ref. 20), 92 (ref. 38), 93 (ref. 38), *144*

Gordon, M. P., 181 (ref. 7), *183*

Gorsuch, J. D., 38 (ref. 59), *40*

Graham-Bryce, I. J., 108 (ref. 102), *146*

Grauer, R. C., 50 (ref. 25), *76*

Green, M. E., 123 (ref. 163), *147*

Griswold, R., 86 (ref. 18), 140 (ref. 18), *143*

Gropper, H., 93 (ref. 42), *144*

Grupe, H., 93 (ref. 41), *144*

Gudmundsen, R. A., 160 (ref. 56), *166*

Gurney, R. W., 104, *145*

H

Haenni, E. O., 75 (ref. 107), *78*

Halverson, F., 153 (ref. 16), 160 (ref. 58), *165*, *167*

Hammond, G. S., 100, 103, *145*

Hardwick, R., 102 (ref. 79), 140, *145*, *149*

Harteck, P., 187 (ref. 2), *193*

Hartman-Leddon Co., 51, *77*

Hartmann, G., 188 (ref. 8), *193*

Hatchard, C. G., 22 (ref. 22), 35 (ref. 48), 36 (ref. 53), *40*, 51 (ref. 54), 57 (ref. 76), 73 (refs. 54, 95), *77*, *78*, 120 (refs. 151, 152), 121 (refs. 151, 152), 122, 123, *147*, 175, *184*

Haugen, G. P., 75 (ref. 116), *79*

Haylock, J. C., 131, *148*

Heckman, R. C., 93 (ref. 40), *144*

Hedin, P. A., 51 (ref. 50), *77*

Heicklen, J., 83 (ref. 7), 84 (ref. 8), *143*

Heidel, R. H., 47 (ref. 13), *76*, 158 (ref. 32), *166*

Heimbuch, A. H., 112 (refs. 127, 128), *146*

Held, M., 196 (ref. 5), *215*

Heller, A., 109, *146*

Heller, W. R., 104, *145*

Hengge, E., 75, *79*, 93 (ref. 41), *144*

Hercules, D. M., 1, 38 (ref. 59), *40*, 46, 52 (ref. 56), 55 (ref. 73), 57 (ref. 8), 58 (ref. 8), 74 (ref. 97), *76–78*, 127, 136, 140 (ref. 224), 141 (ref. 224), *148*, *149*, 151 (ref. 8), 152 (ref. 8), *165*, 192, *193*

Herkstroeter, W. G., 100 (ref. 68), *145*

Hess, S. M., 51 (ref. 43), *77*

Hetherington, A., 111 (ref. 123), 112 (ref. 123), *146*

Higa, S., 160 (ref. 46), *166*

Hirschberg, Y., 99 (ref. 64), *145*

Hirt, R. C., 41 (ref. 1), *76*, 132 (ref. 195), *148*

Ho, M., 54 (ref. 69), 55 (ref. 69), *77*, 178 (ref. 20), *184*

Hobbins, P. C., 219 (ref. 7), *239*

Hochstrasser, R. M., 88, 99 (ref. 63), 103 (ref. 23), 104, 117 (ref. 147), 118, 121, *144*, *145*, *147*

Holzbecher, Z., 175, *183*

Hormats, F., 142 (ref. 227), *149*

Horton, C. A., 151 (ref. 6), *165*

Howerton, H. K., 47 (ref. 15), *76*

Huke, F. B., 47 (ref. 13), *76*

Hutton, E., 36 (ref. 52), *40*, 114, *146*

I

Irvine, J. W., Jr., 88 (ref. 24), 113 (ref. 24), *144*

Isaks, M., 133 (ref. 199), 134 (ref. 199), *148*

Ivanova, T. V., 114 (ref. 132), *147*

J

Jablonski, A., *239*

Jackson, G., 38 (ref. 61), *40*, 51 (ref. 53), *77*, 129, 132, *148*

Jacobs, J., 130 (ref. 188), *148*

Jaffé, H. H., *39*, 132 (ref. 197), 133 (refs. 197–199), 134, *148*

James, C. G., 75 (ref. 110), *78*

Johnson, H., 108 (ref. 109), *146*, 181, 183, *184*

Johnson, J. A., 50 (ref. 24), *76*

Jolley, J. E., 83 (ref. 5), *143*

Jones, H. L., 133 (refs. 198, 199), 134 (refs. 198, 199), *148*

Jones, L. D., 67 (ref. 91), *78*

Joop, N., 224 (ref. 16), *239*

Jorgensen, C. K., 160 (ref. 62), 162 (ref. 62), *167*

Jortner, J., 104 (ref. 89), *145*

K

Kaifu, Y., 24 (ref. 23), *40*, 50 (refs. 28, 31, 33), *76*, 137 (ref. 212), 138 (ref. 217), *148*, *149*

Kaihara, M., 47 (ref. 15), *76*

Kalenichencho, Y. I., 154 (ref. 22), *166*

Kallmann, H., 109, 110 (ref. 117), 111 (refs. 112, 119), 115 (ref. 148), 118 (ref. 148), *146*, *147*

Kamen, M., 238 (ref. 37), *240*

Kanda, Y., 92 (ref. 37), 124 (ref. 167), *144*, *147*

Karyakin, A. V., 154 (ref. 22), *166*

Kasha, M., 9 (ref. 4), 20 (ref. 19), 21 (ref. 4), *39*, 86, 87, 90, 91 (ref. 17), 92, 96, 99, 108, *143*, *144*, *146*, 151 (refs. 9, 10), 152 (refs. 9, 10, 15), 154 (ref. 23), 156 (ref. 10), 159 (ref. 40), *165*, *166*, 175, *184*, 188, *193*

Kasper, K., 36 (refs. 50, 51), 37 (ref. 51), *40*, 107 (ref. 96), 113, 114, *146*

Katz, J. L., 104 (ref. 89), *145*

Kauzmann, W., 82 (ref. 2), *143*

Kawski, A., 137, *149*

Kearns, D. R., *40*

Keirs, R. J., 175, *184*

Kellogg, R. E., 29 (ref. 35), *40*, 102 (ref. 76), *145*

Kern, J., 124 (ref. 166), *147*

Khan, A. U., 94 (ref. 43), *144*

Khan, A. V., 188, *193*

Kiers, R. J., 74, *78*

King, R. M., 46, 74 (ref. 97), *76*, *78*

King, T. A., 115 (ref. 140), *147*

Kinmonth, R., 41 (ref. 1), *76*

Klimova, L. A., 140 (ref. 221), *149*

Kobayashi, M., 139 (ref. 220), *149*

Kochemirovskii, A. S., 138 (ref. 215), *149*

Kohen, E., 74 (ref. 105), *78*

Koizumi, M., 24 (ref. 23), *40*, 50 (ref. 31), *76*, 137 (ref. 212), 139, *148*, *149*

Kokubun, H., 128 (ref. 182), 139 (ref. 220), *148*, *149*

Kolobkov, V. P., 88 (ref. 26), *144*

Kolthoff, I. M., 134, *148*

Kortüm, G., 54 (ref. 66), *77*

Krishna, V. G., 86, 87 (ref. 20), *144*

Krishman, K. S., 218 (ref. 6), *239*

Kropp, J. L., 153 (ref. 17), *165*

Kruger, H. G., 75 (ref. 115), *79*

Kubsa, H., 75 (ref. 115), *79*

Kusuhara, S., 102 (ref. 79), *145*

L

Lacroix, G., 181, 183 (ref. 14), *184*

Ladner, S. J., 92 (ref. 36), 141, *144*

Laikin, M., 61 (ref. 81), *78*

Lamola, A. A., 100 (ref. 69), *145*

Lang, L., 16 (ref. 7), *39*

Langevin, P., 237 (ref. 30), 238 (ref. 30), *240*

Lasher, G., 191 (ref. 15), *193*

Latz, H. W., 175–178, 182 (refs. 10, 21), *184*

Laurence, D. J. B., 239, *240*

Lee, B., 52 (ref. 60), *77*

Lee, S. M., 160 (refs. 46, 52), *166*

Leermakers, P. J., 103 (ref. 81), *145*

Legallis, V., 74, *78*

Lehrer, S. S., 114, *147*

Leiner, K. Y., 62 (ref. 83), *78*

Leininger, E., 85, 86, 92 (ref. 30), 135 (ref. 30), *143*, *144*

Lempicki, A., 142 (ref. 231), *149*, 159 (ref. 42), 160 (refs. 42, 45, 49–51), *166*

Leonhardt, H., 33 (ref. 39), *40*

Lerman, L. S., 203 (ref. 11), *215*

Leto, J. R., 153 (ref. 16), 160 (ref. 58), *165*, *167*

Levinson, G. S., 96 (ref. 57), 97, *144*

Lewis, G. N., 99 (ref. 65), 120, 122, 123, *145*, *147*, 175, *184*, 191, *193*

Lewis, J., 160 (ref. 63), *167*

Lewis, R., 181, *184*

Lim, E. C., 20 (ref. 18), *39*, 124, *147*, 191, *193*

Linschitz, H., 123, *147*, 191, *193*

Lipkin, D., 99 (ref. 65), 120, 122 (ref. 149), 123 (ref. 159), *145*, *147*, 191 (ref. 16), *193*

Lippert, E., *40*, 46 (ref. 10), 50, 54 (refs. 10, 66), 55 (ref. 10), 56, 57 (ref. 10), 59 (ref. 10), 64 (ref. 10), *76*, *77*, 137, 140, *149*

Lipsett, F. R., 55 (ref. 70), 74, *77*, 103 (refs. 84, 85), *145*

Lipsky, S., 111, *146*

Liptay, W., 137 (ref. 214), *149*

Liquori, A. M., 205 (refs. 13, 14), *215*, *216*

Livingston, R., 51 (ref. 53), 58 (ref. 77), 60 (ref. 77), 61 (ref. 77), *77*, *78*, 117 (ref. 142), *147*

Lloyd, R. A., 188, *193*

Löber, G., 137, *149*

Longin, P., 84 (ref. 12), *143*

Longuet-Higgins, H. C., 20 (ref. 20), *39*

Lott, P. F., 55 (ref. 71), *77*

Lowry, O. H., 62 (refs. 83, 84), *78*

Lucchesi, P. J., 16 (ref. 16), *39*, 126 (ref. 180), 127 (ref. 180), 128, 132, *148*

Luckey, G. W., 84 (ref. 9), *143*

Ludwig, P. K., 75 (ref. 114), *79*

Lüder, W., 140 (ref. 225), *149*

Lumry, R., 95 (ref. 51), 114 (ref. 51), *144*

Lyons, H., 160 (ref. 53), *166*

M

McBride, W. R., 47 (ref. 14), *76*

McClure, D. S., 27 (refs. 29–31), *40*, 58 (ref. 78), 60 (ref. 78), 61 (ref. 78), *78*, 83 (ref. 3), 88, 100, 103 (ref. 22), 124 (ref. 168), *143–145*, *148*

Maccoll, A., 162 (ref. 67), *167*

McElroy, W. D., 186 (ref. 1), *193*

McGlynn, S. P., 33 (refs. 37, 38), 35 (ref. 49), 36 (ref. 55), *40*, 108, 120 (ref. 150), 122–124, *146*, *147*, 152 (refs. 13, 14), 154 (ref. 23), *165*, *166*, 173, 180, 183 (ref. 13), *184*

McRae, E. G., 96, 137, *144*, *148*, *149*

Magel, T. T., 99 (ref. 65), 120, 122 (ref. 149), *145*, *147*

Mallet, L., 187, *193*

Marcus, R. A., 104, *145*

Marcus, R. J., 75 (ref. 116), *79*

Margerum, J. D., 96 (ref. 57), *144*

Marsh, O. J., 142 (ref. 230), *149*, 160 (refs. 56, 57), *166*

Masin, F., 196 (ref. 4), *215*

Masin, M., 196 (ref. 4), *215*

Mason, S. F., 131, *148*

Massucci, M. A., 51 (ref. 48), *77*

Mataga, N., 24 (ref. 23), *40*, 50 (refs. 28, 31–33), 76, 92 (ref. 33), 137–139, *144*, *148*, *149*

Matheson, Coleman, and Bell, 51, 64 (ref. 44), *77*

Matovich, E., 160 (ref. 56), *166*

Meek, E. S., 238, *240*

Melhuish, W. H., 50, 54 (ref. 66), 55 (refs. 20, 72), 58 (ref. 21), 59, 60 (refs. 21, 26, 80), 61 (refs. 21, 26), 73 (ref. 26), 74 (ref. 98), *76–78*, 101 (ref. 71), 110, *145*, *146*

Memming, R., 229 (ref. 21), *239*

Meyer, K. O., 137 (ref. 214), *149*, 238, *240*

Mika, N., 93 (ref. 42), *144*

Milkey, R. G., 163, *167*

Miller, B. S., 50 (ref. 24), *76*

Miller, G. D., 50 (ref. 24), *76*

Millich, F., 96, *144*

Miwa, T., 139, *149*

Möll, F., 137 (ref. 204), 140 (ref. 225), *149*

Mokeeva, G. A., 114 (ref. 132), *147*

Mooney, R. W., 71 (ref. 93), *78*

Morantz, D. J., 142 (ref. 228), *149*

Mott, N. F., 104, *145*

Moureu, C., 189, *193*

Moye, H. A., 178, 181, 183 (ref. 22), *184*

Muel, B., 181, 183 (ref. 14), *184*

Mulliken, R. S., 238, *240*

Munro, I. H., 115 (ref. 139), *147*

Murad, E., 84 (refs. 10, 11), *143*

Murashige, R. H., 74 (ref. 98), *78*

Murray, R. W., 188, *193*

Murrell, J. N., 11 (ref. 8), *39*, 132, *148*, 226, *239*

N

Naboikin, Y. V., 131 (ref. 193), *148*

Nägle, W., 46 (ref. 10), 50 (ref. 10), 54–57 (ref. 10), 59 (ref. 10), 64 (ref. 10), *76*

Nag-Chadhuri, J., 33 (ref. 37), *40*

Nathan, M. I., 191, *193*

Nebbia, G., 54 (refs. 66, 68), *77*

Nedderman, H. C., 142 (ref. 227), *149*

Neely, B. T., 173, 180, 183 (ref. 13), *184*

Neely, W. C., 173, 180, 183 (ref. 13), *184*

Nehrich, R. B., Jr., 160 (ref. 48), *166*

Neish, W. J. P., 208 (ref. 17), *216*

Neparko, E., 106 (ref. 93), *145*

Neporent, B. S., 220 (ref. 9), *239*

Nieman, G. C., 36 (ref. 54), *40*, 124 (ref. 169), *148*

Nishijima, Y., 95 (ref. 49), *144*

Noble, B., 52 (ref. 60), *77*

Noyes, W. A., Jr., 83 (refs. 5, 7), 84 (refs. 9, 13), *143*

Nugent, L. J., 160 (refs. 46, 52), *166*

Nyholm, R. S., 162 (ref. 67), *167*

O

Obreimov, I. V., 220 (ref. 10), *239*

Oesterlin, H.-G., 92 (ref. 31), *144*

Ogryzlo, E. A., 187, *193*

Ohnesorge, W. E., 151, 158 (ref. 31), 163 (refs. 73–76), 164 (ref. 79), *166*, *167*

Olson, J. M., 74, *78*

Olson, R. A., 62 (ref. 86), 74, *78*

Orchin, M., *39*

Orgel, L. E., 117 (ref. 141), *147*, 160 (ref. 61), 162 (refs. 61, 67), *167*

Orr, S. F. D., 205 (ref. 12), *215*

Oster, G., 94 (ref. 43), 96, 97, 98 (ref. 60), *144*, *145*, 203, *215*

Oster, G. K., 97 (ref. 59), *145*

P

Palumbo, D. T., 71 (ref. 93), *78*

Pardee, A. B., 51 (ref. 47), 58 (ref. 79), *77*, *78*

Paris, J. P., 38 (ref. 59), *40*, 153 (ref. 20), 154 (refs. 20, 24), 158 (ref. 20), 161, *165*, *166*, 185, *193*

Parker, C. A., 22 (ref. 22), 35 (ref. 48), 36 (ref. 53), *40*, 43, 45 (ref. 5), 47, 49 (refs. 4, 17), 50 (ref. 4), 51 (refs. 17, 52, 54), *53–55*, 57 (refs. 5, 17, 75, 76), 58, 59 (refs. 3, 4), 60, 61 (ref. 4), 73 (refs. 54, 95), 74, *75–78*, 105 (ref. 92), 120 (refs. 151, 152), 121–123, *145*, *147*, 151 (ref. 3), *165*, 175, 178 (ref. 15), *184*

Parmenter, C. S., 84 (ref. 13), *143*

Pavlopoulos, T., 89 (ref. 28), *144*

Pavlova, E. N., 131 (ref. 193), *148*

Peattie, C. G., 151, *165*

Perrin, F., 33 (ref. 40), *40*, 222 (ref. 12), 229 (ref. 20), 230 (ref. 20), 231, 233 (ref. 20), 234 (ref. 25), 238 (ref. 12), *239*, *240*

Pheofilov, P., 236 (ref. 27), *240*

Pimentel, G. C., 189, *193*

Platt, J. R., 12 (ref. 14), *39*

Plitt, K. F., 95 (ref. 48), *144*

Pope, R., 117 (ref. 144), *147*

Popov, A. I., 165 (ref. 80), *167*

Popovych, O., 155 (ref. 25), 156 (refs. 25, 29), 157 (ref. 25), *166*
Porter, G., 37 (ref. 56), 38 (ref. 61), *40*, 102 (ref. 78), 107 (ref. 100), 129, 132, *145, 146, 148*, 192, *193*
Porter, G. B., 83 (ref. 5), *143*
Preston, L. M., 75 (ref. 117), *79*
Price, J. M., 47, *76*
Prichotko, A. F., 220 (ref. 10), *239*
Pringsheim, P., *39*, 115 (ref. 138), *147*, 158 (ref. 33), 160 (ref. 59), 162 (ref. 68), *166, 167*
Pugh, A. C., 51 (ref. 53), *77*

R

Rammensee, H., 196 (ref. 5), *215*
Ramsay, D. A., 6 (ref. 13), 14 (ref. 13), *39*, 187, *193*
Reay, N. W., 75 (ref. 117), *79*
Redlich, D., 62 (ref. 82), *78*
Reed, C. W., 103 (ref. 85), *145*
Rees, W. T., 43, 49 (ref. 4), 50 (ref. 4), 53–55, 58, 59 (refs. 3, 4), 60 (ref. 4), 61 (ref. 4), *75, 76*, 105 (ref. 92), *145*, 151 (ref. 3), *165*
Reeves, R. R., 187, *193*
Rehwoldt, R. H., 74 (ref. 97), *78*
Reynolds, M. J., 108 (ref. 105), *146*, 152 (ref. 14), *165*
Reznikova, I. I., 88 (ref. 26), *144*
Rhodes, W., 99 (ref. 62), *145*
Rice, S. A., 104, *145*
Rickard, E. F., 94 (ref. 44), 112 (ref. 44), *144*
Ripamonti, A., 205 (ref. 13), *215*
Roberts, N. R., 62 (ref. 83), *78*
Robinson, G. W., 9 (ref. 10), 16 (ref. 10), 36 (ref. 54), *39, 40*, 124 (ref. 169), *148*
Röllig, K., 75 (ref. 112), *79*
Rogers, D. A., 96 (ref. 57), *144*
Rogers, L. B., 50 (refs. 19, 29, 34), 59 (ref. 19), 60 (ref. 34), *76*, 81, 127, 130, 131 (ref. 190), 132 (ref. 181), 134 (ref. 181), 136, 140 (ref. 224), 141 (ref. 224), *148, 149*, 151, 155 (ref.

25), 156 (refs. 25, 29), 157 (ref. 25), 158 (ref. 31), 162, *165–167*
Rollefson, G. K., 75 (ref. 108), *78*
Rosebrook, D. D., 132 (ref. 195), *148*
Rosen, P., 74 (ref. 100), *78*
Rosenblatt, G. M., 75 (ref. 110), *78*
Rossotti, F. J. C., 163 (ref. 77), *167*
Rossotti, H., 163 (ref. 77), *167*
Rowley, G. R., 46 (ref. 7), 55 (ref. 7), *76*

S

Sahu, J., 52, *77*, 140 (ref. 223), *149*
St. John, P. A., 50 (ref. 38), 73 (ref. 38), *77*, 174, 177 (ref. 23), 179, *184*
Salmre, W., 175, 177, *183*
Saltiel, J., 100 (refs. 68, 69), *145*
Samelson, H., 142 (ref. 231), *149*, 159 (ref. 42), 165 (refs. 42, 45, 49–51), *166*
Sandel, V. R., 15 (ref. 15), *39*
Sandorfy, C., 130 (ref. 187), *148*
Sandros, K., 22 (ref. 21), 35 (ref. 46), *40*
Sangster, R. C., 88 (ref. 24), 113 (ref. 24), *144*
Sawicki, E., 51 (ref. 49), *77*, 108 (ref. 109), *146*, 181, 183, *184*
Schachter, M. M., 75 (ref. 107), *78*
Schäfer, F. P., 75 (ref. 112), *79*
Scheibe, G., 124 (ref. 166), *147*
Schimitschek, E. J., 160 (refs. 47, 48), *166*
Schmidkung, H., 188 (ref. 8), *193*
Schmillen, A., 217 (ref. 3), *239*
Schoener, B., 74, *78*
Schram, E., 109 (ref. 113), 112 (ref. 113), *146*
Schwarz, W. J., 112 (ref. 128), *146*
Schweitzer, D., 123, *147*, 191, *193*
Schwenker, R. P., 102 (ref. 76), *145*
Scott, A. B., 162 (ref. 69), *167*
Scott, D. R., 73 (ref. 37), *77*
Seaman, D., 52 (ref. 57), *77*
Searle, N. Z., 41 (ref. 1), *76*
Seibold-Blankenstein, I., 46 (ref. 10), 50 (ref. 10), 54–57 (ref. 10), 59 (ref. 10), 64 (ref. 10), *76*

Seliger, H. H., 186 (ref. 1), *193*
Seshan, P. K., 218 (ref. 6), *239*
Shabaldas, K. G., 220 (ref. 10), *239*
Sheftel, M. S., 67 (ref. 90), *78*
Shore, P. A., 51 (ref. 43), *77*
Shore, V. G., 58 (ref. 79), *78*
Shpol'skii, E. V., 86 (ref. 19), 140 (ref. 19), *144*
Shull, H., 140 (ref. 222), *149*
Sidman, J. W., 9 (ref. 11), *39*, 83 (ref. 3), *143*
Simpson, W. T., 96 (ref. 55), 97, *144*
Slavin, W., 71, *78*
Smith, B. E., 131, *148*
Smith, F. J., 108 (ref. 104), *146*, 152 (ref. 13), *165*
Snider, N. S., 16 (ref. 16), *39*, 126 (ref. 180), 127 (ref. 180), 128, 132, *148*
Soleillet, P., 224, *239*
Sommers, A. L., 55 (ref. 74), 57 (ref. 74), 58 (ref. 74), *77*, 94, *144*, 178 (ref. 3), 181, *183*
Sonntag, F. I., 192, *193*
South, D., 181 (ref. 7), *183*
Sponer, H., 92 (ref. 37), 124 (ref. 167), *144, 147*
Sprince, H., 46 (ref. 7), 55 (ref. 7), *76*
Stafford, F. E., 75 (ref. 110), *78*
Staiger, U., 46 (ref. 10), 50 (ref. 10), 54–57 (ref. 10), 59 (ref. 10), 64 (ref. 10), *76*
Stanley, T. W., 108 (ref. 109), *146*
Staudinger, H., 50 (ref. 40), *77*
Stauff, J., 188, *193*
Steiner, R. F., 232 (ref. 23), 233 (ref. 23), *240*
Steinlicht, H., 36 (ref 54), *40*
Stenger, V. A., 134, *148*
Stephen, V. A., 50 (ref. 22), 59 (ref. 22), *76*
Stern, O., 32, *40*
Sternlicht, H., 124 (ref. 169), *148*
Stevens, B., 36 (ref. 52), *40*, 88 (ref. 25), 106 (ref. 95), 114, 115 (ref. 137), 117, 119, *144, 146, 147*
Stevens, H. M., 157, 158 (ref. 30), *166*
Stirpe, D., 142 (ref. 227), *149*

Stoessell, L., 33 (ref. 37), *40*
Stone, A. L., 196 (ref. 8), 197 (ref. 8), *215*
Strickler, H. S., 50 (ref. 25), *76*
Strickler, S. J., 217 (ref. 2), *239*
Sunseri, R., 33 (ref. 38), *40*, 108 (ref. 103), *146*
Surash, J. J., 52 (ref. 56), *77*
Sutton, L. E., 162 (ref. 67), *167*
Suzuki, C. K., 142 (ref. 230), *149*, 160 (ref. 57), *166*
Sveshnikov, B. Ya., 114 (ref. 132), *147*, 236 (ref. 27), *240*
Svitashev, K. K., 91 (ref. 29), *144*
Swank, R. K., 111 (ref. 121), 112 (ref. 126), *146*
Swenson, G. W., 124 (ref. 164), *147*, 191, *193*
Szent-Gyorgyi, A., 181, *184*

T

Tanner, D. W., 117 (ref. 142), *147*
Taylor, W., 117 (ref. 141), *147*
Teale, F. W. J., 46 (ref. 9), 55 (ref. 9), 57 (ref. 9), 58 (ref. 9), 60 (ref. 9), 61 (ref. 9), *76*, 84 (ref. 14), 104 (ref. 14), 105 (ref. 14), *143*, 219 (ref. 8), *239*
Telk, C. L., 142 (ref. 230), *149*, 160 (refs. 46, 55, 57), *166*
Terenin, A. N., 34 (refs. 44, 45), *40*, 102 (ref. 75), *145*
Thomas, G. J., 51 (ref. 47), *77*
Thommes, G. A., 85, 86, 92 (ref. 30), 135 (ref. 30), *143, 144*
Tin, M., 173 (ref. 24), 174 (ref. 24), 177, 182 (refs. 24, 25), *184*
Tolmach, L. J., 108 (ref. 108), *146*
Tomaschek, R., 159 (ref. 43), *166*
Toner, S. D., 95 (ref. 48), *144*
Torihashi, Y., 50 (ref. 28), *76*
Trasciatti, M., 205 (ref. 14), *215*
Trozzolo, A. M., 188, *193*
Tsuno, S., 92 (ref. 33), 138 (ref. 216), 139 (ref. 216), *144, 149*
Turner, G. K., 72, 73, *78*
Turro, N. J., 100 (ref. 69), 103 (refs. 81, 82), *145*

U

Udenfriend, S., 48, 51 (ref. 41), 52 (refs. 16, 55), 53 (ref. 41), 54 (ref. 16), 55 (ref. 16), 61 (ref. 16), 68 (ref. 92), 74, 75–78, 173 (ref. 19), 176 (ref. 19), 184, 195 (ref. 1), 215

Ultra-Violet Products, 45 (ref. 6), 76

Unterleitner, F., 142 (ref. 227), 149

Urban, W., 128 (ref. 176), 148

V

Van Duuren, B. L., 24 (ref. 27), 40, 50, 76, 77, 135, 137, 148, 149, 195, 196 (ref. 6), 207 (ref. 16), 215, 216

Veening, H., 155 (ref. 28), 156 (ref. 28), 161, 166

Velick, S. F., 239, 240

Veljković, S. R., 137, 149

Vise, M. H., 177, 183 (ref. 6), 183

Viswanath, G., 20 (ref. 19), 39

Vogt, V., 100 (ref. 69), 145

Volmer, M., 32, 40

Von Bertalanffy, L., 196 (ref. 4), 215

Voss, W., 40, 46 (ref. 10), 50 (ref. 10), 54–57 (ref. 10), 59 (ref. 10), 64 (ref. 10), 76

W

Wadman, W. H., 51 (ref. 47), 77

Wahl, P., 95 (ref. 50), 144

Walker, C. A., 41, 76

Ware, W. R., 51 (ref. 51), 77, 106 (ref. 94), 146, 217 (ref. 4), 239

Wasserman, E., 188, 193

Weber, G., 46 (ref. 9), 55 (ref. 9), 57 (ref. 9), 58 (ref. 9), 60 (ref. 9), 61 (ref. 9), 76, 84 (ref. 14), 104 (ref. 14), 105 (ref. 14), 143, 217, 219 (ref. 8), 222 (ref. 13), 224 (refs. 15, 18), 225, 226 (ref. 18), 227, 228, 229 (ref. 15), 232 (ref. 15), 233 (ref. 24), 234, 236 (ref. 18), 237, 238 (ref. 34), 239 (ref. 38), 239, 240

Weber, K., 125

Wehry, E. L., 81, 127 (ref. 181), 134 (ref. 181), 148

Weill, G., 96 (ref. 54), 144

Weil-Malherbe, H., 205 (ref. 15), 208 (ref. 15), 216

Weimer, E. O., 54 (ref. 69), 55 (ref. 69), 77, 178 (ref. 20), 184

Weinberg, M., 160 (ref. 46), 166

Weinreb, A., 111 (ref. 122), 112, 146

Weir, D. S., 83 (ref. 6), 143

Weiss, J., 117 (ref. 141), 147

Weissler, A., 64 (refs. 88, 89), 75 (refs. 88, 89), 75, 78, 151 (refs. 2, 4), 158 (ref. 4), 165

Weissman, S. I., 28 (ref. 32), 40, 152 (ref. 12), 153 (ref. 19), 154 (ref. 19), 158 (refs. 12, 19), 159, 165

Weller, A., 16 (ref. 17), 33 (ref. 39), 38 (ref. 60), 39, 40, 50 (ref. 36), 76, 125 (ref. 172), 126, 127 (refs. 173, 174, 177, 179), 128 (ref. 176), 129, 131, 148

Weller, J. F., 75 (ref. 118), 79

Wen, W., 124 (ref. 165), 147

Wentworth, W. E., 74 (ref. 96), 78, 175, 184

West, K., 107 (ref. 99), 140 (ref. 99), 146

West, W., 39, 81, 85 (ref. 1), 89 (ref. 1), 100 (ref. 1), 143

Whan, R. E., 153 (ref. 18), 154 (ref. 18), 159, 160 (ref. 35), 161 (ref. 18), 165, 166

White, B. G., 142 (ref. 228), 149

White, C. E., 50, 54 (refs. 23, 69), 55 (refs. 23, 69), 56, 57, 59 (ref. 23), 64 (refs. 87–89), 67 (ref. 90), 75, 75–78, 151 (refs. 1, 2, 4, 5), 155 (refs. 1, 5, 27), 156 (ref. 26), 158 (refs. 4, 5), 163, 165–167, 178 (refs. 1, 20), 183, 184

Wiame, J. M., 201, 215

Wick, G., 237 (ref. 29), 240

Wilkins, R. G., 160 (ref. 63), 167

Wilkinson, F., 37 (ref. 57), 40, 51 (ref. 46), 77, 83, 102 (ref. 78), 143, 145

Wilkinson, G., 160 (ref. 60), 161 (ref. 60), 167

Willard, H. H., 151 (ref. 6), 165

Williams, A. H., 26 (ref. 28), 40

Williams, R., 35 (ref. 47), *40*, 122, *147*
Wilson, D. J., 52, *77*
Wilson, R. M., 51 (ref. 49), *77*
Windsor, M. W., 107 (ref. 100), 142 (ref. 229), *146*, *149*, 153 (ref. 17), *165*
Winefordner, J. D., 50 (ref. 38), 73 (ref. 38), *77*, 169, 173 (ref. 24), 174–178, 182 (refs. 21, 24, 25), 183 (ref. 22) ,*184*
Winston, H., 142 (ref. 230), *149*, 160 (ref. 57), *166*
Witzke, H., 187 (ref. 4), *193*
Wokes, F., 49 (ref. 18), 52, *76*
Wolf, M. K., 196 (ref. 7), 197 (ref. 7), 204, *215*
Wright, A. J. C., 142 (ref. 228), *149*
Wu, M. L., 62 (ref. 83), *78*
Wyman, G. M., 96 (ref. 57), *144*

Y

Yanari, S. S., 95 (ref. 51), 114 (ref. 51), *144*
Yates, J. M., 192, *193*
Yguerabide, J., 109 (ref. 114), *146*
Young, L. B., 233 (ref. 24), 234, *240*
Yuster, P., 28 (ref. 32), *40*, 152 (ref. 12), 158 (ref. 12), *165*

Z

Zadorozhny, B. A., 131 (ref. 193), *148*
Zanker, V., 196 (ref. 5), *215*
Zarowin, G. B., 75 (ref. 113), *79*
Zelinskii, V. V., 88 (ref. 26), *144*
Zhmyreva, L. A., 138 (ref. 215), *149*
Zimmerman, H., 224 (ref. 16), *239*
Zimmerman, H. E., 15 (ref. 15), *39*

Subject Index

A

Absorption, 10, 11, 218
Acetylene, geometry of, 14
N-Acetyl-L-tyrosine ethyl ester, determination of, 178
Acridine, fluorescence of, 24
Acridine Orange (AO), binding to mononucleotides, 199
  binding to nucleic acids, 196
  binding to polyanions, 195
Adsorption, errors due to, 52
Aggregation, of dyes, 196
Aliphatic compounds, luminescence of, 82
Alkaloids, determination of, 176
Alkyl halides, effect on intersystem crossing, 33
Anabasine, determination of, 178
Analgesics, determination of, 176
Analytical application of chelate luminescence, 162
Aniline polarization spectrum, 225
Anthraquinone, photoreduction of, 3,37
Apparent fluorescence spectra, 54
Aromatic carbonyl compounds, luminescence of, 91
Aromatic hydrocarbons. See Hydrocarbons, aromatic
Aspirin, determination of, 176
Atropine, determination of, 177
Azulene, fluorescence of, 20

B

Benzene, electronic states of, 17, 20
Benzophenone, energy transfer in, 35
Benzo(a)pyrene, TMU complex with, 205
3,4-Benzopyrene, determination of, 181
Biacetyl, luminescence of, 83

Binding, of acridine orange, to mononucleotides, 199
  to nucleic acids, 196
  to polyanions, 195
  electrostatic, 204
Binding equilibria, effect on fluorescence polarization, 239
Biphenyl, determination of, 179
Blood serum, analysis of, 176
Bonding, hydrogen, effect on fluorescence, 50, 135
Bromobenzene, fluorescence efficiency of, 27

C

Calibration, of monochromator–detector combination, 55
Calibration curves, for fluorescence, 58
Cancer, induction by aromatic hydrocarbons, 205
Carbene reactions, 188
Carbonyl compounds, aromatic, luminescence of, 91
Cell geometry, 43, 47
Charge transfer fluorescence, 154, 161
Chelates, fluorescent, 158
  luminescent, effect of ligand field on, 160
    effect of ligand structure on, 155
    effect of metal ion on, 157
    paramagnetic metal, 33
    solvent effect on, 156
    Transition metal, 160
Chemiluminescence, 185
1-Chloroanthracene, energy transfer of, 34
Chlorobenzene, fluorescence efficiency of, 27
Chlorpromazine, determination of, 177
Chromatography, thin-layer, 178
Cocaine, determination of, 177

253

Collisional quenching, 31, 32
Compensating spectrofluorometers, 63, 71
Concentration quenching, 58
Coronene, TMU complexes of, 205
Correction, of excitation spectra, 56
of luminescence spectra, 54
Coupling, spin-orbit, 27
vibrational, 34

D

$d^* \rightarrow d$ transitions, 161
Delayed fluorescence, 35, 118, 122
Detectability, limits of, 2, 181
Detectors, 46
Dibenz(a,h)anthracene, fluorescence of, 207
Diffusion coefficient, 230
9,10-Dihydroxyanthracene, photoreduction of, 38
Dipole moment, of excited singlet states, 237
of organic molecules, 137, 237
Dissociation, of peroxides, 189
protolytic, 125 et seq.
Dyes, aggregation of, 196
fluorescence of, 95

E

Electric field, polarization of fluorescence in, 237
Electroluminescence, 190
Electrolysis, of aromatic hydrocarbons, 192
Electron-donating groups, effect on fluorescence, 29
Electronic absorption, 10
intensity of, 11
Electronic states, 2, 6, 17, 20
vibrational levels of, 9
Electrostatic binding, 204
Electrostatic transitions, intensity of, 12
probability of, 26
symmetry restrictions on, 26

Emission, stimulated, 142
Energy transfer, 32–34, 101, 104, 159, 233
noncollisional, 33
resonant, 34
EPA, 22, 170
Errors, due to absorption, 52
E-type delayed fluorescence, 122
Excimers, 36, 96, 107, 113
Excitation, energy, radiationless transfer of, 30
molecular, 9
mechanisms in chemiluminescence, 185
sources, 45
spectra, 44
correction of, 56
Excited organic molecules, dipole moments of, 137, 237
Excited state geometry, 6, 14
Excited state ionization, 15, 38
Excited state lifetimes, 21, 31, 238
Excited states, chemical properties of, 14
radiationless deactivation of, 28
External heavy-atom effect, 108

F

Filter fluorometers, 42, 62
Filters, 42
Flavin, fluorescence polarization of, 231
Fluorescence, calibration curves for, 58
charge transfer, 154, 161
delayed, 35, 118, 122
identification of compounds by, 62
of inorganic complexes, 162
lifetimes, instrumentation for determination of, 75
process, 19
quenching, 31, 33, 49–51, 101, 106, 189, 196
reference compounds, 49
sensitivity, 53, 60
sensitized, 102
solvent effect on, 50, 135
solvents for, 50

spectra, 54, 55
temperature effects on, 28, 52, 136, 139, 173
viscosity effects on, 52
Fluorescence polarization, 217, 232, 237
effect of binding equilibria on, 239
of flavin, 231
spectra, 224, 226
Fluorescent chelates, 158
Fluorescent indicators, 134
Fluorobenzene, fluorescence efficiency of, 27
Fluorograph, 75
Fluorometers, 42, 62
Formaldehyde, electronic states of, 6
electronic transitions of, 11
geometry of, 14
Franck-Condon principle, 18, 135
Functional groups, effect on luminescence, 88

G

Gallium arsenite, 190
Geometry, of acetylene, 14
of cells, 43, 47
of excited states, 6, 14
of formaldehyde, 14
Grating monochromators, 43
Ground state, 3

H

Heavy-atom effect, 88, 97
external, 108
Heterocycles, nitrogen, 92
Hund's rule, 8
Hydrocarbons, aromatic, cancer induction by, 205
electrolysis of, 192
fluorescence of, 88
luminescence of, 85, 91
oxygen quenching of fluorescence in, 106, 189
solubilization of, 205
Hydrogen bonding, effect on fluorescence, 50, 135

I

Identification, of compounds by fluorescence, 62
Indicators, fluorescent, 134
Indole, determination of, 177
fluorescence polarization spectrum of, 226
Inner filter effect, 49, 58, 105, 107
Inorganic complexes, fluorescence of, 162
Instrumental sensitivity, 59
Intensity of electronic absorption, 11
Intercalation theory, 203
Internal conversion, 19
Intersystem crossing, 21, 23, 27, 28
effect of alkyl halides on, 33
quantum efficiency of, 29
Intramolecular energy transfer, 104, 159
Intramolecular heavy-atom effect, 88
Ion-exchange resins, 112
Ionization, excited-state, 15, 38
Isomerism, effect on fluorescence, 97, 99, 100

K

Ketones, luminescence of, 83

L

Lasers, 160
Lifetime, excited-state, 21, 31, 238
phosphorescence, 22, 44, 73, 170
Ligand field, effect on chelate luminescence, 160
Ligand structure, effect on chelate luminescence, 155
Light, scattered, 47
Limits of detectability, 2, 181
Luminescence, of aliphatic compounds, 82
of aromatic compounds, 91
of chelates, 162
crystal, 88, 103
definition of, 1

effect of functional groups on, 88
effect of molecular geometry on, 98
effect of molecular structure on, 24, 85
effect of substituent groups on, 29
instrumentation, 62
of ketones, 83
of nitrogen heterocycles, 92
processes, 16
processes competing with, 29
recombination, 191
spectra, correction of, 54

M

Mercury arc, 41
Mesoporphyrin (IX) dimethyl ester, fluorescence of, 28
Metal chelate compounds, fluorescence of, 151
Metal ion, effect of chelate fluorescence, 157
Mirror image relationship, 100
Mixed excimers, 107
$m^* \rightarrow m$ transitions, 154
Molecular excitation, 9
Molecular geometry, effect on luminescence, 98
Molecular structure, effect on luminescence, 24, 85
Monochromator, 43, 45, 55
Mononucleotides, binding of acridine orange to, 199
Multiplicity, 4

N

Naphthalene, determination of, 180
phosphorescence of, 35
β-Naphthol, excited state ionization of, 38
Nicotine, determination of, 178
Nitrogen heterocycles, luminescence of, 92
p-Nitrophenol, determination of, 179
Noncollisional energy transfer, 33
Noncollisional quenching mechanisms, 31

Nornicotine, determination of, 178
n,π^* excited states, 8, 23
$n \rightarrow \pi^*$ transitions, 23, 29, 92
n,σ^* excited states, 8
Nucleic acids, binding of acridine orange to, 196

O

Organic crystal scintillators, 112
Organic liquid scintillators, 109
Organic molecules, excited, dipole moments of, 137, 237
Organic oxidations, chemiluminescence in, 188
Organic plastic scintillators, 111
Organic polymers, fluorescence of, 94
Oxidations, organic, chemiluminescence in, 188
Oxygen quenching of fluorescence, 106, 189

P

Paramagnetic metal chelates, 33
Parathion, determination of, 179
Peroxide dissociation, 189
Perylene, energy transfer in, 34
fluorescence quenching by amines in, 33
Phenanthrene, determination of, 180
Phenobarbital, determination of, 177
Phenol absorption, emission, and polarization, 224
Phosphorescence, 1, 21, 35, 44
emission and excitation spectra of, 169
impurities in, 174
instrumentation for, 73
intensity of, 173
lifetimes for, 22, 44, 73, 170
quantum efficiency of, 25, 29
sensitized, 102
α-Phosphorescence, 120
Phosphoroscope, 170
Phosphorimetric limits of detection, 181

Phosphorimetry, 169
Phosphoroscopic resolution in analysis, 172, 179
Photolysis, 51
Photomultiplier tubes, 44, 46
Photochemical isomerizations, 100
Photoionization, 191
Photoperoxides, 189
Photoreduction, of anthroquinone, 3, 37
of 9, 10-dehydroxyanthracene, 38
Photosynthesis, 238
Photochemical reactions, 30, 37, 82
π-electron distribution, 15
systems, 4
$\pi^* \to m$ transition, 154
$\pi^* \to n$ fluorescence, 92
π, π^* excited states, 4, 7, 23
of fluorescent metal chelates, 157
$\pi \to \pi^*$ transitions, 6, 13, 23
Polarization of fluorescence, 217, 232, 237
in an electric field, 237
Polarization shifts, in fluorescence spectra, 136, 224
Polarization spectrum, 225
Polarized light absorption, 218
Polyadenylic acid, 200
Polyanions, binding of Acridine Orange to, 195
Potassium bromide, pellets, 207
Predissociation, 82
Probability, of an electronic transition, 26
Procaine, determination of, 177
Processes competing with luminescence, 29
Proteins, polarization of fluorescence of, 232
Protolytic dissociation, of excited organic molecules, 125 et seq.
P-type delayed fluorescence, 122
Pyrene, fluorescence of, 206

Q

Quantum efficiency, of fluorescence, 19, 24, 53, 58, 59, 71

of intersystem crossing, 29
of phosphorescence, 25, 29
Quenching, collisional, 31, 32
concentration, 58
of fluorescence, 31, 49–51, 101, 196
noncollisional, 31
by oxygen, 106, 189
solvent, 107, 141
Quinine, as fluorescence standard, 50, 53
Quinoline, solvent effect on fluorescence, 24

R

Radiationless deactivation, of an excited state, 28
Radiationless processes, 19
Radiationless transfer, of excitation energy, 30
Radical–radical reactions, 187
Raman spectra, 47
Rare earth fluorescence, 158
Recombination luminescence, 191
Reference compounds, in fluorescence, 49, 56
Relative fluorescence quantum yields, 24
Relaxation, times, 230
vibrational, 18
Reserpine, determination of, 177
Resolution, phosphoroscopic, 172, 179
Resonant energy transfer, 34
Rotational diffusion coefficient, 230
Rotational relaxation time, 230

S

Sample cell geometry, 47
Scattered light, 47
Scintillating ion-exchange resins, 112
Scintillators, organic crystal, 112
organic liquid, 109
organic plastic, 111
Sensitivity, of analysis, 55, 59, 170, 172
instrumental, 59

Sensitized fluorescence, 102
Sensitized phosphorescence, 102
Serotonin, determination of, 177
Singlet–singlet transitions, 22
Singlet state, excited, dipole moment
    of, 237
Single–triplet mixing, 27
Solubilization, of aromatic hydro-
    carbons, 205
Solvent effect, on chelate fluorescence,
    156
  on fluorescence, 50, 135
Solvent quenching, of fluorescence,
    107, 141
Solvents, for fluorescence, 50
  for low temperature spectral meas-
    urements, 50, 174
Spectral data, reporting of, 54
Spectrofluorometers, 41, 54, 63, 68
  compensating, 63, 71
Spectrophotometers, fluorescence ac-
    cessories for, 67
Spin–orbit coupling, 27
Stereofluorograph, 75
Stern-Volmer law, 32
Stimulated emission, 142
Stokes shift, 19
Substituted aromatic hydrocarbons,
    fluorescence of, 88
Sulfa drugs, determination of, 176
Symmetry restrictions, in electronic
    transitions, 26

T

Temperature effects, on fluorescence,
    28, 52, 136, 139, 173
1,2,4,5-Tetramethylbenzene,   deter-
    mination of, 180
1,3,7,9-Tetramethyluric acid (TMU),
    205
Thermoluminescence, 190
Thin-layer chromatography, use with
    phosphorescence, 178
TMU.   See 1,3,7,9-Tetramethyluric
    acid.
Transition metal chelates, fluorescence
    of, 160
Transition states, 3
Triplet-singlet transitions, 22
Triplet states, 4
Triplet–triplet energy transfer, 34
Triplet–triplet transitions, 18
Tryptophan, determination of, 177

V

Vibrational coupling, 34
Vibrational levels of electronic states, 9
Vibrational relaxation, 18
Viscosity effects, on fluorescence, 52

W

Wavelength shifter, 110

X

Xenon arcs, 41